Bus Restored

2006

Buses
Restored
2006

OXFORD
TEL. 2173

1
MORRIS WORKS

956

956 AJO

Ian Allan
PUBLISHING

Contents

Front cover: Midland General 175 (KRR 255) is a 1949 AEC Regal III with B35F bodywork by Weymann. It was new to Mansfield and District, and is kept by the museum of the Midland Road Transport Group at Butterley near Chesterfield. *Philip Lamb*

Half-title: Ex-Ulsterbus Bristol RELL6G 2583 (BXI 2583) at the Enniskillen depot of Ulsterbus on 30 July 2005, taking Irish Transport Trust members on a visit to Bus Eireann at Sligo. *Paul Savage*

Title page: City of Oxford 956 (956 AJO), a 1957 Park Royal-bodied AEC Regent V, is owned by the Oxford Bus Museum at Long Hanborough.

First published 2006

ISBN (10) 0 7110 3123 1
ISBN (13) 978 0 7110 3123 4

© Ian Allan Publishing Ltd 2006

Published by Ian Allan Publishing

an imprint of Ian Allan Publishing Ltd, Hersham, Surrey KT12 4RG.
Printed by Ian Allan Printing Ltd, Hersham, Surrey KT12 4RG.

Code: 0603/A2

Note: Please be aware that vehicles on display can vary from time to time as not all museums display their entire 'fleet'. Visitors wishing to see a particular vehicle should make enquiries prior to their visit.

Useful addresses
NARTM, PO Box 5141, Burton-upon-Trent DE15 OZF.
The Transport Trust, 202 Lambeth Road, London SE1 7JW.
British Bus Preservation Group, 25 Oldfield Road,
Bexleyheath, Kent DA7 4DX.
The PSV Circle, 26 Ashville Grove, Halifax HX2 OPN.

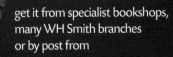

Introduction

Welcome to *Buses Restored 2006* which now includes more colour that we hope regular readers will appreciate. *Buses Restored* was first published in 2000 as a companion to the established *Railways Restored* and it has been updated annually ever since. The information in the book is derived from data supplied by the member organisations of the National Association of Road Transport Museums (NARTM) with the help of Ian Allan Publishing.

NARTM is now in its 25th year, having started as a small informal group of bus enthusiasts who aspired to run their own transport museums in their spare time, and some of them actually did run museums open to the public on a limited basis. Over the years, more and more groups have joined NARTM and we now have around 60 member groups, although not all have museums open to the public. Some members have private collections and their vehicles may be accessible by arrangement or at the many historic vehicle rallies held each year. Details of these events can be found in this book and each month in *Bus and Coach Preservation*, another Ian Allan publication.

NARTM is still a relatively informal organisation and exists to serve its members as an information exchange, source of advice and a clearing house for old vehicle spares and equipment. Increasingly, NARTM is representing the interests of historic buses and their owners at a national level, to ensure that their specific needs are known and recognised alongside the needs of other sectors of our heritage. Most of the NARTM member museums are still run by volunteers with some notable exceptions such as the Glasgow Museum of Transport and the Museum of London's Transport.

If you or your organisation is interested in joining NARTM, or if you would like to have more detail about our collections, please have a look at our website at www.nartm.org.uk, send us an e-mail to mail@nartm.org.uk or write to NARTM, PO Box 141, Burton-upon-Trent, Staffordshire, DE15 0ZF.

A quick lesson in bus history

As I write this introduction, old buses are actually in the news for a change as the last traditional Routemaster buses work out their last days in London. For many people, all old buses with the engine at the front are Routemasters, but many readers of this book will know that that is not the case. On the other hand, in many areas of Britain outside London, the general public will not have been familiar with buses having open rear platforms and a conductor for the last 30 years or more, so it is not surprising that the only buses of this style they know are those familiar vehicles in the capital.

The Routemaster was designed in the early 1950s and after a few years of trials it entered service from 1959. It was actually a technical advance in many ways from its contemporaries and this, together with its durability and the varying local politics of the London area, has seen the Routemaster remain in service for a remarkably long time. At the time it was being built, many other bus operators were changing over to the double deck buses with the engine at the back which are now so familiar. Others switched to single deck buses with the engines under the floor or at the back and it was the latter that have now developed into the low floor, easy access buses in use today. While I can't think of any true 'low floor' buses in preservation yet, the buses listed in this book span the last century of motor bus history and the various museums give the enthusiast and interested visitors the opportunity to see and learn more about the development of the bus.

Early motor buses were in turn evolved from the nineteenth century horse buses, with similar open top timber framed bodies fitted to high steel chassis with primitive petrol engines. Engines improved and became more reliable and increasingly lower chassis frames were introduced over the years, making access easier. Roofs were added to the top decks from the 1920s, and more economical diesel engines were fitted from the 1930s. This produced the same basic design as the Routemaster, so the end of their lives in service really was the end of a long story of bus development and not just of one particular type.

Trolleybuses have also not been familiar vehicles to many of the British public for over forty years now. (All right, only 34 years if you lived in Bradford!) A British trolley bus was usually similar to the traditional open platform motor bus, but was fitted with an electric motor rather than an engine and collected its power from twin overhead wires. This meant that they were fast and quiet in operation, and clean at the point of use, although their electricity was probably generated in a coal fired power station. In the 1950s and 1960s it was simpler and more economical to replace them in

Britain with motor buses although they have remained popular in other countries, especially in Europe and China.

Whose chassis is it anyway...?

If you are new to the world of old buses, please read on despite the number of chassis numbers and types in the first part below – it is all explained later on...

Here is a spot of number crunching for all our readers who champion the merits of one type of bus chassis over and above all others. Some chassis makes have been popular through the years with operators because of their reliability, economy or longevity while the enthusiast and preservationist may favour those vehicles which they remember from their childhood, the ones with the melodious gearbox sounds or those with a really throaty exhaust note. Drivers of these machines would have their own views – to them ease of steering, gear changing and pedal operation would be more important, although not as vital as the cab heater, adjustable seat and space for the brew can. And why not?

The NARTM database now includes details of almost 3,500 buses and coaches, which is up by about 800 vehicles since the last time I did any analysis of it in the pages of *Buses Restored* about 3 years ago. The biggest single increase was when the data collected by the British Bus Preservation Group about their members' vehicles was added and we thank them for access to that data. It should be noted that with the exception of the BBPG information, the majority of vehicles listed are those owned by museums and collections. This means that many of the recently preserved Routemasters which are in private ownership are not included and a large number of their predecessors, the London RT and RF family buses, are also not recorded here. There are many other privately owned buses up and down the country (and with our friends overseas of course) which would then bring the total of preserved buses and coaches to over 5,000 which is a number quoted for a number of years now.

The benefit of using the NARTM database is that it is updated annually before each edition of *Buses Restored* is published so it is as accurate as the annual updates provided by our contributors. By the way, don't try to add up the various vehicles in the book to arrive at the numbers quoted below, as not all the owners of vehicles on the database have given permission for their details to be published.

So, with the above 'health warnings' about the completeness of our data, here are the five most numerous chassis makes in preservation today. Following the tradition of such competitions, we will list them in reverse order. Coming in at number five is Bedford, with 180 examples in preservation, just beaten by Daimler with 196 although you could argue that the 34 preserved 'Leyland' Fleetlines should also sit in the Daimler camp…? Third most numerous chassis builder by some margin is Bristol with 530 vehicles listed. AEC retain their second place spot with 639 examples (plus quite a few more RMs, RMLs, RTs etc as noted above) while Leyland have increased their lead with 1,097 preserved buses and coaches. For completeness, in positions 6 to 10 on this listing are, in descending order this time, Guy (106), Dennis (84), Ford (55), Albion (45) and then Sunbeam (36).

From the above broad numbers, which are the most numerous passenger vehicle chassis models in preservation? Remembering the notes about the London buses above, the top ten chassis models are shown below. I know there are some quite arbitrary divisions between types here, depending on individual manufacturers, but I have tried to group them on their wider appeal rather than by technical differences.

Leyland Titan (PD1, 2 and 3 variants)	296
AEC Regent (postwar II, III and V series)	194
Leyland Atlantean (PDR and AN68 variants)	193
AEC Reliance (underfloor engines)	147
Daimler and Leyland Fleetline	126
Leyland National	106
Bristol RE	104
Bristol Lodekka (LD and F series)	90
AEC/PRV Routemaster	84
Guy Arab (utility and postwar Mk I to V)	77

A very close runner up was the popular Bristol VR with 76 preserved examples at the time of compilation, although probably a few more will have entered preservation now as the type's days in service are coming to an end. Once again the number of Routemasters in existence although out of service is likely to be many more than the 84 above.

Buses simplified…

So that was a bit of fun for the enthusiasts amongst our readers. If you are relatively new to the world of old buses and wouldn't know a Daimler Fleetline if you got on to one, don't panic! By looking through the many illustrations in this book, you will find lots of examples of each chassis type pictured. However, that is where life might just become more confusing for you, for just when you have found a picture of a Fleetline, so you know what one looks like, along comes another one that looks nothing like the first…

Unfortunately, or fortunately, buses and coaches are not like cars and traditionally they have been bought in two parts – the chassis and the body. The chassis is the heart of the vehicle, but since the front engine and exposed radiator fell from favour in the 1950s it has been difficult to tell the various chassis types apart at a glance. ('No it isn't!' I hear the experts cry, but quiet please, this bit is written for the newcomer with the hope that by demystifying the subject they might become more interested). It took me years to work out the difference between a Daimler Fleetline and a Leyland Atlantean, perhaps because many of the local examples carried bodywork from the same coachbuilders.

So buying a bus or coach is more complex than buying a car. Even today, if you buy a car, you buy the whole thing – a Ford Focus, Vauxhall Vectra or Nissan Micra – all in one go. If you were to buy a new bus (and had the required £100,000 plus) you might choose a Volvo or Scania chassis and then have a body built by Alexander or East Lancashire according to the work you have for the vehicle, the money available and your own perception of each manufacturer and their products.

It was the same in the past and out of the 20 or so Leyland Titans in the collection of the Manchester Museum of Transport, hardly any two are identical. All right, some are quite similar, but built for use in different local towns. That is where the fascination of old buses starts. Why did Salford and Manchester have buses the same but different? It was the same in Leeds and Bradford, Liverpool and Birkenhead, Glasgow and Edinburgh, Birmingham and Wolverhampton and so on. The buses didn't really do very different jobs, so why go to the expense of having a 'bespoke' product for each town? Local municipal identity and pride, the preferences of the General Manager and those of his Chief Engineer were usually responsible although local conditions did make their contribution.

In more recent times, there has been much less local influence in the design of buses and coaches, so a FirstGroup bus from Aberdeen, Manchester or Leicester will be to an almost identical design and such buses are often exchanged between the individual operating centres as the needs of the operations change. London buses are no longer designed specially for the capital, but they are still different to provincial ones; the recent introduction of large numbers of articulated 'bendy' buses is a case in point.

Local identity has also been lost in recent years by the adoption of nationwide liveries by the big three bus groups – Arriva, First and Stagecoach. So when a bus from Edinburgh is transferred to Manchester most people would never notice, unless the eagle eyed spotted its Scottish registration number, or the not so eagle eyed might notice the route branding for the 'Falkirk Wheel'… In the past every local authority and independent company had its own very distinctive colour scheme and their buses were very much a part of the local scene. Hull's blue and white streamlined buses would not have looked right anywhere else and the same applied to Oxford's, Portsmouth's and so on.

Coaches, used on long distance services as well as day trips and longer tours were even more distinctive than the local buses. With the exception of National Express with their white livery and the familiar blue of Shearings, the same applies today. Many small operators specify their own requirements of interior and exterior trim and have their own distinctive colours and designs, often applied in vinyl today with some striking results.

The Body Shop
So then, which are the most popular body makes in preservation today? Based on the NARTM database again (please see above for the inputs to the database) here are the top ten, in descending order.

Eastern Coach Works	467
Park Royal	294
Alexander (Falkirk and Belfast)	256
Metro-Cammell (and MCW)	222
Plaxton	184
Duple	158
Weymann	147
East Lancashire	144
Northern Counties	138
Roe	131

Readers who are still following this will notice that in the chassis builders' league table, Bristol were third and here in the body builders table, Eastern Coach Works (ECW) are far and away the most numerous manufacturer. This is largely due to the nationalisation of many of bus companies after the Second World War when these companies were made to buy the products of Bristol and ECW which were also nationally owned. Not that this was a great hardship, for Bristol chassis were well engineered and reliable and the ECW body was renowned for its durability. When the controls were relaxed, both ECW and Bristol sold a good number of their products to operators outside the National Bus Company. Sadly, this did not stop them both closing during the 1980s, along with many other famous names from the bus industry.

Of the other manufacturers, Alexander predominantly produced bodies for their sister operating companies in Scotland, Plaxton and Duple concentrated on coach body construction and Park Royal built thousands of buses for London and for smaller municipal operators. These were not always local preferences either, for both East Lancs and Northern Counties who were based in Lancashire built bodies for South Coast operators.

I think the time has now come to let you carry on and browse through the rest of the book. By and large, the museums and collections listed house examples of vehicles that were used in the area around that museum. This helps to give each of the collections its own distinct atmosphere and identity. So when you have visited one bus museum, please look out for others when you are in other areas. You will be sure to find something of interest and a warm welcome at each one.

In this introductory section we have focussed on the vehicles themselves. The buses and coaches do form the largest and most visible part of the museum collections listed, but there is a tremendous amount of smaller objects, photographs and documents in each of the collections. These items really fill in a lot of gaps in the story of local road public transport and are an important resource for students, local historians, people tracing their family history as well as the general public who are simply interested to see something different and to understand why all these vehicles were built, who travelled on them and why.

Dennis Talbot,
Chairman, NARTM.

Other Titles of Interest

Classic Bus Yearbook-12

Edited by Gavin Booth

Since it was first published in 1995, Classic Bus Yearbook has firmly established itself as one of the most popular road transport titles in the Ian Allan Publishing range. Its annual publication each Spring, is eagerly awaited by bus enthusiasts.

The book always offers an eclectic mix of articles and photo-features portraying the passenger transport scene in the period up to the mid-1970s. It is an entertaining exercise in nostalgia for all those who remember the era of the half-cab bus.

ISBN: 0 7110 3126 6 | 235 x 172mm | c128pp | HB
b/w and colour photos throughout

£14.99

Bus Operators 1970:
South-West and Southern England

Gavin Booth

By 1970, bus and coach operations in the south-west of England was dominated by the subsidiaries of the newly-created National Bus Company, most notably Devon General, Southern National, Western National, Bristol and Hants & Dorset, although there were still municipal operations in places such as Plymouth. Whilst the NBC would later impose its corporate image on its subsidiaries, in 1970 the pre-1967 liveries were still in use and the variety of vehicle types was also impressive. As one of the country's leading domestic holiday destinations, the West Country operators provided numerous summer-only services and these, along with the vehicles used, will also be featured in the book which is comprehensively illustrated throughout with both mono and colour photographs.

ISBN: 0 7110 3034 0 | 280 x 215mm | 80pp | HB
c200 b/w and colour photos

£16.99

What is NARTM ?

The National Association of Road Transport Museums (NARTM) is an informal organisation of museums and collections. Volunteers operate many of them, although others, such as the Glasgow and London Transport Museums, are managed by full-time staff. This mix of museum types gives the opportunity to share ideas and experiences and the volunteers involved each bring their own professional skills to their projects and best practices can then be shared by all the member collections.

NARTM has been in existence for almost 20 years and now has around 30 member organisations, with more joining each year. The buses and coaches that form part of the NARTM collections are generally regarded as forming the nucleus of the National Collection of Buses and Coaches. However, it must be stressed that many important examples are in private hands outside the scope of NARTM and its members.

What does NARTM do?

Many of the people involved in running transport museums are busy people and have little spare time after making significant contributions to their own projects, such as the Museum in Manchester. This is why NARTM only holds two meetings each year at the various member museums and in recent years we have visited Devon, Lincoln, Glasgow, Oxford and Portsmouth. In between meetings, the quarterly *Bulletin* keeps members in touch with each other and we are often in touch. Indeed, one of the main functions of NARTM is to put people in touch with each other and there are many instances of restoration projects progressing and spare parts being located through NARTM contacts. Discussion topics at recent meetings have included the encouragement and role of Junior members, bus services, grant applications, museum registration, visitor facilities, risk assessment, documentation and links with other bodies.

NARTM's unique service to its members is also as an information exchange about running museums — after all, as so many of our members are volunteers, their skills and experiences are not within the heritage and leisure industry. It is often the case that another project in another area has already been faced with exactly the same issues as we have today, and by sharing ideas and pooling resources, progress can be made more quickly.

Over the years NARTM has also taken a lead role in campaigning on new legislation to lessen its impact on the historic bus preservation movement. Vehicle licensing, driver licensing, tachographs and the retention of original registration numbers have all received our attention, with some success in each case through our work in conjunction with other groups within the movement. NARTM is also a club authorised to endorse applications from historic vehicle owners to retain, or regain, the original registration of their vehicle.

The future

NARTM is currently working closely with the Transport Trust to define the bus preservation sector of the heritage transport industry. It is also addressing the major issues currently facing the movement — storage, documentation, human resources and skills, public access and the future of vehicles in preservation. A database is now maintained which lists all vehicles in NARTM and associated collections and this will eventually form part of a decision-making process to ensure that the most historically important vehicles have a secure long-term future.

For more information about NARTM please contact:
NARTM, PO Box 5141, Burton-upon-Trent,
Staffordshire, DE15 0ZF.
Website: **www.nartm.org.uk**
e-mail: **email@nartm.org.uk**

Useful addresses

The Transport Trust, 202 Lambeth Road, London SE1 7JW.

British Bus Preservation Group, 18 Greenriggs, Hedley Park, Stopsley, Luton LU2 9TQ.

The PSV Circle, 26 Ashville Grove, Halifax HX2 0PN.

How to Use this Book

This book lists both formal museums and the more informal types of collection, and gives details of opening times, contact addresses and the facilities available, together with a list of the buses, trolleybuses and coaches on display. Many of the sites are open to the public on a regular basis. Admission fees vary and some are even free to visitors, although donations towards the upkeep of the collections are always welcome. Please be aware that the vehicles on display can vary from time to time. Not all museums are able to display their entire 'fleet', and some practise the regular rotation of exhibits for added interest. In addition, some of the vehicles may be in the process of restoration in a workshop off-site, and there is always the possibility that a bus may be on loan to another museum! Visitors wishing to see a particular vehicle should make enquiries prior to the visit.

Some collections are not normally available for public access. However, the owners usually welcome visitors and will arrange for viewing by prior application. In addition, many such groups do have open or public days from time to time. Contact addresses are provided in this book, and those wishing to visit a particular site are asked to contact the address given. Please bear in mind that most are run by volunteers — please enclose a stamped self-addressed envelope when writing and respect the privacy of individuals. This book does not grant or imply any permission whatsoever to enter premises to look at old buses except by the agreement of the group involved. Note that where buses are licensed for use on public passenger-carrying services, the use of individual vehicles will vary from time to time, as the demands of their preservation dictate.

Whilst some of the restored vehicles detailed here have been 'officially' preserved by their former operators, the majority have been restored and conserved by volunteers, often working in difficult conditions with limited resources of time, money and materials. That there are so many buses and coaches fully restored is a testimony to the

dedication of bus enthusiasts over the last 40 years or more, and it is intended that the vehicles will have a long and secure future.

The information used in this book is as provided by the organisations listed, for which the authors express their thanks. Any information on further collections not included in the current edition will be most welcome. If you own vehicles, or are associated wih such an organisation, please contact NARTM at the address given on page 7.

For each vehicle, details given include the present registration number, year first registered, brief chassis and body details (including seating) and original operator. Standard PSV Circle body codes are used, as outlined below.

Body type (before seating capacity):

A	articulated
B	single-deck bus
C	coach (single-deck)
CH	double-decker coach
Ch	charabanc
CO	convertible open-top double-decker
DP	dual-purpose (eg coach seats in bus shell)
F	full-front (where not normal for chassis)
H	Highbridge double-decker
L	Lowbridge double-decker (ie with sunken side gangway upstairs; all other types — with conventional gangways — are 'H', regardless of overall height)
O	open-top double-decker
OB	open-top single-decker
PO	partially-open-top double-decker
R	single-decker with raised rear saloon (eg over luggage compartment)
T	Toastrack

Seating capacity:

For double-deckers this is shown with the upper-deck capacity first, eg 43/31

Door position (after seating capacity):

C	centre entrance/exit
D	dual doors (usually front entrance and centre exit)
F	front or forward entrance/exit
R	open rear platform
RD	rear entrance/exit with doors
RO	open rear platform with open staircase
T	triple doors (eg on articulated vehicles)

Suffix:

t	fitted with toilet
l	fitted with wheelchair lift

The restoration state is given in accordance with the following code:

R	restored;
RP	restoration in progress;
A	awaiting restoration.

Note: Please be aware that vehicles on display can vary from time to time as not all museums display their entire 'fleet'. Visitors wishing to see a particular vehicle should make enquiries prior to their visit.

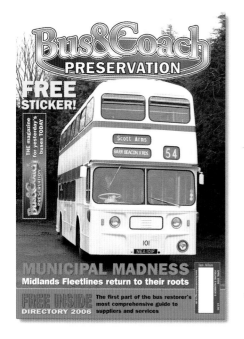

Part 1

Museums Normally Open to the Public

City of Oxford Motor Services L166 (PWL 413), a Weymann-bodied AEC Regent III of 1950, resides at the Oxford Bus Museum at Long Hanborough. *Philip Lamb*

A	Audio/visual displays	H	Baby-changing facilities
B	Bus rides (regular)	L	Lecture theatre
B(e)	Bus rides (at events)	M	Band stand
C	Children's information pack	P	Car parking
D	Access for disabled	R	Refreshments
E	Picnic facilities	S	Enthusiasts' shop
F	School activity pack	T	Toilets
G	Gift shop		

Note: Please be aware that vehicles on display can vary from time to time as not all museums display their entire 'fleet'. Visitors wishing to see a particular vehicle should make enquiries prior to their visit.

Abbey Pumping Station
Leicester

Contact address: Corporation Road, Leicester LE4 5PX
Phone: 0116 299 5111
Fax: 0116 299 5125
Brief description: The Museum is a Victorian pumping-station dating from 1892 with four beam-engines. The vehicle collection is on view on special open days. On these occasions, one of the beam-engines is steamed.
Events planned: Opening times for special events: Saturdeys 11.00-14.30, Sundays 13.00-17.00
1 April, 6 May, 3 June, 1 July, 5 August, 2 September, 7 October 2006 — Railway Running Days;
9 April 2006 — Little & Large Steam Day
6 May 2006 — Classic Vehicles
3 June 2006 — Teddy Bears Day
24/25 June 2006 — Urban Rally Weekend
5 August 2006 — Preserved Vehicles
10 September 2006 — Art & Craft Day
10 December 2006 — Christmas Toys Steam Day
14 January 2007 — Meccano Day
4 February 2007 — Steam Toys in Action
Please see the enthusiast press for further details.
Opening days/times:
1 February-31 November, plus 10 December and 14 January 2007. Saturday, Monday to Thursday 11.00-16.30; Sundays 13.00-13.60.
Museum closed Decamber and January except for above dates
Directions by car: A6 (north of Leicester) joins Abbey Lane at Redhill Island. Corporation Road is off Abbey Lane.
Directions by public transport: From City Centre (Charles Street) take bus 54 to top of Corporation Road.
Charges: Free except on special open days.
Facilities: C D E G H P R (on open days) T

Registration	Date	Chassis	Body	New to	Fleet No	Status
CBC 921	1939	AEC Renown O664	Northern Counties H32/32R	Leicester City Transport	329	R
MTL 750	1958	Leyland Tiger Cub PSUC1/2	Yeates DP43F	Delaine Coaches of Bourne	47	R
TBC 164	1958	Leyland Titan PD3/1	Willowbrook H41/33R	Leicester City Transport	164	R
JMC 121K	1972	AEC Reliance 6MU4R	Plaxton C34C	Glenton Tours of London	121	R
OUM 727P	1976	Bedford J2SZ10	Caetano C16F	Anderton Tours of Keighley		R
B401 NJF	1984	Ford Transit 190D	Rootes B16F	Midland Fox	M1	R

Notes:
CBC 921   On view at Snibston Discovery Park
B401 NJF   On view at Snibston Discovery Park

Note: Please be aware that vehicles on display can vary from time to time as not all museums display their entire 'fleet'. Visitors wishing to see a particular vehicle should make enquiries prior to their visit.

Amberley Working Museum

Contact address: Amberley, Arundel, West Sussex, BN18 9LT
Phone: 01798 831370
Fax: 01798 831831
E-mail: office@amberleymuseum.co.uk
Brief Description: The industrial museum has a wide range of attractions, including rail and bus operations. Some buses in the collection are museum-owned, others are owned by the Southdown Omnibus Trust or are in private hands.
Events planned:
17 September 2006 — Annual Bus Show 'London to Brighton' theme.
Opening days/times:
March to October: Weds to Sun (also Mon and Tues during school holidays)
Directions by car: Situated close to Amberley railway station on the B2139. Approach from the north and west via the A29 and from the east via the A24 and A283.
Directions by public transport: Hourly rail service calls at Amberley station which is adjacent to the museum.
Charges: Adults £7.50, OAP £6.50.
Facilities: A B B(e) C D E F G H L P R T

Registration	Date	Chassis	Body	New to	Fleet No	Status
IB 552	1914	Tilling Stevens TS3 Petrol Electric	Newman O22/16R	Worthing Motor Services	52	R
CD 5125	1920	Leyland N	Short O27/24R	Southdown Motor Services	125	R
CD 4867	1923	Tilling Stevens TS3A Petrol Electric	(chassis only)		67	RP
BP 9822	1924	Shelvoke & Drewery Freighter	Hickman (replica) B18F	Tramocar of Worthing	1	R
MO 9324	1927	Tilling Stevens B9A	Brush B32R	Thames Valley Traction Co	152	R
UF 1517	1927	Dennis 30cwt	Short B19R	Southdown Motor Services	517	R
BR 7132	1929	Leyland Lion LT1	Leyland B34F	Sunderland Corporation	2	R
UF 4813	1929	Leyland Titan TD1	Brush O27/24R	Southdown Motor Services	813	A
UF 6473	1930	Leyland Titan TD1	Leyland H24/24R	Southdown Motor Services	873	R
UF 6805	1930	Tilling Stevens B10A2	Short B31R	Southdown Motor Services	1205	RP
UF 7428	1931	Leyland Titan TD1	Short H26/24R	Southdown Motor Services	928	R
ECD 524	1937	Leyland Cub KPZ2	Park Royal B20F	Southdown Motor Services	24	RP
EUF 184	1938	Leyland Titan TD5	Leyland -	Southdown Motor Services	0184	R

Notes:

IB 552	Petrol-electric transmission. Body new 1909
CD 5125	Restored using a P or Q 5- or 6-ton chassis. Rebodied 1928
CD 4867	Petrol-electric. To be restored as Southdown replica charabanc
BP 9822	Solid tyres. Replica body built at Amberley
UF 1517	All-metal body
MO 9324	Mechanical Transmission. Restored at Amberley
BR 7132	Stored off-site
UF 4813	On loan from Southdown Motor Services Ltd, unrestored but operational
UF 6805	Mechanical transmission
EUF 184	Converted from bus 184; fitted with breakdown vehicle body ex Leyland TD1 872 (UF 6472)

Aston Manor Road Transport Museum

Contact address: The Old Tram Depot, 208-216 Witton Lane, Aston, Birmingham B6 6QE
Phone: 0121 322 2298
Fax: 0121 449 4768
Web site: www.amrtm.org.uk
Affiliation: NARTM

Brief description: The 19th-century former tram depot houses a selection of buses, coaches, commercial vehicles and tramcar bodies in an authentic setting — the depot still has tram tracks and stone sets in situ. There are also many small exhibits, working model layouts and video presentations.

Events planned:
29 May 2006 — Two Museums Running Day. Bus service linking Aston Manor and Wythall.
9 July 2006 — Open day/Outer Circle running day.
9/10 Sept 2006 — Heritage Open Days.
26 Nov 2006 — Collectors' fair with free bus rides.
Please see the enthusiast press for other events.

Opening days/times:
Saturdays, Sundays and Bank Hols 11.00 to 17.00. Other times by arrangement.
Opening times may vary over Christmas/New Year period.

Directions by car: Easy access from M6 junction 6.

Directions by public transport: Rail to Witton Station and a short walk (170yd)
Bus No 7 from Birmingham City Centre or bus No 11, Outer Circle to Witton Square.

Charges:
Adults £1.50, Child and Concessions 75p, Family £4.00.
Admission charges may vary on special event days.

Facilities: A B(e) D H P R S T

Other information: Not all of the vehicles listed are on display at the museum. To view any vehicle not normally accessible, visitors should enquire at the museum as to arrangements for viewing.

Registration	Date	Chassis	Body	New to	Fleet No	Status
note z	1925	AEC S	Buckingham	Birmingham Corporation Tramways	215	A
OP 237	1926	(no chassis)	Short H32/26R	Birmingham Corporation Tramways	208	A
EA 4181	1929	Dennis E	Dixon B32F	West Bromwich Corporation	32	RP
HA 4963	1930	SOS RR	(chassis only)	BMMO ('Midland Red')	963	A
JF 2378	1931	AEC Regal 662	Burlingham C32R	Provincial of Leicester	R1	R
OJ 9347	1933	Morris Commercial Dictator	Metro Cammell B—F	Birmingham Corporation Tramways	47	RP
AOG 679	1935	Daimler COG5		Birmingham Corporation Tramways	83	A
CDH 501	1935	Dennis Lance	Park Royal H28/24R	Walsall Corporation	110	A
EHA 775	1938	SOS SON	(chassis only)	BMMO ('Midland Red')	2207	A
RC 7927	1940	BMMO SON	Willowbrook DP34F	Trent Motor Traction Co	417	R
FON 630	1942	Leyland Titan TD7	(chassis only)	Birmingham City Transport	1330	A
KHA 301	1948	BMMO C1	Duple C30C	BMMO ('Midland Red')	3301	R
KTT 689	1948	Guy Vixen	Wadham FC29F	Court Cars of Tourquay		R
ARC 515+	1949	Sunbeam F4	Brush H30/26R	Derby Corporation	215	R
GUJ 608	1950	Sentinel STC4	Sentinel B40F	Sentinal demonstrator		R
JOJ 222	1950	Leyland Titan PD2/1	Park Royal H29/25R	Birmingham City Transport	2222	RP
JOJ 526	1950	Guy Arab IV	Metro Cammell H30/24R	Birmingham City Transport	2526	A
JOJ 548	1950	Guy Arab IV	Metro Cammell H30/24R	Birmingham City Transport	2548	RP
KHA 352	1950	BMMO CL2	Plaxton C26C	BMMO ('Midland Red')	3352	RP
SB 8155	1950	Guy Wolf	Ormac B20F	Alexander MacConnacher of Ballachulish		R
JOJ 847	1952	Daimler CVG6	Crossley H30/25RD	Birmingham City Transport	2847	A
LOG 301	1952	Guy Arab IV	Saunders Roe H30/25R	Birmingham City Transport	3001	RP
LJW 336	1953	Guy LUF	Saunders Roe B44F	Guy Demonstrator		R
LOG 302	1954	Daimler CLG5	Metro Cammell H30/25R	Birmingham City Transport	3002	R
MOF 90	1954	Guy Arab IV	Metro Cammell H30/25R	Birmingham City Transport	3090	RP
RRU 903	1955	Leyland Tiger Cub PSUC1/1	Park Royal B40F	Bournemouth Corporation	266	R
773 FHA	1958	BMMO D9	BMMO H40/32RD	BMMO ('Midland Red')	4773	A
1294 RE	1959	Guy Arab LUF	Burlingham C41F	Harper Bros of Heath Hayes	60	R
WLT 506	1960	AEC Routemaster R2RH	Park Royal H36/28R	London Transport	RM506	R
264 ERY	1963	Leyland Titan PD3A/1	Park Royal O41/33R	Leicester City Transport	264	R
3035 HA	1963	BMMO D9	BMMO O40/32RD	BMMO ('Midland Red')	5035	RP
334 CRW	1963	Daimler CVG6	Metro Cammell H34/29R	Coventry City Transport	334	RP
6370 HA	1964	BMMO D9	BMMO H40/32RD	BMMO ('Midland Red')	5370	R
KOX 663F	1967	AEC Swift MP2R	MCW B37D	Birmingham City Transport	3663	RP
LHA 870F	1967	BMMO S21	BMMO DP49F	BMMO ('Midland Red')	5870	R
UHA 969H	1970	BMMO S23	BMMO/Plaxton B51F	BMMO ('Midland Red')	5969	A
XNX 136H	1970	Leyland Leopard	Alexander DP49F	Stratford-upon-Avon Blue Motors	36	R

Registration	Date	Chassis	Body	New to	Fleet No	Status
XON 41J	1971	Daimler Fleetline CRG6LX	Park Royal H43/33F	West Midlands PTE	4041	R
OFR 989M	1974	AEC Swift 3MP2R	Marshall B47D	Blackpool Corporation	589	RP
PHA 319M	1974	Leyland Leopard PSU3B/2R	Marshall DP49F	Midland Red Omnibus Co	319	RP
GOH 357N	1974	Leyland Leopard PSU3B/2R	Marshall DP49F	Midland Red Omnibus Co	357	R
JOV 714P	1976	Bristol VRTSL/6LX	MCW H43/33F	West Midlands PTE	4714	R
OOX 825R	1977	Leyland National 11351A/1R	Leyland National DP45F	West Midlands PTE	6825	RP
BVP 784V	1979	Leyland Leopard PSU3E/4R	Plaxton C53F	Midland Red Omnibus Co	784	A
WDA 700T	1979	Leyland Fleetline FE30AGR	MCW H43/33F	West Midlands PTE	7000	A
A110 WVP	1984	MCW Metrobus GR133/1	MCW H43/30F	West Midlands PTE	8110	RP
F685 YOG	1988	MCW Metrorider MF150/113	MCW B23F	West Midlands PTE	685	A
+ Trolleybus						

Notes:

note z	Registration not known	LOG 302	Chrome-plated chassis exhibited 1952 Commercial Motor Show
HA 4963	Chassis only		
OJ 9347	Renumbered 77 in 1935	RRU 903	Converted for OMO and rear door removed in 1957
AOG 679	Originally bus 679 with Northern Counties H26/22R body; rebodied 1947 as a van	3035 HA	Originally H40/32RD; converted to open-top by Marshall ('Obsolete Fleet') London (OM6)
EHA 775	Chassis only	264 ERY	Originally H41/33R
RC 7927	On loan from Trent Motor Traction	OOX 825R	Volvo engine fitted by WMPTE
KHA 352	Rebodied 1963	A110 WVP	Guided wheel experimental vehicle

Black Country Living Museum Transport Group
Dudley

Contact address: Tipton Road, Dudley, West Midlands DY1 4SQ
Phone: 0121 557 9643
Web site: wwww.bclm.co.uk
Brief description: Tramway operation daily. Trolleybus operation on Sundays and Bank Holidays.
Opening days/times: Summer: daily 10.00-17.00. Winter: Wednesdays to Sundays 10.00-16.00. Some evening openings
Events planned: 3-18 June 2006 — 'Trolleybus' event, trolleybuses running every day
Directions by car: M5 (jct 2) signposted on Motorway. follow signs on A4123 to 'Black Country Living Museum'.
Directions by public transport: Central Trains to Tipton station. Travel West Midlands 224, 263, 270, 311-313 to Museum.
Facilities: A, B, B(e)C, D, E, F, G, H, L, P, R, T
Contact (Transport Group): Black Country Museum Transport Group, 28 Farm Close, Etchinghill, Rugeley, Staffs WS15 2XT.

Registration	Date	Chassis	Body	New to	Fleet No	Status
UK 9978+	1931	Guy BTX	Guy H26/24R	Wolverhampton Corporation	78	A
HA 8047	1933	SOS REDD	Metro Cammell H26/26R	BMMO ('Midland Red')	1047	RP
DKY 735+	1946	Karrier W	East Lancs H37/29F	Bradford Corporation	735	RP
DUK 833+	1946	Sunbeam W	Roe H32/28R	Wolverhampton Corporation	433	R
FEA156	1949	Daimler CVG5	Metro Cammell B38R	West Bromwich Corporation	156	RP
GEA 174	1952	Daimler CVG6	Weymann H30/26R	West Bromwich Corporation	174	RP
TDH 912+	1955	Sunbeam F4A	Willowbrook H36/34RD	Walsall Corporation	862	R
SCH 237+	1960	Sunbeam F4A	Roe H37/28R	Derby Corporation	237	R
UCX 275	1961	Guy Wulfrunian	Roe H43/32F	County Motors of Lepton	99	R
VRD 186+	1961	Sunbeam F4A	Burlingham H38/30F	Reading Corporation	186	RP
6342 HA	1963	BMMO D9	BMMO H40/32RD	BMMO ('Midland Red')	5342	RP
GHA 327D	1965	Leyland Leopard PSU4/4R	Plaxton -	Midland Red Omnibus Co	5827	R
XDH 519G	1969	Daimler Fleetline CRG6LX	Northern Counties H41/27D	Walsall Corporation	119	RP
+ Trolleybus						

Note: Please be aware that vehicles on display can vary from time to time as not all museums display their entire 'fleet'. Visitors wishing to see a particular vehicle should make enquiries prior to their visit.

Notes:

HA 8047	Sole surviving SOS double decker
DKY 735	Rebodied 1959
DUK 833	Rebodied 1959
UCX 275	On loan from Dewsbury Bus Museum
VRD 186	Operated at Teeside 1968-71 and currently in their livery
GHA 327D	Converted to breakdown vehicle in 1979.

British Commercial Vehicle Museum
Leyland

Contact address: King Street, Leyland, Lancashire, PR25 2LE
Phone: 01772 451011
Fax: 01772 451015
Brief description: A unique line-up of historic commercial vehicles and buses spans a century of truck and bus building. More than 50 exhibits are on display in this national collection.
Events planned: Please see the enthusiast press for details.
Opening days/times:
April to end of September: Sundays, Tuesdays, Wednesdays, Thursdays and Bank Holidays, 10.00 to 17.00
October: Sundays only, 10.00 to 17.00
Directions by car: Close to the M6 Junction 28.
Directions by public transport:
By train to Leyland station (on West Coast main line).
Buses from Preston and Chorley bus stations.
Charges: Adult £4, Child/OAP £2, Family £10.
Facilities: A B(e) D F G L P R S T

Registration	Date	Chassis	Body	New to	Fleet No	Status
note t	1896	Horse bus	O14/12R	Edinburgh & District Tramways		R
XW 9892	1925	Tilling Stevens TS7	Tilling B30R	Thomas Tilling	0172	R
YT 3738	1927	Leyland Lioness PLC1	Thurgood C22F	King George V		R
KGU 284	1949	Leyland Titan 7RT	Park Royal H30/26R	London Transport	RTL325	R
JRN 29	1956	Leyland Tiger Cub PSUC1/2	Burlingham C41F	Ribble Motor Services	963	R
OED 217	1956	Foden PVD6	East Lancs H30/28R	Warrington Corporation	112	R
301 LJ+	1962	Sunbeam MF2B	Weymann H37/28D	Bournemouth Corporation	301	R
+ Trolleybus						

Notes:

note t	Unregistered
301 LJ	On loan from Bournemouth Heritage Transport Collection

Castle Point Transport Museum
Canvey Island

Contact address: 105 Point Road, Canvey Island, Essex SS8 7TP
Phone: 01268 684272
Affiliation: NARTM
Brief description: This historic former Canvey & District bus depot, built in 1935, houses approximately 35 commercial vehicles spanning the years 1944 to 1988. Exhibits include buses, coaches, lorries, fire engines and military vehicles. They can be seen in varying stages from the totally restored to those in need of complete restoration. Completely run by volunteers, membership of the society is available at £10 per annum.

Events planned: Please see enthusiast press for details
Opening days/times: Open on 1st/3rd Sundays, April to mid October.
Directions by car: A130 to Canvey Island; follow brown tourism signs on reaching the island.
Directions by public transport: By rail to South Benfleet, then by bus to Leigh Beck, Canvey Island.
Charges: Free admission. Donations welcome. A charge is made on the Transport Show day in October.
Facilities: B(e) P T
Other information: Hot drinks available.

Registration	Date	Chassis	Body	New to	Fleet No	Status
BTW 488	1935	Dennis Lancet I	(chassis only)	Eastern National Omnibus Co	3549	A
FOP 429	1944	Daimler CWA6	Duple O33/26R	Birmingham Corporation Tramways	1429	R
JVW 430	1944	Bristol K5G	ECW L27/28R	Eastern National Omnibus Co	3885	R
MPU 52	1947	Leyland Titan PD1A	ECW L27/26R	Eastern National Omnibus Co	3991	RP
CFV 851	1948	Bedford OB	Duple C29F	Seagull Coaches of Blackpool		R
LYR 997	1949	AEC Regent III O961 RT	Weymann H30/26R	London Transport	RT2827	RP
NEH 453	1949	Leyland Titan OPD2/1	Northern Counties L27/26RD	Potteries Motor Traction Co	L453	R
ONO 49	1950	Bristol L5G	ECW B35R	Eastern National Omnibus Co	4029	R
PTW 110	1950	Bristol L6B	ECW FC31F	Eastern National Omnibus Co	4107	RP
WNO 478	1953	Bristol KSW5G	ECW O33/28R	Westcliff-on-Sea Motor Services		R
XVX 19	1954	Bristol Lodekka LD5G	ECW H33/25R	Eastern National Omnibus Co	4208	R
381 BKM	1957	AEC Reliance MU3RV	Harrington C41F	Maidstone & District Motor Services	C381	RP
PHJ 954	1958	Leyland Titan PD3/6	Massey L35/32R	Southend Corporation	315	RP
217 MHK	1959	Bristol MW6G	ECW DP41F	Eastern National Omnibus Co	480	R
236 LNO	1959	Bristol Lodekka LDL6LX	ECW H37/33R	Eastern National Omnibus Co	1541	RP
VLT 44	1959	AEC Routemaster R2RH	Park Royal H36/28R	London Transport	RM44	RP
SGD 407	1960	Leyland Titan PD3/2	Alexander H41/31F	Glasgow Corporation	L405	RP
373 WPU	1961	Guy Arab IV	Massey L34/33R	Moore Bros of Kelvedon		R
138 CLT	1962	AEC Routemaster R2RH	Park Royal H36/28R	London Transport	RM1138	R
28 TKR	1962	AEC Reliance 2MU3RV	Harrington C29F	Maidstone & District Motor Services	C28	R
918 NRT	1963	AEC Regent V MD3RV	Massey H33/28R	Lowestoft Corporation	8	RP
SDX 57	1963	AEC Regent V 2D2RA	East Lancs Neepsend H37/28R	Ipswich Corporation	57	RP
CUV 233C	1965	AEC Routemaster R2RH/1	Park Royal H36/29RD	London Transport	RCL2233	R
NTW 942C	1965	Bristol Lodekka FLF6G	ECW H38/32F	Eastern National Omnibus Co	2849	R
AVX 975G	1968	Bristol Lodekka FLF6LX	ECW H38/32F	Eastern National Omnibus Co	2614	RP
CPU 979G	1968	Bristol VRTSL6LX	ECW H39/31F	Eastern National Omnibus Co	3000	R
GNM 232N	1975	Bristol LHS6L	Plaxton C33F	Epsom Coaches		RP

Notes:

JVW 430	Renumbered 1274 in 1954
FOP 429	Originally H33/26R; later operated by Eastern National Omnibus Co and Southend Corporation (244)
MPU 52	Renumbered 1121 in 1954
LYR 997	In Osbornes of Tollesbury livery
ONO 49	Renumbered 309 in 1954 and 1107 in 1964
PTW 110	Renumbered 328 in 1954
WNO 478	Built as H33/28R; numbered 1423 in 1954; passed to Eastern National Omnibus Co in 1955; renumbered 2380 in 1964 and converted to open-top in 1965/6
XVX 19	Renumbered 1431 in 1954 and 2400 in 1964
VLT 44	In Southend Transport livery
236 LNO	Renumbered 2510 in 1964
217 MHK	Renumbered 1402 in 1964
AVX 975G	Delivered as CH37/18F; fitted with bus seats and renumbered 2946 in 1969

Note: Please be aware that vehicles on display can vary from time to time as not all museums display their entire 'fleet'. Visitors wishing to see a particular vehicle should make enquiries prior to their visit.

Cavan & Leitrim Railway
Dromod

Contact address: Cavan & Leitrim Railway, Narrow Gauge Station, Station Road, Dromod, Co Leitrim, Eire
Phone/fax: 00353 71 9638599
Brief description: Half mile 3ft gauge steam railway with a collection of railway vehicles (steam, diesel, carriages, wagons and railcars) together with a selection of vintage road vehicles, military equipment and vintage aircraft.
Opening days/times:
Daily April-September. Rest of year by request
Directions by car: to Dromod on N4 from Dublin. R202 from Dromod, 500yds.
Directions by public transport: Train to Dromod Irish Rail station from Dublin Connolly (Dublin-Sligo line). Narrow gauge station next to main line
Charges: Adult 8 Euro, Child 5 Euro, Family 17 Euro, Senior citizen 5 Euro
Facilities: B(e) C D E G R (on request) S T

Registration	Date	Chassis	Body	New to	Fleet No	Status
KID 154	1947	Leyland Tiger PS1	Northern Ireland Road Transport Board B34R	Northern Ireland Road Transport Board	A8520	A
FCI 323	1950	Bristol LL5G	ECW B39R	Crosville Motor Services	KG156	RP
ZJ 5904	1950	Leyland Tiger OPS3/1	CIE	CIE	P164	R
IY 7383	1951	GNR Gardner	Park Royal/GNR B33R	Great Northern Railway (Ireland)	G389	R
IY 8044	1952	GNR Gardner	Park Royal/GNR B33R	Great Northern Railway (Ireland)	G396	A
ZO 6960	1953	Leyland Titan OPD2/1	CIE H37/31R	CIE	R541	RP
ZU 5000	1953	Leyland Royal Tiger PSU1/9	Saunders Roe B44C	Irish Army		RP
ZY 1715	1955	AEC Regal IV	Park Royal/GNR B40F	Great Northern Railway (Ireland)	345	R
ILI 98	1958	Bristol SC4LK	ECW B35F	Eastern National Omnibus Co	455	RP
OST 502	1959	AEC Reliance 2MU3RV	Alexander B41F	Highland Omnibuses	B24	RP
3945 UE	1960	Leyland Tiger Cub PSUC1	Park Royal B45F	Stratford-upon-Avon Blue Motors	45	A
71 AHI	1960	Leyland Tiger Cub PSUC1/2	Metro Cammell B41F	Western Welsh Omnibus Co	1274	A
AZD 203	1964	Leyland Leopard L2	CIE B45F	CIE	E140	R
BLH 123B	1964	Bedford VAS2	Duple (Midland) B—F	London County Council		RP
EZH 155	1965	Leyland Leopard PSU3/4R	CIE B—F	CIE	C155	A
EZH 170	1966	Leyland Leopard PSU3/4R	CIE B45F	CIE	C170	R
UZH 258	1966	Leyland Leopard PSU3/4R	CIE B55F	CIE	C258	R
ZS 8621	1971	Daimler Fleetline CRG6LX	Park Royal H—/—F	West Midlands PTE	4130	A
177 IK	1972	Leyland Leopard PSU5/4R	CIE B48F	CIE	M177	A
78 D 140	1978	Bedford SB5	Marshall B40F	Royal Navy		R
78 D 824	1978	Bristol RELL6G	Alexander (Belfast) B52F	Ulsterbus	2193	R
85 D 2412	1978	Bedford SB5	Marshall B40F	Royal Air Force		A
643 MIP	1980	Volvo B58	Duple C—F	North West Coachlines		A

Notes:

KID 154	Originally registered GZ7588
FCI 323	Originally registered LFM737
ZJ 5904	Converted to recovery vehicle by CIE in 1971
ZU 5000	Spent 28 years as garden shed
ZO 6960	Sole survivor of a batch of 6 Airport buses
ZY 1715	Converted to 3ft gauge railway carriage 1971
ILI 98	Originally registered 9579 F
71 AHI	Originally registered UKG 274
AZD 203	Worked on hire to County Donegal Railways
EZH 155	Converted to mobile workshop
ZS 8621	Converted to playbus. Originally registered YOX130K
177 IK	Daf engine fitted early 1980s.
85 D 2412	Originally registered 48 AC 14
78 D 140	Originally registered 42 RN 98
78 D 824	Originally registered POI 2193
643 MIP	Originally registered GRN 896W

Cobham Bus Museum

Contact address: Redhill Road, Cobham, Surrey, KT11 1EF
Phone: 01932 868665
Web site: www.lbpt.org
E-mail: cobhambusmuseum@aol.com
Affiliation: AIM, NARTM
Brief description: This well-established museum is home to the London Bus Preservation Trust. It was formed by a small group of enthusiasts in 1966. The collection has steadily grown over the years and now over 30 preserved buses, coaches and service vehicles are located at Cobham.
Events planned: 2 April 2006 — Annual Open Day, for other events please see the enthusiast press for details.
Opening days/times: Open days as advertised.
Viewing possible at weekends 11.00 to 17.00 but please telephone in advance to confirm.
Directions by car: From M25 junction 10 take A3 north and turn left on to A245. Museum is 1 mile on left.
Directions by public transport: Museum bus service from Weybridge station on main events. Network of special services on annual open day. Infrequent bus service at other times to Brooklands Road/Byfleet.
Charges: £5 but higher charges on open days.
Facilities: B B(e) G P R(limited) S T

Registration	Date	Chassis	Body	New to	Fleet No	Status
XO 1038	1923	AEC 405 (NS)	(chassis only)	London General Omnibus Co	NS144	RP
XX 9591	1925	Dennis 4-ton	Dodson O24/24RO	Dominion Omnibus Co		R
UU 6646	1929	AEC Regal 662	LGOC B30R	London General Omnibus Co	T31	R
GJ 2098	1930	AEC Regent 661	Thomas Tilling H27/25RO	Thomas Tilling	ST922	R
GN 8242	1931	AEC Regal 662	Weymann B30F	Queen Line Coaches of London	T357	A
GO 5170	1931	AEC Renown 664	LGOC B35F	London General Omnibus Co	LT1059	A
AXM 693	1934	AEC Regent 661	LPTB H30/26R	London Transport	STL441	RP
CGJ 188	1935	AEC Q O762	Birmingham R C & W B35C	London Transport	Q83	R
CXX 171	1936	AEC Regal O662	Weymann C30F	London Transport	T448	RP
DLU 92	1937	AEC Regent O661	LPTB H30/26R	London Transport	STL2093	A
EGO 426	1937	AEC Regent O661	LPTB H30/26R	London Transport	STL2377	R
ELP 228	1938	AEC Regal O662	LPTB C30F	London Transport	T504	R
HGC 130	1945	Guy Arab II	Park Royal UH30/26R	London Transport	G351	R
HLX 410	1948	AEC Regent III O961 RT	Weymann H30/26R	London Transport	RT593	R
JXC 288	1949	Leyland Tiger PS1	Mann Egerton B30F	London Transport	TD95	R
KGK 803	1949	Leyland Titan PD2/1 7RT	Park Royal H30/26R	London Transport	RTL139	R
KGU 142	1949	AEC Regent III O961 RT	(chassis only)	London Transport	RT2213	R
MYA 590	1949	Leyland Comet CPO1	Harrington C29F	Scarlet Pimpernel of Minehead		R
LUC 210	1951	AEC Regal IV 9821LT RF	Metro Cammell DP35F	London Transport	RF10	RP
LYR 826	1952	AEC Regent III O961 RT	Park Royal H30/26R	London Transport	RT2775	RP
LYR 910	1952	AEC Regent III O961 RT	Park Royal H30/26R	London Transport	RT3491	R
MLL 740	1953	AEC Regal IV 9822E	Park Royal RC37C	British European Airways		R
MXX 334	1953	Guy Special NLLVP	ECW B26F	London Transport	GS34	R
NLE 672	1953	AEC Regal IV 9821LT RF	Metro Cammell B41F	London Transport	RF672	R
CDX 516	1954	AEC Regent III 9613E	Park Royal H30/26R	Ipswich Corporation	16	R
SLT 58	1958	Leyland Routemaster	Weymann H34/30R	London Transport	RML3	R
461 CLT	1962	AEC Routemaster R2RH	Park Royal H32/25RD	London Transport	RMC1461	R
EGN 369J	1971	AEC Swift 4MP2R	Park Royal B33D	London Transport	SMS369	R
JPA 190K	1972	AEC Reliance 6U2R	Park Royal DP45F	London Country Bus Services	RP90	R
OJD 172R	1976	Leyland Fleetline FE30GR	(chassis only)	London Transport	DMS2172	R
WYW 6T	1979	MCW Metrobus DR101/8	MCW H43/28D	London Transport	M6	R

Note: Please be aware that vehicles on display can vary from time to time as not all museums display their entire 'fleet'. Visitors wishing to see a particular vehicle should make enquiries prior to their visit.

Notes:

XX 9591	Restored as London General Omnibus Co D142
GJ 2098	On loan to BMMO during World War 2
CXX 171	Used as an ambulance during World War 2
DLU 92	Original metal-framed Park Royal body replaced in 1949
ELP 228	Used as an ambulance during World War 2
HGC 130	Only remaining example of a London utility bus
MYA 590	Converted from petrol to diesel in 1966
JXC 288	Toured Europe and USSR 1963-1967
LYR 826	Toured USA and Canada when new
LYR 910	Fitted with AEC 11.3 litre engine in 1998
SLT 58	Prototype Leyland Routemaster; renumbered RM3 in 1961
OJD 172R	Shortened chassis only

Coventry Transport Museum

Contact address: Coventry Transport Museum, Millenium Place, Hales Street, Coventry CV1 1PN

Phone: 024 7623 4270

Fax: 024 7623 4284

E-mail: enquiries@transport-museum.com

Brief Description: The museum has over 250 cars and commercial vehicles, over 100 motorcycles and around 300 bicycles. Various tableaux chart the development of the motor vehicle from the early years and Coventry's contribution to this can be seen in the many marques on display. Other exhibits include the Thrust 2 and Thrust SSC land speed record car, several thousand die-cast models and a walk through audio visual display of the Coventry Blitz experience.

Opening days/times:

Open all year, 10.00-17.00 (last admission 16.30) except 24/25/26 December.

Directions by car: Coventry ring road circles the city centre and is encountered whichever direction you come from. Once on it follow the brown 'Motor Museum' signs and turn off at junction 1. Nearest car park (pay & display) is signposted and is in Tower Street at the back of the Museum.

Directions by public transport: The Museum is opposite Pool Meadow bus/coach station. Use Travel West Midlands bus 17 or 27 from Coventry railway station to Broadgate (5min walk downhill to Museum from Broadgate).

Facilities: R, T, L, D, S, G, F, Be, H

Note: The vehicles are frequently stored off site while new developments are built. Please phone to check which vehicles are on display

Registration	Date	Chassis	Body	New to	Fleet No	Status
SR 1266	1916	Maudslay Subsidy A	(chassis only)			A
EKV 966	1944	Daimler CWA6	Roe H31/25R	Coventry Corporation	366	R
JNB 416	1948	Maudslay Marathon II	Trans-United C33F	Hackett's of Manchester		R
KOM 150	1950	Daimler CVD6	Wilsdon -	Birmingham Post & Mail		R
SRB 424	1953	Daimler CD650	Willowbrook L27/28RD	Tailby & George ('Blue Bus Services') Willington		R
PBC 734	1954	Karrier Bantam Q25	Reading C14F	Mablethorpe Homes of Leicester		R
333 CRW	1963	Daimler CVG6	Metro Cammell H34/29R	Coventry Transport	333	R
PDU 125M	1973	Daimler Fleetline CRG6LX	East Lancs O44/30F	Coventry Transport	125	R
K232 DAC	1993	Peugeot J5	C11F	Peugeot UK		A

Notes:

SR 1266	To be restored as replica of 1921 Hickman bodied bus for Coventry Corporation
EKV 966	Rebodied 1951; converted to mobile repair workshop (O2) in 1960
KOM 150	Built as mobile print shop for the Birmingham Post and Mail and currently used as museum promotional vehicle
PBC 734	Welfare bus
PDU 125M	Originally H44/30F; converted to open top in 1986
K232 DAC	Prototype electric minibus

Dover Transport Museum
Whitfield

Contact address: Willingdon Road, Port Zone White Cliffs Business Park, Whitfield, Dover, CT16 2HJ
Phone: 01304 822409
Affiliation: NARTM, Transport Trust, AIM, ASTRO
Brief description: The museum displays local transport and social history. Road vehicles of all types. A maritime room, railway room, bygone shops and a garage. Hundreds of transport models including a working model tramway.
Events planned: Please see the enthusiast press for details.
Opening days/times: All year round — Sundays 10.00 to 17.00 (except when Chrisatmas Day falls on a Sunday)
Easter to end September — Sundays and Bank Holidays 10.00 to 17.00; Wednesday, Thursdays and Fridays 14.00 to 17.00.
Last entry 45 minutes before closing
Open at other times for pre-arranged groups.
Directions by car: Approximately one mile from the A2 Whitfield roundabout on the Dover bypass.
Directions by public transport: Dover Priory station then bus to Old Park, Whitfield.
Charges: Adult £2.50, Senior Citizen £2, Child £1, Family £6.
Facilities: B(e) D E G P R T

Registration	Date	Chassis	Body	New to	Fleet No	Status
CC 9305	1929	Dennis G	Roberts T19	Llandudno UDC	4	R
569 KKK	1960	AEC Reliance 2MU3RA	Duple C41C	Ayers Coaches of Dover		R
WFN 912	1961	Ford 570E	Duple C41F	Seath Coaches		A
GJG 751D	1966	AEC Regent V 2D3RA	Park Royal O40/32F	East Kent Road Car Co		R
NPD 145L	1973	Leyland National 1151/1R	Leyland National B30D	London Country Bus Services	LNC45	A

Notes:
GJG 751D   Originally H40/32F; used as promotional vehicle
NPD 145L   Converted to Rally Control/Hospitality unit

East Anglia Transport Museum
Carlton Colville

Contact address: Chapel Road, Carlton Colville, Lowestoft, Suffolk, NR33 8BL
Phone: 01502 518459
Web site: www.eatm.org.uk
Affiliation: NARTM, London Trolleybus Preservation Society, Transport Trust.
Brief description: A working transport museum on a four-acre site, first opened in 1972 and run entirely by volunteers. Tram and trolleybus services operate regularly within a developing street scene and the tramway has a woodland section. There is also a narrow-gauge railway. A wide variety of other vehicles on display and sometimes operated includes buses, lorries, steam rollers, battery-electrics, tower wagons and a London taxi. The museum is a registered charity.
Events planned:
10/11 June 2006 — Steam & Vintage Weekend.
9 July 2006 — Annual Bus Rally.
9/10 September 2006 — Trolleybus Weekend. Free bus service to Lowestoft and Beccles.
Opening days/times: April to end of September:
Sundays and Bank Holidays — 11.00 to 17.00;
Thursdays and Saturdays (June to Sept) — 14.00 to 17.00;
Daily, except Mondays (late July and Aug) — 14.00 to 17.00.
Last entry 1 hour before closing.
Directions by car: Situated just off the A1384. Follow the brown signs from the A12, A146 and A1117. Free car parking.

Note: Please be aware that vehicles on display can vary from time to time as not all museums display their entire 'fleet'. Visitors wishing to see a particular vehicle should make enquiries prior to their visit.

Directions by public transport:
Monday to Saturday: Eastern Counties bus 111 or 112 from Lowestoft bus station to Carlton Colville Church.
Every day X2 Lowestoft to Norwich, to Carlton Crown PH then 5min walk.
By train to Oulton Broad South then 35min walk or bus 606 or 607.
Bus service 606 or 607 links Oulton Broad North and Oulton Broad South railway stations with the museum (Chapel Road bus stop), also gives a direct link to Great Yarmouth (Mondays to Saturdays only). For more details of this or other public transport information please ring the travel line on 08459 583358.
Charges: £5.00 adults, £4 Senior Citizens, £3.50 children. Admission includes free rides within the museum.
Facilities: B(e) D E F G H P R S T
Other information: Regular tram, train and trolleybus rides

Registration	Date	Chassis	Body	New to	Fleet No	Status
AH 79505+	1926	Garrett O type	Strachan & Brown B26D	NESA Copenhagen	5	RP
KW 1961	1927	Leyland Lion PLSC3	Leyland B35F	Blythe & Berwick of Bradford		A
ALJ 986+	1935	Sunbeam MS2	Park Royal O40/29R	Bournemouth Corporation	202	R
CUL 260+	1936	AEC 664T	Metro Cammell H40/30R	London Transport	260	R
EXV 201+	1938	Leyland LPTB70	Leyland H40/30R	London Transport	1201	R
FXH 521+	1940	Metro Cammell	Metro Cammell H40/30R	London Transport	1521	R
GBJ 192	1947	AEC Regent II O661	ECW H30/26R	Lowestoft Corporation	21	R
BDY 809+	1948	Sunbeam W	Weymann H30/26R	Hastings Tramways Co	34	RP
KAH 408	1948	Bristol L4G	ECW B35R	Eastern Counties Omnibus Co	LL108	A
note d+	1948	Berna	Hess B37D	Biel (Switzerland)	39	R
LLU 829	1950	Leyland Titan PD2/1 7RT	Park Royal H30/26R	London Transport	RTL1050	R
NBB 628+	1950	BUT 9641T	Metro Cammell H40/30R	Newcastle Corporation	628	A
ERV 938+	1951	BUT 9611T	Burlingham H28/26R	Portsmouth Corporation	313	RP
SG 2030+	1952	Henschel ,HIII/s	Uerdingen B32T	Solingen (Germany)	1	R
DRC 224+	1953	Sunbeam F4	Willowbrook H32/28R	Derby Corporation	224	R
LCD 52+	1953	BUT 9611T	Weymann H30/26R	Brighton Corporation -	52	R
YTE 826+	1956	BUT 9612T	Bond H32/28R	Ashton-under-Lyne Corporation	87	A
2206 OI+	1958	Sunbeam F4A	Harkness H36/32R	Belfast Corporation	246	R
YLJ 286+	1959	Sunbeam MF2B	Weymann H35/28D	Bournemouth Corporation	286	R
557 BNG	1962	Bristol Lodekka FL6G	ECW H37/33RD	Eastern Counties Omnibus Co	LFL57	R
AEX 85B	1964	AEC Reliance 2MU3RA	Pennine B39F	Great Yarmouth Corporation	85	RP
YRT 898H	1969	AEC Swift 2MP2R	ECW B45D	Lowestoft Corporation	4	R
OCK 985K	1972	Bristol VRTSL/6LX	ECW H39/31F	Ribble Motor Services	1985	R
D103 DAJ	1986	Mercedes L608D	Reeve Burgess B20F	Hartlepool Transport	13	R

+ Trolleybus

Notes:

AH 79505	Danish registration	OCK 985K	Acquired by Eastern Counties Omnibus Co (VR385) in 1985
ALJ 986	Converted to open top 1958		
note d	Swiss Trolleybus; unregistered	D103 DAJ	Restored in Lincolnshire Road Car (Roadrunner) livery
SG 2030	German registration		
LCD 52	Built 1950. First used 1953; Preserved in colours of subsequent operator Maidstone Corporation		

Grampian Transport Museum
Alford

Contact address: Alford, Aberdeenshire AB33 8AE
Phone: 01975 562292
Fax: 01975 562180
E-mail: info@g-t-m.freeserve.co.uk
Web site: www.gtm.org.uk
Brief description: Dramatic displays, working exhibits and video presentations trace the history of travel and transport.
Opening days/times: April to October inclusive, 10.00 to 17.00 (10.00-16.00 in October).
Directions by car: On A944 west from Aberdeen (27 miles).

Directions by public transport: Stagecoach bus services from Aberdeen.
Charges: £5 Adults, £4.40 Senior Citizens, £2.40 Children, £13.Family.
Facilities: A B(e) C D E FG H L M P R S T

Registration	Date	Chassis	Body	New to	Fleet No	Status
SP 5139	1922	Ford Model T	B6	Lochgelly Post Office		R
JFM 238D	1966	Bristol Lodekka FS6G	ECW H33/27RD	Crosville Motor Services	DFG238	R
NRG 154M	1974	Leyland Atlantean AN68/1R	Alexander H45/29D	Grampian Regional Transport	154	R

Notes:

SP 5139	Post Bus. On loan from Drambuie Liqueur Co Ltd.
JFM 238D	Last rear entrance Bristol ever built
NRG 154M	Used as a video theatre

Imperial War Museum
London

Contact address: Lambeth Road, London SE1 6HZ
Phone:
020 7416 5320
0891 600140 (Recorded information)
E-mail: website: www.iwm.org.uk
Brief description: Revel in the history of the nation, through the world wars and much more besides. Regular exhibitions and displays of considerable educational value. The one bus in the collection fills a significant gap in transport history and is on display in museum atrium.
Opening days/times: Daily 10.00 to 18.00 (closed 24, 25 and 26 December)
Directions by car: South of Waterloo Station, close to the Elephant & Castle. Parking difficult but Coach Park at Vauxhall Bridge and disabled parking by prior arrangement only — phone 020 7416 5397.
Directions by public transport:
Underground to Lambeth North, Waterloo or Elephant & Castle.
Rail to Waterloo.
Bus routes 1, 3, 12, 53, 59, 68, 148, 155, 159, 168, 171, 172, 176, 188, 344, 453, 468 and C10 with 45, 63, 100 nearby.
Charges: Free entry to main displays.
Facilities: A C D G H R T

Registration	Date	Chassis	Body	New to	Fleet No	Status
LN 4743	1911	LGOC B	LGOC O18/16RO	London General Omnibus Co	B43	R

Notes:

LN 4743	Named "Ole Bill" after wartime cartoon character

Ipswich Transport Museum

Contact address: Old Trolleybus Depot, Cobham Road, Ipswich IP3 9JD
Phone: 01473 715666
E-mail: www.ipswichtransportmuseum.co.uk.html
Affiliation: NARTM, ASTRO, SEMS, AFSM
Brief description: The collection includes most forms of road transport from the last 200 years, including bicycles, horse-drawn vehicles, trucks and service vehicles. There are displays of vehicles and other products of Ipswich engineering companies including six mobile cranes.
Events planned: Please see enthusiast press for details
Opening days/times: April to November: Sundays and Bank Holidays 11.00 to 16.00. School holidays, Monday to Friday 13.00 to 16.00

Above: Park Royal-bodied Guy Arab G351 (HGC 130) of 1946 is a perfect example of the London Transport utility bus specified during and immediately after World War 2. It is seen displayed outside Cobham Bus Museum on Rally Day, 3 April 2005. *Matthew Wharmby*

Left: Midland Red 4943 (943 KHA) is one of only two underfloor-engined BMMO D10 double-deckers built, and survives in the hands of the Transport Museum at Wythall. *Philip Lamb*

Right: Southdown Leyland TD5 EUF 184, new in 1937, was converted to a towing lorry during the 1950s and now resides at Amberley Museum. *Philip Lamb*

Below: 'Bradford's Last Trolleybus', Sunbeam F4 844 (FWX 914), was also Britain's last trolleybus in service on 26 March 1972. It now forms part of the collection at Keighley Bus Museum. *Philip Lamb*

Directions by car: From A12/A14 junction with A1189 (Nacton and Ipswich East) head towards Ipswich on Nacton Road. Turn right into Lindburgh Road. Museum is on left in Cobham Road.
Directions by public transport: By train to Ipswich. Take any bus to Tower Ramparts bus station. Then Ipswich Buses route 6.
Charges: Adult £3.50, Child £2.50, Concessions £2.50, Family £9.50. Special event rates may apply
Facilities: A B(e) D G P R T, picnic area

Registration	Date	Chassis	Body	New to	Fleet No	Status
DX 3988+	1923	Railless	Short B30D	Ipswich Corporation	2	R
DX 5610+	1926	Ransomes Sims & Jefferies D	Ransomes Sims & Jefferies B31D	Ipswich Corporation	9	A
DX 5629+	1926	Garrett O type	Strachan & Brown B31D	Ipswich Corporation	26	A
DX 6591	1927	Tilling Stevens B9B	Eastern Counties B36R	Eastern Counties Road Car Co	78	A
VF 2788	1928	ADC 425A	Eastern Counties B36R	United Automobile Services	J379	A
DX 7812	1929	Tilling Stevens B10A2	(chassis only)	Eastern Counties Road Car Co	116	R
VF 8157	1930	Chevrolet LQ	Bush & Twiddy C14D	Final of Hockwold		R
WV 1209	1932	Bedford WLB	Waveney B20F	Alexander of Devizes		A
PV 817+	1933	Ransomes Sims & Jefferies	Ransomes Sims & Jefferies H24/24R	Ipswich Corporation	46	A
CVF 874	1939	Bristol L5G	ECW B35R	Eastern Counties Omnibus Co	LL574	A
CAH 923	1940	Dennis Ace	ECW B20F	Eastern Counties Omnibus Co	D23	A
PV 8270+	1948	Karrier W	Park Royal H30/26R	Ipswich Corporation	105	RP
KAH 407	1949	Bristol L4G	ECW B35R	Eastern Counties Omnibus Co	LL407	R
KNG 374	1949	Bristol K6B	ECW L27/28R	Eastern Counties Omnibus Co	LK374	RP
PV 9371	1949	Bedford OB	Duple C27F	Mulleys Motorways		R
ADX 1	1950	AEC Regent III 9612E	Park Royal H30/26R	Ipswich Corporation	1	R
ADX 196+	1950	Sunbeam F4	Park Royal H30/26R	Ipswich Corporation	126	R
MAH 744	1951	Bristol LSX4G	ECW B42F	Eastern Counties Omnibus Co	LL744	R
BPV 9	1953	AEC Regal IV 9822E	Park Royal B42D	Ipswich Corporation	9	A
ADX 63B	1964	AEC Regent V 2D2RA	Massey H37/28R	Ipswich Corporation	63	R
APW 829B	1964	Bristol MW6G	ECW C39F	Eastern Counties Omnibus Co	LS829	RP
GNG 125C	1965	Bristol Lodekka FS5G	ECW H33/27RD	Eastern Counties Omnibus Co	LFS125	RP
DPV 68D	1966	AEC Regent V 2D2RA	East Lancs Neepsend H37/28R	Ipswich Corporation	68	A
JRT 82K	1971	AEC Swift 2MP2R	Willowbrook B40D	Ipswich Corporation	82	R
MRT 6P	1976	Leyland Atlantean AN68/1R	Roe H43/29D	Ipswich Corporation	6	R
XNG 770S	1978	Leyland National 11351/1R	Leyland National B53F	Eastern Counties Omnibus Co	LN770	A

+ Trolleybus

Notes:

DX 3988	Believed the oldest trolleybus on display in the world		PV 817	First Ipswich double decker
DX 5610	Changed from solid to pneumatic tyres in 1930		CVF 874	Originally numbered LL74
DX 6591	New with charabanc body; rebuilt in 1934		CAH 923	Originally fitted with Gardner 4LK engine
VF 2788	Original United body replaced in 1934		PV 8270	Originally fitted with wooden seats
DX 7812	Rebodied twice while with Eastern Counties		KNG 374	Engine changed Gardner 5LW by Eastern Counties OC
VF 8157	Body swapped with VF9126; acquired by Mulleys Motorways of Ixworth in 1940		ADX 1	Ipswich Corporation's first motor bus
			MAH 744	Bristol LS prototype

Isle of Wight Bus Museum
Newport (Isle of Wight)

Contact address: Seaclose Quay, Newport, Isle of Wight, PO30 2EF
Phone: 01983 533352
Affiliation: NARTM
Brief description: The collection ranges from a 1927 Daimler CK to a 1979 Ford R-series. Many of the vehicles are of Southern Vectis origin.
Events planned: 15th October 2006 — Running day.
Opening days/times: 8-23 April: daily 10.30-16.00 then Tuesdays only until 23 May;
28 May-28 September: Tuesdays, Wednesdays, Thursdays and Sundays 10.30-16.00

27 May-4 June and 22 July-3 September: daily 10.30 to 16.00
October: Sundays 10.30-16.00
Directions by car: Bus museum is adjacent to Boat Museum (both signposted) off Fairlee Road through Sea Close Park to Quay past Travel Inn.
Directions by public transport: Bus to Newport bus station. Walk 12min to north of town.
Charges: £3 Adult, £2.50 Senior Citizen, £1.50 child.
Facilities: B(e) D G S
Other information: Car parking nearby. Refreshments and toilets at adjacent Boat Museum.

Registration	Date	Chassis	Body	New to	Fleet No	Status
DL 5084	1927	Daimler CK	Dodson B26R	Dodson Bros ('Vectis')	11	A
NG 1109	1931	Reo Pullman	Taylor Ch26D	Reynolds of Overstrand		R
JT 8077	1937	Bedford WTB	Duple C25F	South Dorset Coaches		R
DDL 50	1940	Bristol K5G	ECW O30/26R	Southern Vectis Omnibus Co	703	R
FDL 676	1949	Bedford OB	Duple C29F	Southern Vectis Omnibus Co	216	
GDL 764	1950	Leyland Titan PD2/1A	Leyland L27/26R	Seaview Services		R
ODL 400	1957	Bedford SBG	Duple C41F	Moss Motor Tours of Sandown		RP
PDL 519	1958	Bristol Lodekka LD6G	ECW CO33/27R	Southern Vectis Omnibus Co	559	R
SDL 268	1959	Bristol Lodekka LD6G	ECW H33/27R	Southern Vectis Omnibus Co	563	R
ADL 459B	1964	Bedford SB3	Duple C41F	Pauls Tours of Ryde	9	RP
CDL 479C	1965	Bristol Lodekka FLF6G	ECW H38/32F	Southern Vectis Omnibus Co	611	R
FDL 927D	1966	Bristol MW6G	ECW B43F	Southern Vectis Omnibus Co	806	R
KDL 885F	1968	Bristol RESH6G	Duple C45F	Southern Vectis Omnibus Co	301	R
SDL 638J	1971	Bristol VRTSL6G	ECW H39/31F	Southern Vectis Omnibus Co	628	R
TDL 564K	1971	Bristol RELL6G	ECW OB50F	Southern Vectis Omnibus Co	864	R
VDL 264K	1972	Bedford YRQ	Plaxton B47F	Seaview Services		R
MDL 880R	1976	Leyland National 11351A/1R	Leyland National B52F	Southern Vectis Omnibus Co	880	A
YDL 135T	1979	Ford R1014	Duple B47F	Isle of Wight County Council	5809	A

Notes:

PDL 519	Originally H33/27R
DDL 50	Converted to open top 1959, became tree-lopper in 1969

Keighley Bus Museum
Keighley

Contact address: 47 Brantfell Drive, Burnley, Lancs BB12 8AW
Phone: 01282 413179
Web site: www.kbmt.org.uk
Affiliation: AIM, FBHVC, NARTM, ROOA, Y&HMC
Brief description: A collection of 50 buses, coaches and ancillary vehicles. Some 50% are owned by the Trust and others by private individuals. The Trust aims to establish a permanent home for the collection in central Keighley.
Events planned:
2006 events not yet finalised
Opening days/times: Tuesday evenings 19.00-22.00, and most Sundays (please check in advance) at Riverside, off Dalton Lane adjacent to railway station.
Car parking: Dalton Lane.
Directions by public transport: Keighley (5min from main line station) and 10min walk from bus station. Frequent buses from Keighley (zone routes 708/711, alight at Dalton Mills).
Charges: Special events: £2 Adult, £1 concession. Otherwise free but donations welcome.
Facilities: B(e) P T

Note: Please be aware that vehicles on display can vary from time to time as not all museums display their entire 'fleet'. Visitors wishing to see a particular vehicle should make enquiries prior to their visit.

Registration	Date	Chassis	Body	New to	Fleet No	Status
WT 7101+	1924	Straker Clough	Brush H50R	Keighley Corporation Tramways	5	R
KW 2260	1927	Leyland Lion PLSC3	Leyland B35R	Bradford Corporation	325	A
KY 9106	1931	AEC Regent I	Metro-Cammell	Bradford Corporation	046	A
TF 6860	1931	Leyland Lion LT3	Leyland B36R	Rawtenstall Corporation	61	RP
ANW 682	1934	AEC Regent 661	Roe H30/26R	Leeds City Transport	139	R
CWX 671	1938	Bristol K5G	Roe L27/28R	Keighley-West Yorkshire Services	KDG 26	R
FWX 914+	1948	Sunbeam F4	East Lancs H37/29F	Mexborough & Swinton Traction Co		R
MNW 86	1948	Leyland Tiger PS1	Roe B36R	Leeds City Transport	28	R
LFM 767	1950	Bristol LL6B	ECW B39R	Crosville Motor Services	SLB186	RP
JWU 886	1951	Bristol LL5G	ECW B39R	West Yorkshire Road Car Co	SGL16	R
LYR 533	1951	AEC Regent III O961 RT	Park Royal H30/26R	London Transport	RT3314	R
UUA 214	1955	Leyland Titan PD2/11	Roe H33/25R	Leeds City Transport	214	RP
GJX 331	1956	Daimler CVG6	Roe H37/26R	Halifax Corporation	119	R
VTU 76	1956	Daimler CVG6	Northern Counties H35/23C	SHMD Board	76	R
XLG 477	1956	Atkinson Alpha PL745H	Northern Counties B34C	SHMD Board	77	A
7514 UA	1959	Daimler CVG6-30	Roe H38/32R	Leeds City Transport	514	A
XYJ 418	1961	AEC Routemaster	Park Royal H36/28R	London Transport	RM736	RP
PJX 232	1962	Leyland Leopard L1	Weymann B44F	Halifax Joint Omnibus Committee	232	R
WJY 758	1962	Leyland Atlantean PDR1/1	MCW	Plymouth Corporation	158	R
WBR 246	1963	Atkinson Alpha PM746HL	Marshall B45D	Sunderland Corporation	46	RP
6203 KW	1964	AEC Regent V 2D3RA	Metro Cammell H40/30F	Bradford Corporation	203	A
6204 KW	1964	AEC Regent V 2D3RA	Metro Cammell H40/30F	Bradford Corporation	204	A
6220 KW	1964	AEC Regent V 2D3RA	MCW H40/30F	Bradford Corporation	220	R
ENW 980D	1966	AEC Regent V 2D2RA	Roe H39/31R	Leeds City Transport	980	RP
HNW 131D	1966	Daimler Fleetline CRG6LX	Roe H45/33F	Leeds City Transport	131	R
KVH 473E	1966	Daimler Fleetline CRG6LX	Roe H44/31F	Huddersfield Corporation	473	R
KWT 642D	1966	Bristol Lodekka FS6B	ECW H33/27RD	West Yorkshire Road Car Co	DX210	R
NWU 265D	1966	Bristol Lodekka FS6B	ECW H33/27RD	York - West Yorkshire Services	YDX221	R
TWW 766F	1967	Bristol RELH6G	ECW C47F	West Yorkshire Road Car Co	CRG6	R
YLG 717F	1967	Bristol RESL6G	Northern Counties B43F	SHMD Board	117	A
LAK 309G	1969	Leyland Titan PD3A/12	Alexander H41/29F	Bradford Corporation	309	R
LAK 313G	1969	Leyland Titan PD3A/12	Alexander H41/29F	Bradford Corporation	313	RP
TKU 467K	1971	Leyland Atlantean PDR2/1	Alexander H47/29D	Bradford Corporation	467	RP
WFM 801K	1972	Leyland National 1151/2R/0403	Leyland National B44D	Crosville Motor Services	SNL801	R
XAK 355L	1972	Daimler Fleetline CRL6	Alexander H43/31F	Bradford Corporation	355	RP
GWY 690N	1975	Leyland Leopard PSU4B/4R	Plaxton C45F	West Yorkshire PTE	64	A
DNW 840T	1978	Leyland National 10351B/1R	Leyland National B44F	West Yorkshire Road Car Co	1002	R
JUM 505V	1980	MCW Metrobus	MCW H43/30F	West Yorkshire PTE	7505	A
NKU 245X	1981	Leyland National 2	Leyland National B52F	Yorkshire Traction Co	245	A
D275 OOJ	1987	Freight Rover Sherpa	Carlyle B20F	Carlyle demonstrator		RP

+ Trolleybus

Notes:

WT 7101	Solid tyres
KY 9106	Former double-decker converted to gritter. On loan from Bradford Museums Service
TF 6860	Used as a tow bus and snow plough 1950-1963
CWX 671	Rebodied 1950
FWX 914	Originally single-deck. Rebodied as double-decker for Bradford Corporation 1963
JWU 886	Single block experimental Gardner engine
UUA 214	Leeds City Transport driver trainer 1972/78
XYJ 418	Original registration WLT 736
WJY 758	Converted to open-top in 1975. Restored as Keighley Corporation Tramways 59
NWU 265D	Renumbered 3821 in 1971
KWT 642D	Renumbered 1810 in 1971
TWW 766F	Renumbered 1019 in 1971; restored in later guise as 2508
WFM 801K	Second production Leyland National; operated single door with Greater Manchester Buses (South)

Lincolnshire Road Transport Museum
North Hykeham

Contact address: Whisby Road, North Hykeham, Lincoln LN6 3QT
Phone: 01522 689497
Web site: www.lvvs.org.uk
Affiliation: NARTM
Brief description: An impressive collection of over 50 vehicles including classic cars, commercials, buses and motor cycles, mostly with Lincolnshire connections. Sixty years of road transport history is represented in the museum hall, which was built in 1993. An extension to the hall is planned.
Events planned: Please see enthusiast press and web site.
16 April 2006 — Easter Sunday open day
5 November 2006 — Autumn open day
Opening days/times:
May to October: Monday to Friday 12.00 to 16.00; Sunday 10.00 to 16.00;
November to April: Sunday 13.00 to 16.00. Other times by appointment.
Directions by car: Just off A46 Lincoln by-pass on Whisby Road, which links A46 to B1190.
Directions by public transport:
1 mile from North Hykeham railway station.
Whisby Road is just off Doddington Road, served by several bus routes from city centre.
Charges: £2 adult. Accompanied children free. Other charges may apply at special events — please see web site.
Facilities: A B(e) D P T
Other information: Refreshments available on open days. Please check beforehand if you wish to se aparticular vehicle as a few are rotated with other accommodation.

Registration	Date	Chassis	Body	New to	Fleet No	Status
KW 474	1927	Leyland Lion PLSC1	Leyland B31F	Blythe & Berwick of Bradford		R
TE 8318	1929	Chevrolet LQ	Spicer C14D	Jardine of Morcambe		R
VL 1263	1929	Leyland Lion LT1	Applewhite B32R	Lincoln Corporation	5	R
WH 1553	1929	Leyland Titan TD1	Leyland L27/24RO	Bolton Corporation	54	R
KW 7604	1930	Leyland Badger TA4	Plaxton B20F	Bradford Education Committee	023	R
TF 818	1930	Leyland Lion LT1	Roe B30F	Lancashire United Transport	202	R
FW 5698	1935	Leyland Tiger TS7	Burlingham B35F	Lincolnshire Road Car Co	1411	R
RC 2721	1935	SOS DON	Brush B—F	Trent Motor Traction Co	321	R
FHN 833	1940	Bristol L5G	ECW B35F	United Automobile Services	BG147	RP
BFE 419	1941	Leyland Titan TD7	Roe H30/26R	Lincoln Corporation	64	R
VV 8934	1945	Daimler CWD6	Duple UH30/26R	Northampton Corporation	129	RP
AHE 163	1946	Leyland Titan PD1	Roe H31/25R	Yorkshire Traction Co	726	RP
DBE 187	1946	Bristol K6A	ECW H30/26R	Lincolnshire Road Car Co	2115	R
GUF 727	1947	Leyland Tiger PS1/1	ECW B32R	Southdown Motor Services	677	R
DFE 383	1948	Guy Arab III	Guy H30/26R	Lincoln Corporation	23	R
HPW 133	1949	Bristol K5G	ECW H30/26R	Eastern Counties Omnibus Co	LKH133	R
OHK 432	1949	Daimler CVD6	Roberts H30/26R	Colchester Corporation	4	R
ONO 59	1949	Bristol K5G	ECW L-/-R	Eastern National Omnibus Co	4038	R
FFU 860	1950	AEC Regal III 9621E	Willowbrook DP35F	Enterprise of Scunthorpe	60	R
FDO 573	1953	AEC Regent III 9613E	Willowbrook H32/28RD	J W Camplin & Sons ('Holme Delight') of Donington		RP
OLD 714	1954	AEC Regent III O961 RT	Weymann H30/26R	London Transport	RT4494	R
LFW 326	1955	Bristol Lodekka LD6B	ECW H33/25RD	Lincolnshire Road Car Co	2318	R
OVL 465	1960	Bristol MW5G	ECW B45F	Lincolnshire Road Car Co	2245	R
RFE 416	1961	Leyland Titan PD2/41	Roe H33/28R	Lincoln Corporation	89	R
952 JUB	1964	AEC Regent V 2D2RA	Roe H39/31R	Leeds City Transport	952	RP
CVL 850D	1966	Bristol RELH6G	ECW C47F	Lincolnshire Road Car Co	1431	RP
EVL 549E	1967	Leyland Panther PSUR1/1R	Roe DP45F	Lincoln Corporation	41	RP

Note: Please be aware that vehicles on display can vary from time to time as not all museums display their entire 'fleet'. Visitors wishing to see a particular vehicle should make enquiries prior to their visit.

Registration	Date	Chassis	Body	New to	Fleet No	Status
UVL 873M	1973	Bristol RELL6L	Alexander B48F	Lincoln Corporation	73	RP
NFW 36V	1980	Bristol VRTLL3/6LXB	East Lancs H50/36F	Lincoln City Transport	36	A
PFE 542V	1980	Bristol VRTSL3/6LXB	ECW H43/31F	Lincolnshire Road Car Co	1958	R

Notes:

KW 474	Restored as Lincoln Corporation No 1
FW 5698	Originally fleet No 368. Rebodied in 1949
FHN 833	Originally fleet No BLO 133
DBE 187	Originally fleet No 661. Rebuilt by ECW in mid 1950s
DFE 383	Ruston Hornsby air-cooled engine
ONO 59	Renumbered 1427 in 1954 and 2255 in 1964; subsequently converted to caravan
FFU 860	Passed to Lincolnshire Road Car Co (860) in 1950
CVL 850D	Later renumbered 2231

London's Transport Museum Depot
Acton

Contact address: 39 Wellington Street, London WC2E 7BB.
Phone: 020 7565 7299 — 24hr recorded information; 020 7379 6344 — Admin etc
Fax: 020 7565 7250
E-mail: enquiry@ltmuseum.co.uk
Web site: www.ltmuseum.co.uk
Affiliation: HRA, NARTM, TT
Brief description: The museum at Covent Garden, London, is now closed for major refurbishment until spring 2007.
The Depot is a working museum store and treasure trove of over 370,000 objects. Attractions include rare road and rail vehicles, station models, signs, ticket machines, posters and original artworkk.
Depot location: 118-120 Gunnersbury Lane, Acton, London W3 8BQ
Opening days/times: Open weekends are planned for:
4/5 March 2006 — Model Weekend
20/21 May 2006 — 150 Years of London General Omnibus Co
21/22 October 2006 — Family Weekend.
Pre-booked private views for groups, these can be booked for any date available or pre-booked guided tours for individuals on the last Friday and Saturday in the month (except December).
Car parking: On site parking is reserved for Blue Badge holders and must be requested in advance. Limited parking in the local area.
Facilities for the disabled: Full disabled access including toilets
Charges:
Open Weekends — Adult £6.95, Concession £4.95, Accompanied children under 16 free
Guided Tours — Adult £10, Concession £8.50
Facilities: L S (weekends only)

Registration	Date	Chassis	Body	New to	Fleet No	Status
note m	1829	Horse bus	LGOC	George Shillibeer		R
note n	1875	Horse bus	Thomas Tilling -24-	Thomas Tilling		R
note p	1888	Horse bus	LGOC -26-	London General Omnibus Co		R
LC 3701	1906	De Dion	(chassis only)	London General Omnibus Co	L7	R
LA 9928	1911	LGOC B	LGOC O18/16RO	London General Omnibus Co	B340	RP
XC 8059	1921	AEC K	LGOC O24/22RO	London General Omnibus Co	K424	R
MN 2615	1923	Tilling Stevens TS3A Petrol Electric	(chassis only)	Douglas Corporation	10	R
XM 7399	1923	AEC S	LGOC O28/26RO	London General Omnibus Co	S742	R
YR 3844	1926	AEC NS	LGOC H28/24RO	London General Omnibus Co	NS1995	R
GK 3192	1931	AEC Regent 661	LGOC H28/20R	London General Omnibus Co	ST821	R
GK 5323	1931	AEC Renown 663	LGOC H33/23R	London General Omnibus Co	LT165	R
GK 5486	1931	AEC Regal 662	Duple C30F	London General Omnibus Co	T219	R

Registration	Date	Chassis	Body	New to	Fleet No	Status
GO 5198	1931	AEC Renown 664	LGOC B35F	London General Omnibus Co	LT1076	R
HX 2756+	1931	AEC 663T	UCC H32/24R	London United Tramways	1	R
AXM 649	1934	AEC Regent 661	Chalmers -	London Transport	830J	R
AYV 651	1934	AEC Regent 661	LPTB H30/26R	London Transport	STL469	R
BXD 576	1935	AEC Q O762	Birmingham R C & W B35C	London Transport	Q55	R
CLE 122	1936	Leyland Cub KP03	Weymann B20F	London Transport	C94	R
EXV 253+	1939	Leyland LPTB70	Leyland H40/30R	London Transport	1253	R
FJJ 774	1939	Leyland FEC	LPTB B34F	London Transport	TF77	R
HYM 768+	1948	BUT 9641T	Metro Cammell H40/30R	London Transport	1768	R
MXX 364	1953	Guy Special NLLVP	ECW B26F	London Transport	GS64	R
NLE 537	1953	AEC Regal IV 9821LT RF	Metro Cammell B39F	London Transport	RF537	R
NXP 997	1954	AEC Regent III O961 RT	Park Royal H30/26R	London Transport	RT4712	R
OLD 589	1954	AEC Regent III O961 RT	Park Royal H30/26R	London Transport	RT4825	R
SLT 56	1956	AEC Routemaster	Park Royal/LTE H36/28R	London Transport	RM1	R
SLT 57	1957	AEC Routemaster	Park Royal/LTE H36/28R	London Transport	RM2	RP
737 DYE	1963	AEC Routemaster 2R2RH	Park Royal H36/28R	London Transport	RM1737	R
CUV 229C	1965	AEC Routemaster R2RH/1	Park Royal H36/29RD	London Transport	RCL2229	R
KGY 4D	1966	AEC Routemaster FR2R	Park Royal H41/31F	London Transport	FRM1	R
AML 582H	1969	AEC Merlin 4P2R	MCW B25D	London Transport	MBA582	R
EGP 1J	1970	Daimler Fleetline CRG6LXB	Park Royal H44/24D	London Transport	DMS1	R
KJD 401P	1976	Bristol LH6L	ECW B39F	London Transport	BL1	A
TPJ 61S	1977	Bristol LHS6L	ECW B35F	London Country Bus Services	BN61	R
NUW 567Y	1982	Leyland Titan TNLXB/2RR	Leyland H44/24D	London Transport	T567	R
C526 DYT	1986	Volkswagen LT55	Optare B25F	London Buses Ltd	OV2	R
F115 PHM	1988	Volvo B10M-50	Alexander H75D	Grey Green	VA115	R
note r	1993	Optare Metrorider	Optare B26F	London Buses Ltd	MRL242	R

+ Trolleybus

Notes:

note m	Unregistered reconstruction
note n	Unregistered; Knifeboard type
note p	Unregistered; Garden Seat type
AXM 649	Rebuilt with Breakdown Vehicle body in 1950
SLT 56	Prototype new 9/1954. First Registered 1/1956
SLT 57	Prototype new 1955. First Registered 5/1957
TPJ 61S	Support collection vehicle
F115 PHM	On loan from Arriva London
note r	Unregistered sectioned exhibit built especially for LT Museum

Manchester Museum of Transport
Cheetham

Contact address: Boyle Street, Cheetham, Manchester M8 8UW
Phone: 0161 205 2122
Fax: 0161 202 1110
E-mail: email@gmts.co.uk
Web site: www.gmts.co.uk or www.manchester.bus.museum
Affiliation: AIM, MLA-NW, NARTM
Brief description:
The museum houses over 70 buses and coaches from the Greater Manchester area, from an 1876 horse bus to a 1990 Metrolink tram. Travel back to a time of twopenny singles and coach trips to Blackpool. Extensive displays of photos, uniforms and models complement the vehicles, and visitors may enter many of the vehicles and view the museum's workshop.

Note: Please be aware that vehicles on display can vary from time to time as not all museums display their entire 'fleet'. Visitors wishing to see a particular vehicle should make enquiries prior to their visit.

Events planned:
25/26 March 2006 — Spring Transport Festival
23 April 2006 — London Bus Event
20/21 May 2006 — Lancashire United (LUT) Weekend
17/18 June 2006 — Accessible Transport Weekend
22/23 July 2006 — Festival of Model Tramways
3 September 2006 — Trans-Lancs Rally
14/15 October 2006 — ManchesterBus 100
2/3 December 2006 — Christmas Cracker
Opening days/times: Wednesdays, Saturdays, Sundays & Bank Holidays: 10.00-17.00 March to October, 10.00 to 16.00 November-February inclusive (please phone for Christmas/New Year opening)
Directions by car:
From M62/M60 junction 18, follow 'Castlefields' signs to Cheetham Hill; from City, follow A665 (Cheetham Hill Road) — Museum signposted.
Directions by public transport:
Bus 135 or 59 to Queen's Road; Metrolink tram to Woodlands Road (10min walk)
Charges: £4 adult, £2 concession (5-15, over 60, students and unemployed), £9 family. Free under 5 and registered disabled. Season tickets available. School parties free
Facilities: B(e) C D F G H P R S T
Other information: Archives available for study by arrangement.

Registration	Date	Chassis	Body	New to	Fleet No	Status
note b	1876	Horse bus	Manchester Carriage Co O18/14RO	Manchester Carriage Co	2	R
DB 5070	1925	Tilling Stevens TS6 Petrol Electric	Brush O54RO	North Western Road Car Co	170	R
CK 3825	1927	Leyland Lion PLSC1	Leyland B31F	Ribble Motor Services	295	R
VM 4439	1928	Leyland Tiger TS1	Metro Cammell/Crossley B—R	Manchester Corporation	138	A
VY 957	1929	Leyland Lion PLSC1	Ribble B32R	York Corporation	2	R
VR 5742	1930	Leyland Tiger TS2	Manchester Corporation Car Works B30R	Manchester Corporation	28	R
ANB 851	1934	Crossley Mancunian	Crossley/MCT H28/26R	Manchester Corporation	436	A
AXJ 857	1934	Leyland Titan TD3	(chassis only)	Manchester Corporation	526	R
JA 7585	1935	Leyland Tiger TS7	English Electric B35C	Stockport Corporation	185	A
RN 7824	1936	Leyland Cheetah LZ2	Brush C31F	Ribble Motor Services	1568	RP
EFJ 92	1938	Bedford WTB	Heaver C25F	Taylor of Exeter		RP
AJA 152	1939	Bristol K5G	Willowbrook L27/26R	North Western Road Car Co	432	R
BBA 560	1939	AEC Regent O661	Park Royal H26/22R	Salford Corporation	235	R
JP 4712	1940	Leyland Titan TD7	Leyland L24/24R	Wigan Corporation	70	RP
FTB 11	1941	Leyland Titan TD7	Northern Coachbuilders UL27/26R	Leigh Corporation	84	A
BJA 425	1946	Bristol L5G	Willowbrook B38R	North Western Road Car Co	270	R
HTB 656	1946	Leyland Tiger PS1	Roe B35R	Ramsbottom UDC	17	R
HTF 586	1947	Bedford OB	Scottish Motor Traction C29F	Warburton Bros of Bury		R
CDB 224	1948	Leyland Titan PD2/1	Leyland L27/26R	North Western Road Car Co	224	R
CWH 717	1948	Leyland Titan PD2/4	Leyland	Bolton Corporation	367	R
DBU 246	1948	Leyland Titan PD1/3	Roe H31/25R	Oldham Corporation	246	RP
JND 791	1948	Crossley DD42/8S	Crossley H32/26R	Manchester Corporation	2150	R
JNA 467	1949	Leyland Titan PD1/3	Metro Cammell H32/26R	Manchester Corporation	3166	RP
LMA 284	1949	Foden PVSC6	Lawton C35F	Coppenhall of Comberbach		R
BEN 177	1950	AEC Regent III 9613A	Weymann H30/26R	Bury Corporation	177	R
CWG 206	1950	Leyland Tiger PS1	Alexander C35F	W Alexander & Sons	PA164	R
FBU 827	1950	Crossley DD42/8	Crossley H30/26R	Oldham Corporation	368	RP
LTC 774+	1950	Crossley Empire TDD42/2	Crossley H30/26R	Ashton-under-Lyne Corporation	80	RP
MTB 848	1950	Leyland Tiger PS2/1	East Lancs B35R	Rawtenstall Corporation	55	R
EDB 549	1951	Leyland Titan PD2/1	Leyland O30/20R	Stockport Corporation	295	R
EDB 562	1951	Leyland Titan PD2/1	Leyland H30/26R	Stockport Corporation	308	A
EDB 575	1951	Crossley DD42/7	Crossley H30/26R	Stockport Corporation	321	R
JND 646	1951	Leyland Titan PD2/3	Metro Cammell H32/26R	Manchester Corporation	3245	R
JVU 755+	1951	Crossley Dominion TDD64/1	Crossley H36/30R	Manchester Corporation	1250	R
NNB 125	1953	Leyland Royal Tiger PSU1/13	Northern Counties B41C	Manchester Corporation	25	R
UTC 672	1954	AEC Regent III 9613S	East Lancs L27/28RD	Bamber Bridge Motor Services	4	R

Registration	Date	Chassis	Body	New to	Fleet No	Status
UMA 370	1955	Atkinson PD746	Northern Counties H35/24C	SHMD Board	70	R
JBN 153	1956	Leyland Titan PD2/13	Metro Cammell H34/28R	Bolton Corporation	77	R
NDK 980	1956	AEC Regent V D2RA6G	Weymann H33/28R	Rochdale Corporation	280	R
PND 460	1956	Leyland Titan PD2/12	Metro Cammell H36/28R	Manchester Corporation	3460	R
DJP 754	1957	Leyland Titan PD2/30	Northern Counties H33/28R	Wigan Corporation	115	R
NBU 494	1957	Leyland Titan PD2/20	Roe H31/29R	Oldham Corporation	394	R
116 JTD	1958	Guy Arab IV	Northern Counties H41/32R	Lancashire United Transport	21	R
122 JTD	1958	Guy Arab IV	Northern Counties H41/32R	Lancashire United Transport	27	R
SDK 442	1958	Leyland Worldmaster RT3/2	Plaxton C41F	Ellen Smith of Rochdale		RP
TNA 496	1958	Leyland Titan PD2/40	Burlingham H37/28R	Manchester Corporation	3496	R
TNA 520	1958	Leyland Titan PD2/34	Burlingham H37/28R	Manchester Corporation	3520	R
UNB 629	1960	Leyland Atlantean PDR1/1	Metro Cammell H45/33F	Manchester Corporation	3629	R
YDK 590	1960	AEC Reliance 2MU3RA	Harrington C37F	Yelloway Motor Services of Rochdale		R
HEK 705	1961	Leyland Titan PD3A/2	Massey H41/29F	Wigan Corporation	57	A
TRJ 112	1962	Daimler CVG6	Metro Cammell H37/28R	Salford City Transport	112	R
414 CLT	1963	AEC Routemaster 2R2RH	Park Royal H36/28R	London Transport	RM1414	R
4632 VM	1963	Daimler CVG6K	Metro Cammell H37/28R	Manchester Corporation	4632	R
REN 116	1963	Leyland Atlantean PDR1/1	Metro Cammell H41/33F	Bury Corporation	116	A
8860 VR	1964	AEC Regent V 2D3RA	East Lancs Neepsend H41/32R	A Mayne & Son of Manchester		R
BND 874C	1965	Leyland Panther Cub PSURC1	Park Royal B43D	Manchester Corporation	74	R
DBA 214C	1965	Leyland Atlantean PDR1/1	Metro Cammell H43/33F	Salford City Transport	214	R
DDB 174C	1965	Daimler Fleetline CRG6LX	Alexander H44/31F	North Western Road Car Co	174	R
PTC 114C	1965	AEC Renown 3B3RA	East Lancs H41/31F	Leigh Corporation	15	R
PTE 944C	1965	Leyland Titan PD2/37	Roe H37/28F	Ashton-under-Lyne Corporation	44	R
FRJ 254D	1966	Leyland Titan PD2/40	Metro Cammell H36/28F	Salford City Transport	254	R
JRJ 281E	1967	Leyland Titan PD2/40	Metro Cammell H36/28F	Salford City Transport	281	R
HVM 901F	1968	Leyland Atlantean PDR1/1	Park Royal H45/28D	Manchester City Transport	1001	R
KDB 408F	1968	Leyland Leopard PSU4/1R	East Lancs B43D	Stockport Corporation	408	RP
KJA 871F	1968	Leyland Titan PD3/14	East Lancs H38/32R	Stockport Corporation	71	R
MJA 891G	1969	Leyland Titan PD3/14	East Lancs H38/32R	Stockport Corporation	91	R
MJA 897G	1969	Leyland Titan PD3/14	East Lancs O38/32F	Stockport Corporation	97	R
TTD 386H	1969	Leyland Titan PD3/14	East Lancs H41/32F	Ramsbottom UDC	11	R
SRJ 328H	1970	Leyland Atlantean PDR2/1	MCW H47/31D	SELNEC PTE	1205	RP
TXJ 507K	1972	Leyland National 1151/2R/0202	Leyland National B46D	SELNEC PTE	EX30	R
VNB 101L	1972	Leyland Atlantean AN68/1R	Park Royal H43/32F	SELNEC PTE	7001	R
XVU 352M	1974	Seddon Pennine IV-236	Pennine B19F	Greater Manchester PTE	1722	R
GNC 276N	1975	Seddon Lucas	Pennine B19F	Greater Manchester PTE	EX62	R
HVU 244N	1975	AEC Reliance 6U3ZR	Plaxton C49F	Yelloway Motor Services of Rochdale		R
XBU 17S	1978	Leyland Fleetline FE30AGR	Northern Counties H43/32F	Greater Manchester PTE	8017	A
ORJ 83W	1981	MCW Metrobus DR102/21	MCW H43/30F	Greater Manchester PTE	5083	A
A706 LNC	1984	Leyland Atlantean AN68D/1R	Northern Counties H43/32F	Greater Manchester PTE	8706	A
B65 PJA	1984	Leyland Olympian ONXB/1R	NCME H43/30F	Greater Manchester PTE	3065	A
C208 FVU	1986	MCW Metrobus DR132/8	Northern Counties CH43/29F	Greater Manchester PTE	5208	RP
D63 NOF	1986	Freight Rover 400 Special	Carlyle B18F	Manchester Minibuses (Bee Line Buzz Co)		A
D676 NNE	1987	MCW Metrorider MF151/3	MCW B23F	Greater Manchester Buses	1676	R
M939 XKA	1994	Mercedes Benz 609D	Mercedes - Devon Conversion	Greater Manchester Accessible Transport		R

+ Trolleybus

Notes:

note b	Largest surviving horse bus.	VM 4439	Body new 1935
DB 5070	Petrol Electric transmission	VY 957	Body rebuilt 1983; restored to Ribble livery
CK 3825	Body rebuilt 1981	VR 5742	Rebodied 1937

Note: Please be aware that vehicles on display can vary from time to time as not all museums display their entire 'fleet'. Visitors wishing to see a particular vehicle should make enquiries prior to their visit.

ANB 851	Rebodied 1938
BBA 560	Training bus with dual controls 1948-70. Renumbered 98 in 1950
AJA 152	Rebodied 1951
FTB 11	Originally L27/28R. Refurbished by Thurgood in the 1950s
BJA 425	Originally numbered 125; rebodied 1958 with 1952 body
CWH 717	Originally H30/26R; converted to tower wagon 1963
LMA 284	Body new 1954
EDB 549	Originally H30/26R. Converted to open top in 1968
EDB 562	Used as training bus 1968-1978
UMA 370	Only Atkinson double-decker bodied. Originally H35/25C
122 JTD	Gardner 6LX from new.
SDK 442	New body fited 1970
TNA 520	Fully auto transmission when new and converted to semi-auto in 1963
UNB 629	H43/34F when new. Reseated in 1954 using ex-trolleybus seats
414 CLT	Loaned to Manchester Corporation when new in Feb 1963
HVM 901F	First 'Mancunian' double-decker
KJA 871F	Restored as GMPTE 5871
TTD 386H	Last half-cab double-decker delivered to a British operator
MJA 891G	Last open-rear-platform double-decker delivered to a British operator
MJA 897G	Originally H38/32F; converted to open-top in 1982
SRJ 328H	Mancunian style ordered originally by Salford City Transport
VNB 101L	First SELNEC Standard double-decker
TXJ 507K	First production Leyland National
GNC 276N	Battery-powered
M939 XKA	Wheelchair lift at rear

Midland Road Transport Group — Butterley

Contact address: 21 Ash Grove, Mastin Moor, Chesterfield S43 3AW
Phone: Midland Road Transport Group — 01246 473619
Midland Railway 01773 747674, Visitor Information Line (01773) 570140.
Brief Description: A large purpose-built museum building housing a collection of buses, lorries and fork lift trucks fully or partially restored. Situated at the Swanwick Junction site of the Midland Railway Centre. All vehicles are all privately-owned by individual preservaionists who co-operated together to provide finances to build the museum which was completed in 2004
Events planned:
9 July 2006 — 3rd Annual Road Transport Rally (date to be confirmed)
Opening days/times:
See Railways Restored for details
Directions by car: To Swanwick Junction.
From the north, M1 Jcn 28, follow A38 southbound to B600, turn left to Somercotes, right on to B6016 through Riddings. Follow signs to Codnor/Heanor and turn right onto Coach Road at the bottom of descent from Riddings. Half mile along this narrow lane, take right fork after speed bumps.
From the south, M1 Jcn 26, follow A610 northbound to Codnor, turn right and right again onto B6016 Alfreton/Somercotes. Travel along for three miles and turn left onto Coach Road at bottom of hill after wooded areas on B6016.
Directions by public transport: Trent Barton service H1 from Derby, Heanor or Alfreton. Half mile walk from end of Coach Road, ask for Riddings Dale
Facilities: R, S, T

Registration	Date	Chassis	Body	New to	Fleet No	Status
ESV 811	1947	AEC Regal III	Weymann B30D	Carris of Lisbon	141	R
HVO 937	1947	AEC Regent II	Weymann H30/26R	Mansfield District	126	R
KRR 255	1949	AEC Regal III	Weymann B35F	Mansfield District	9	R
NRA 78F	1968	Bedford TK	Reeve Burgess	Derbyshire County Council		RP
BNU 679G	1969	Bristol VRTSL6LX	ECW H43/32F	Midland General Omnibus Co		RP
PNU 114K	1971	Leyland Atlantean PDR1A/1	Northern Counties H44/28D	Chesterfield Corporation	114	RP
RCH 629L	1972	Bristol VRTSL6LX	ECW H43/34F	Trent Motor Traction Co	629	R
NNU 123M	1973	Daimler Fleetline CRL6-30	Roe H42/29D	Chesterfield Corporation	123	R
NNU 124M	1973	Daimler Fleetline CRL6-30	Roe H42/29D	Chesterfield Corporation	124	R
SHN 80L	1973	Bristol RELH6G	ECW DP49F	United Automobile Services	6080	R
UOA 322L	1973	Leyland National 1151/1R/0401	Leyland National B52F	Eastern National Omnibus Co	1702	RP
LRA 801P	1975	Bristol VRTSL3/501	ECW H43/34F	Midland General Omnibus Co	801	R

Notes:

ESV 811	Original Portugese registration II-14-49
NRA 78F	Library Bus
UOA 322L	Originally registered WNO 551L
LRA 801P	Original Leyland 501 engine replaced by Gardner unit 1980

Museum of Transport
Glasgow

Contact address: Kelvin Hall, 1 Bunhouse Road, Glasgow G3 8DP
Phone: 0141 287 2720 (school bookings on 0141 565 4112/3)
Fax: 0141 287 2692
Affiliation: NARTM
Brief description: The museum displays many items of transport history dating from the 1860s.
Opening days/times: Monday to Thursday and Saturday, 10.00 to 17.00; Friday and Sunday 11.00 to 17.00 (closed 25/26, 31 December and 1/2 January)
Directions by car: From M8 junctions 17 or 19
Directions by public transport: Buses 9, 16, 18, 62, from City Centre (Dumbarton Road) to Kelvin Hall; Underground to Kelvin Hall; nearest main-line railway station is Partick.
Charges: Free admission
Facilities: D F G H R T
Other information: Guided tours, exhibitions and events also held.

Registration	Date	Chassis	Body	New to	Fleet No	Status
EGA 79	1949	Albion Venturer CX37S	Croft H30/26R	Glasgow Corporation	B92	R
FYS 988+	1958	BUT RETB1	Burlingham B50F	Glasgow Corporation	TBS13	R
FYS 998	1958	Leyland Atlantean PDR1/1	Alexander H44/34F	Glasgow Corporation	LA1	R
+ Trolleybus						

Notes:

FYS 988	Exhibited at the 1958 Commercial Motor Show

National Museum of Science and Industry
Wroughton

Contact address: Exhibition Road, London SW7 2DD
Phone: 0207 942 4105 or 01793 814466
E-mail: s.evans@nmsi.ac.uk
Brief description: The bus collection is located at Wroughton airfield (hangar 4), near Swindon, Wiltshire.
Events planned: Open days are held and details of these may be found in the enthusiast press.
Opening days/times: Open only on Transport Festival and Open Days.
Directions by car: On A4361 approx 4 miles south of Swindon.
Directions by public transport: Publicised for Open Days
Charges: Published for each event.

Note: Please be aware that vehicles on display can vary from time to time as not all museums display their entire 'fleet'. Visitors wishing to see a particular vehicle should make enquiries prior to their visit.

Registration	Date	Chassis	Body	New to	Fleet No	Status
LMJ 653G	1913	Fiat 52B		(operator unknown) Yugoslavia		RP
JCP 60F	1928	Leyland Lion PLSC1	Leyland B31F	Jersey Railways & Tramways		A
DR 4902	1929	Leyland Titan TD1	Leyland L51RO	National Omnibus & Transport Co	2849	A
DX 8871+	1930	Ransomes Sims & Jefferies D	Ransomes Sims & Jefferies B31D	Ipswich Corporation	44	A
GW 713	1931	Gilford 1680T	Weymann C30D	Valliant of Ealing		A
VO 6806	1931	AEC Regal 662	Cravens B32F	Red Bus of Mansfield		A
JN 5783	1935	AEC Q 762	(chassis only) -	Westcliff-on-Sea Motor Services		A
CPM 61+	1939	AEC 661T	Weymann H28/26R	Brighton Hove & District	6340	A
FR 1347	1940	Saurer CRD		GFM (Switzerland)	52	A
DHR 192	1943	Guy Arab II	Weymann UH30/26R	Swindon Corporation	51	A
KPT 909	1949	Leyland Titan PD2/1	Leyland L27/26R	Weardale Motor Services of Frosterley		R
LTA 772	1951	Bristol LWL5G	ECW B32R	Western National Omnibus Co	1613	A
HET 513	1953	Crossley DD42/7	Crossley H30/26R	Rotherham Corporation	213	A
NLP 645	1953	AEC Regal IV 9822E	Park Royal RDP37C	British European Airways	1035	A
OTT 55	1953	Bristol LS5G	ECW B41F	Southern National Omnibus Co	1701	A
OLJ 291	1954	Bedford CAV	Bedford B12	Non-psv use		A
VLT 140	1960	AEC Routemaster R2RH	Park Royal H36/28R	London Transport	RM140	R
504 EBL	1963	Bedford VAL 14	Duple C52F	Reliance Motor Services of Newbury	87	A
note u	1970	Moulton MD	Moulton C23F	Moulton Development vehicle		A
BCD 820L	1973	Leyland National 1151/1R/0102	Leyland National B49F	Southdown Motor Services	20	A
+ Trolleybus						

(handwritten beside LTA 772: ① ... B' First 4·12)

Notes:

LMJ 653G	Yugoslavia
JCP 60F	Originally registered J 4601
FR 1347	Displays original Swiss registration FR1347
note u	Eight-wheeled integral development vehicle (unregistered)

(handwritten: 14-9-2012)

North of England Open Air Museum
Beamish

Contact address: Beamish, Co Durham, DH9 0RG
Phone: 0191 370 4000
Fax: 0191 370 4001
E-mail: museum@beamish.org.uk
Web site: www.beamishmuseum.co.uk
Brief description: Beamish is an open-air museum which vividly recreates life in the North of England in the early 1800s and early 1900s Buildings from throughout the region have been brought to Beamish, rebuilt and furnished as they once were. Costumed staff welcome visitors and demonstrate the past way of life in The Town, Colliery Village, Home Farm, Railway Station, Pockerley Manor and 1825 Railway. A one-mile circular period tramway carries visitors around the Museum and a replica 1913 Daimler bus operates between The Town and Colliery Village.
Events planned: (transport related, please contact for non-related events) please contact to confirm actual dates
30 April 2006 — Power from the Past
14 May 2006 — Morgan Car Meeting
410Sept 2006 — Alvis Car Meet
24 Sept 2006 — Classic car day
Opening days/times: 2006
Summer: 1 April to 28 October: (open every day)
Winter 29 October to 23 March 2007: 10.00 to 16.00 (closed Mondays and Fridays); also closed 11 December to 1 January 2007 (inclusive).
Reduced operations in winter.
Last admission always 15.00.
Directions by car: Follow A1(M) to junction 63 (Chester-le-Street exit). Take A693 towards Stanley and follow Beamish Museum signs.
Directions by public transport: Buses 709 from Newcastle, 720 from Durham and 775/778 from Sunderland all serve Beamish.

Charges: — 2006 rates, under 5s free
Summer: Adult £16, Child £10, Over 60s/Students £12.50.
Winter: £6 per person.
Group rates available in summer for parties of 20 or more.
Facilities: B E F G H M P R T
Other information: Free leaflet available in advance for visitors with disabilities and mobility limitations.
Some vehicles not on display. Please telephone for information

Registration	Date	Chassis	Body	New to	Fleet No	Status
WT 7108+	1924	Straker Clough T29	Brush B32F	Keighley Corporation Tramways	12	A
UP 551	1928	BMMO SOS QL	Brush Replica B37F	Northern General Transport Co	338	RP
VK 5401	1931	Dodge UF30A	Robson of Consett B14F	Batey of Rookhope		RP
LTN 501+	1948	Sunbeam S7	Northern Coachbuilders H39/31R	Newcastle Corporation	501	R
J 2503	1988	Renault	Osborne O18/14RO	Beamish of the North of England Open Air Museum		R

J 2007
+ Trolleybus

Notes:
UP 551	Replica body has been constructed
VK 5401	Undergoing restoration off-site
LTN 501	On loan to the Trolleybus Museum at Sandtoft
J 2503	Replica of 1913 Daimler.

North West Museum of Road Transport

Contact address: The Old Bus Depot, 51 Hall Street, St Helens, WA10 1DU
Phone: 01744 451681
E-mail: email@hallstreetdepot.co.uk
website: www.hallstreetdepot.co.uk
Affiliation: NARTM
Brief description: A collection of over 70 historic vehicles representing the transport heritage of the northwest of England.
Events planned: Please see the enthusiast press for details
Opening days/times: Expected to re-open to the public during 2006 after major refurbishment. Please see the enthusiast press for details
Facilities: To be confirmed

Registration	Date	Chassis	Body	New to	Fleet No	Status
AFY 971	1934	Leyland Titan TD3	English Electric O26/25R	Southport Corporation	43	A
ATD 683	1935	Leyland Lion LT7	Massey B30R	Widnes Corporation	39	A
RV 6360	1935	Leyland Titan TD4	English Electric O26/24R	Portsmouth Corporation	117	R
EWM 358	1945	Daimler CWA6	Duple UH30/26R	Southport Corporation	62	A
ANQ 778	1946	AEC Regent III	Commonwealth Engineering	Dept of Road Transport & Tramways of Sydney	1984	A
DED 797	1946	Leyland Titan PD1	Alexander H30/26R	Warrington Corporation	16	RP
HLW 159	1946	AEC Regent III O961 RT	Park Royal H30/26R	London Transport	RT172	R
FFY 404	1947	Leyland Titan PD2/3	Leyland O30/26R	Southport Corporation	87	R
KTD 768	1948	Leyland Titan PD2/1	Lydney L27/26R	Leigh Corporation	16	R
ACB 902	1949	Guy Arab II	Northern Coachbuilders H30/26R	Blackburn Corporation	74	A
KTC 615	1949	Guy Arab III	Guy B33R	Accrington Corporation	10	A
GFY 406	1950	Leyland Titan PD2/3	Leyland H30/26R	Southport Corporation	106	RP

Note: Please be aware that vehicles on display can vary from time to time as not all museums display their entire 'fleet'. Visitors wishing to see a particular vehicle should make enquiries prior to their visit.

Registration	Date	Chassis	Body	New to	Fleet No	Status
NTF 466	1952	Daimler CVG5	Northern Counties B32F	Lancaster City Transport	466	R
RFM 641	1953	Guy Arab IV	Massey H30/26R	Chester Corporation	1	R
CDJ 878	1954	Leyland Titan PD2/9	Davies H30/26R	St Helens Corporation	E78	A
RFM 644	1954	Guy Arab IV	Guy/Park Royal H30/26R	Chester Corporation	4	R
434 BTE	1957	Crossley Regent V D3RV	East Lancs H31/28RD	Darwen Corporation	17	R
GDJ 435	1957	AEC Regent V MD3RV	Weymann H33/26R	St Helens Corporation	H135	A
KRN 422	1957	Leyland Titan PD2/10	Crossley H33/29R	Preston Corporation	31	R
FHF 456	1959	Leyland Atlantean PDR1/1	Metro Cammell H44/33F	Wallasey Corporation	6	A
KDJ 999	1959	AEC Regent V 2D3RA	East Lancs H41/32F	St Helens Corporation	K199	A
LDJ 985	1960	Leyland Titan PD2A/27	Weymann H30/25RD	St Helens Corporation	K175	A
562 RTF	1961	Leyland Titan PD2/40	East Lancs H37/28R	Widnes Corporation	31	R
574 TD	1962	Guy Arab IV	Northern Counties H41/32R	Lancashire United Transport	110	R
PSJ 480	1962	Leyland Titan PD2A/27	Massey H37/27F	Wigan Corporation	35	RP
TRJ 109	1962	AEC Reliance 2MU3RV	Weymann B45F	Salford City Transport	109	RP
201 YTE	1963	Leyland Titan PD2/37	East Lancs O37/28F	Lancaster City Transport	201	R
TDJ 612	1963	AEC Reliance 2MU3RA	Marshall B45F	St Helens Corporation	212	R
4227 FM	1964	Bristol Lodekka FS6G	ECW H33/27RD	Crosville Motor Services	DFG157	R
AJA 139B	1964	Bedford VAL14	Strachan B52F	North Western Road Car Co	139	RP
HTF 644B	1964	Leyland Titan PD2/40	East Lancs H37/28R	Widnes Corporation	38	R
JTD 300B	1964	Guy Arab V	Northern Counties H41/32F	Lancashire United Transport	166	A
BCK 367C	1965	Leyland Titan PD3/6	Leyland/Preston Corporation H38/32F	Preston Corporation	61	A
BED 731C	1965	Leyland Titan PD2/40 Special	East Lancs H34/30F	Warrington Corporation	50	R
FFM 135C	1965	Guy Arab V	Massey H41/32F	Chester Corporation	35	RP
MDJ 555E	1967	Leyland Titan PD2A/27	East Lancs H37/28R	St Helens Corporation	55	A
KJA 299G	1968	Bristol RESL6G	Marshall B43F	North Western Road Car Co	299	R
DFM 347H	1969	Guy Arab V	Northern Counties H41/32F	Chester Corporation	47	R
JFM 650J	1970	Daimler Fleetline CRG6LX	Northern Counties H43/29F	Chester Corporation	50	RP
JDJ 260K	1972	AEC Swift 3MP2R	Marshall B44D	St Helens Corporation	260	R
PDJ 269L	1972	AEC Swift 3MP2R	Marshall B42D	St Helens Corporation	269	RP
RTC 645L	1972	Leyland National 1151/1R/0101	Leyland National B52F	Widnes Corporation	1	R
LED 71P	1976	Bristol RESL6G	East Lancs B41D	Warrington Corporation	71	R
CWG 696V	1979	Leyland Atlantean AN68A/1R	Alexander H--/--D	South Yorkshire PTE	1696	R
XLV 140W	1980	Leyland National 2 NL116AL11/1R	Leyland National B49F	Merseyside PTE	6140	R
YMA 99W	1981	Dennis Dominator DD121B	Northern Counties H43/29F	Chester City Transport	99	RP

Notes:

AFY 971	Originally H26/25R
RV 6360	Originally H26/24R; renumbered 6 following open-top conversion
HLW 159	Acquired by Bradford City Transport (410) in 1958
FFY 404	Originally H30/26R
PSJ 480	Originally registered JJP 502
201 YTE	Originally H37/28F
BCK 367C	Rebuilt from Leyland PD2 by Preston Corporation
DFM 347H	Last Guy Arab delivered to a British operator
LED 71P	Relocated away from museum during refurbishing works

Nottingham Transport Heritage Centre
Ruddington

Contact address: Mere Way, Ruddington, Nottingham NG11 6NX
Phone: 0115 940 5705
Web site: http://www.nthc.co.uk
Affiliation: NARTM
Brief description: The centre offers exhibits covering road and rail transport, and provides the opportunity to experience travel of a bygone age.
Events planned: 30 April 2006 — 'The Big Clear Out' Bus and Coach Autojumble,
13 August 2006 — Annual Bus Gala,
8 October 2006 — End of Season Road Transport Gala.
Opening days/times: Sundays and Bank Holiday Mondays 10.45-17.00. Easter to last weekend in October. Last admission 16.30.
Directions by car: 3 miles south of Nottingham just off A52 ring-road and main A60 road via small roundabout at Ruddington.
Directions by public transport: Buses from Nottingham pass near the museum
Charges: Adults £5, Senior £4.50, Children 4-14 £3, Family (2 adults 3 children) £15.
Facilities: B B(e) D E G H P R S T

Registration	Date	Chassis	Body	New to	Fleet No	Status
VO 8846	1932	Leyland Lion LT5	Willowbrook DP32F	South Notts Bus Co of Gotham	17	A
DJF 349	1947	Leyland Titan PD1	Leyland H30/26R	Leicester City Transport	248	RP
JVO 230	1948	Leyland Titan PD1A	Duple L29/26F	Barton Transport of Chilwell	507	R
MAL 310	1951	Leyland Royal Tiger PSU1/11	Duple DP45F	South Notts Bus Co of Gotham	42	A
APR 167A	1953	Leyland Titan PD2/12	Leyland H30/26RD	Barton Transport of Chilwell	732	A
OTV 161	1953	AEC Regent III 9613E	Park Royal H30/26R	Nottingham City Transport	161	R
PFN 865	1959	AEC Regent V 2LD3RA		East Kent Road Car Co		R
866 HAL	1960	AEC Reliance 2MU3RV	Plaxton C41F	Barton Transport of Chilwell	866	RP
80 NVO	1962	Leyland Titan PD3/4	Northern Counties L33/32F	South Notts Bus Co of Gotham	80	RP
YRC 194	1962	Leyland Tiger Cub PSUC1/1	Alexander DP41F	Trent Motor Traction Co	194	R
CUV 218C	1965	AEC Routemaster R2RH/1	Park Royal H32/25D	London Transport	RCL 2218	R
DAU 370C	1965	AEC Renown 3B3RA	Weymann H40/30F	Nottingham City Transport	370	R
EOD 524D	1966	AEC Regent V 2D3RA	MCW H34/25F	Devon General	524	R
FEL 751D	1966	Bristol MW6G	ECW C39F	Hants & Dorset Motor Services	904	R
LNN 89E	1967	Albion Lowlander LR3	Northern Counties H41/30F	South Notts Bus Co of Gotham	89	RP
STO 523H	1970	Leyland Atlantean PDR1A/1	Northern Counties H47/30D	Nottingham City Transport	523	R
KVO 429P	1975	Leyland National 11351/2R	Leyland National B50F	Trent Motor Traction Co	429	A
ORC 545P	1976	Leyland Atlantean AN68/1R	ECW O--/--F	Northern General Transport Co	3299	R
ARC 666T	1976	Leyland Atlantean AN68A/1R	Northern Counties H47/31D	Nottingham City Transport	666	R
SCH 117X	1981	Leyland Fleetline FE30ALR	ECW H44/31F	South Notts Bus Co of Gotham	117	R

Notes:

APR 167A	Originally registered RAL334
PFN 865	Recovery vehicle
LNN 89E	Last Albion Lowlander delivered badged Leyland
KVO 429P	Originally B44D
ORC 545P	Originally H45/27D and registered MPT299P; used as promotional vehicle

Note: Please be aware that vehicles on display can vary from time to time as not all museums display their entire 'fleet'. Visitors wishing to see a particular vehicle should make enquiries prior to their visit.

Left: The Tameside Transport Collection have begun the restoration of 1929 Crossley Arrow LG 2637, new to S. Jackson & Sons of Crewe. *David Potts*

Below: The Midland Road Transport Group is home to Midland General Weymann-bodied AEC Regal no 175 (KRR 255), new to Mansfield & District in 1949. *Andrew Bagshaw*

Above: Chesterfield 124, a Roe-bodied Daimler Fleetline of 1973, is owned by the Midland Road Transport Group. *Andrew Bagshaw*

Below: City of Oxford's minibus pioneers are represented at the Oxford Bus Museum by Carlyle-bodied Ford Transit 724 (C724 JJO) of 1986.

Oxford Bus Museum
Long Hanborough

Contact address: Station Yard, Long Hanborough, Witney, Oxfordshire, OX29 8LA
Phone: 01993 883617 (Answerphone) or 01993 881662
Affiliation: NARTM
Brief description: Over 40 buses dating from 1915 to 1994, mainly from City of Oxford Motor Services and other local companies. The collection includes many vehicles of AEC manufacture plus cars, fire engines and support vehicles. New Morris Motors Museum now incorporated.
Events planned: Please see enthusiast press for details.
Opening days/times: Wednesdays, Sundays and Bank Holiday Mondays, 10.30 to 16.30. Saturdays open from Easter until the last Saturday in October, 10.30-16.30 (last entries 16.00). Bus rides at 15.00 on the first Sunday of each month from the first Sunday in April to the first Sunday in October inclusive.
Directions by car: The entrance is on the south side of the A4095 (Witney-Bicester), between the villages of Bladon and Long Hanborough.
Directions by public transport: Museum is adjacent to Hanborough railway station on the Oxford-Worcester line, Sunday train services (journey time Oxford 10mins, London Paddington 70mins). Stagecoach bus service from George Street Oxford, weekdays, hourly to Long Hanborough village centre (1 mile).
Charges: Adults £2.50, Children £1.50, OAP £2.50, Family (2+2) £7.
Facilities: B(e) D P R S T
Other information: School parties welcome by arrangement — please telephone for booking.

Registration	Date	Chassis	Body	New to	Fleet No	Status
DU 4838	1915	Daimler Y	City of Oxford Electric Tramways B32R	City of Oxford Electric Tramways	39	A
note e	1916	Daimler Y	(chassis only)			A
note f	1916	Daimler Y	(chassis only)			A
note ao	1917	Daimler Y	O18/16RO	City of Oxford Electric Tramways		RP
YL 740	1925	Morris Commercial 1-ton	Ch14			R
JO 5032	1932	AEC Regal 642	(chassis only)	City of Oxford Motor Services	GC41	R
JO 5403	1932	AEC Regent 661	Brush O28/24R	City of Oxford Motor Services	GA16	R
DBW 613	1948	Bedford OB	Duple C29F	Oliver of Long Handborough		A
JVF 528	1949	Bedford OB	Duple C29F	Bensley of Martham		R
NJO 703	1949	AEC Regal III 9621A	Willowbrook DP32F	City of Oxford Motor Services	703	R
OFC 393	1949	AEC Regent III 9612A	Weymann H30/26R	City of Oxford Motor Services	H892	A
OFC 205	1950	AEC Regal III 6821A	Duple C32F	South Midland Motor Services	66	A
PWL 413	1950	AEC Regent III 9613A	Weymann L27/26R	City of Oxford Motor Services	L166	R
GJB 254	1952	Bristol LWL6B	ECW B39R	Thames Valley Traction Co	616	R
SFC 610	1952	AEC Regal IV 9821S	Willowbrook C37C	City of Oxford Motor Services	610	R
TWL 928	1953	AEC Regent III 9613S	Park Royal H30/26R	City of Oxford Motor Services	H928	RP
956 AJO	1957	AEC Regent V MD3RV	Park Royal H33/28R	City of Oxford Motor Services	H956	R
YNX 478	1958	AEC Reliance MU3RA	Duple Midland B44F	Chiltern Queens of Woodcote		RP
756 KFC	1960	AEC Reliance 2MU3RV	Park Royal B44F	City of Oxford Motor Services	756	R
14 LFC	1961	Morris FF	Wadham C27F	Morris Motors		RP
304 KFC	1961	Dennis Loline II	East Lancs H35/28F	City of Oxford Motor Services	304	R
305 KFC	1961	Dennis Loline II	East Lancs H35/28F	City of Oxford Motor Services	305	R
850 ABK	1962	AEC Reliance 2MU3RA	Duple C43F	Don Motor Coach Co of Southsea		RP
YWB 494M	1964	International Harvester 1853FC	Superior of Ohio B44F	United States Air Force		RP
FWL 371E	1967	AEC Renown 3B3RA	Northern Counties H38/27F	City of Oxford Motor Services	371	RP
NAC 416F	1967	Leyland Atlantean PDR1A/1	Northern Counties H44/31F	Stratford-upon-Avon Blue Motors	10	A
UFC 430K	1971	Daimler Fleetline CRL6	Northern Counties H43/27D	City of Oxford Motor Services	430	A
EUD 256K	1972	AEC Reliance 6MU4R	Plaxton B47F	Chiltern Queens of Woodcote		R
VER 262L	1972	AEC Reliance 6U3ZR	Alexander C53F	Premier Travel of Cambridge	262	RP
HUD 476S	1977	Bristol VRTSL3/6LXB	ECW H43/27D	City of Oxford Motor Services	476	R
BBW 21V	1980	Leyland Leopard PSU3	Duple C49F	City of Oxford Motor Services	21	R
JUD 597W	1980	Ford R1014	Plaxton C45F	House of Watlington		R
A869 SUL	1983	Leyland Titan TNLXB/2RRSp	Leyland H44/26D	London Transport	T869	R
B106 XJO	1985	Ford Transit 160D	Carlyle B16F	South Midland	SM6	RP
C724 JJO	1986	Ford Transit	Carlyle DP20F	City of Oxford Motor Services	724	R
D122 PTT	1987	Ford Transit 190D	Mellor B16F	Thames Transit	122	R
L247 FDV	1994	Iveco 49-10	Mellor B13D	Bay Line of Exeter		R

Notes:

DU 4838	Body new 1920
note f	Chassis only
note e	Chassis only
note ao	Body ex-London built 1906
JO 5032	Passed to Mascot Motors in Jersey and subsequently converted to lorry. Body removed. To be exhibited as chassis.
JO 5403	Originally H28/24R
JVF 528	Restored in Mulleys livery.
OFC 205	Displayed as an unrestored vehicle
YNX 478	Carries 1956 body transferred from Dennis Pelican chassis
305 KFC	Sectioned museum display showing body construction method
14 LFC	Originally used for Morris Motors band
850 ABK	Acquired by Chiltern Queens of Woodcote in 1964
YWB 494M	Original USAF Identity 64 B 2428
NAC 416F	Acquired by City of Oxford Motor Services (905) in 1970
A869 SUL	Acquired by City of Oxford Motor Services (975) in 1993
L247 FDV	Bi-mode Minibus

Scottish Vintage Bus Museum
Lathalmond

Contact address: M90 Commerce Park, Lathalmond, Fife, KY12 OSJ
Phone: 01383 623380
Website: www.busweb.co.uk/svbm
Affiliation: NARTM
Brief description: The collection of over 160 buses was, in the main, operated or manufactured in Scotland, from the late 1920s to the early 1980s. Vehicles are generally owned by private individuals or groups. A fully-equipped workshop enables comprehensive restoration to be undertaken. The 42-acre site is a former Royal Navy depot.
Events planned: Please see enthusiast press for details.
Opening days/times: Easter to end of September, Sundays 13.00 to 17.00
Directions by car: Use M90 junction 4. Take B914 Dollar road. Left B915 Dunfermline (2 miles). 2 miles to M90 Commerce Park on right.
Directions by public transport: Nearest bus/train Dunfermline. No public transport to site.
Charges: Sunday opening £3. Other charges apply at special events.
Facilities: B B(e) D E P R S T

Registration	Date	Chassis	Body	New to	Fleet No	Status
CD 7045	1922	Leyland G7	Short O27/24R	Southdown Motor Services	135	R
GE 2446	1928	Leyland Titan TD1	Leyland L27/24RO	Glasgow Corporation	111	R
RU 8678	1929	Leyland Lion PLSC3	Leyland B35F	Hants & Dorset Motor Services	268	RP
SO 3740	1929	Leyland Tiger TS2	Alexander B32F	Scottish General (Northern) Omnibus Co	P63	R
VD 3433	1934	Leyland Lion LT5A	Alexander B36F	Central SMT Co		R
WG 1620	1934	Gilford Hera L176S	(chassis only)	Alexander	Y49	R
AAA 756	1935	Albion Victor PK114	Abbott C20C	King Alfred Motor Services		R
WG 3260	1935	Leyland Lion LT5A	Alexander B35F	W Alexander & Sons	P705	A
WS 4522	1935	Leyland Tiger TS7	Cowieson B—R	Scottish Motor Traction Co		RP
ATF 477	1937	Leyland Tiger TS7T	Fowler B39F	Singleton of Leyland		A
AUX 296	1939	Sentinel-HSG	Cowieson B32R	Sentinel of Shrewsbury (demonstrator)		RP
WG 8107	1939	Leyland Tiger TS8	Alexander -	W Alexander & Sons	P528	RP
WG 8790	1939	Leyland Tiger TS8	Alexander B39F	W Alexander & Sons	P573	RP
ETJ 108	1940	Leyland Tiger TS11	Roe -	Leigh Corporation	79	A
HF 9126	1940	Leyland Titan TD7	Metro Cammell	Wallasey Corporation	74	A
WG 9180	1940	Leyland Titan TD7	Leyland L27/26R	W Alexander & Sons	R266	R
DSG 169	1942	Leyland Titan TD5	Alexander L27/26R	Scottish Motor Traction Co	J66	R
CDR 679	1943	Guy Arab II	Duple UH30/26R	Plymouth Corporation	249	R
JWS 594	1943	Guy Arab II	Duple/Nudd H31/24R	London Transport	G 77	R

Note: Please be aware that vehicles on display can vary from time to time as not all museums display their entire 'fleet'. Visitors wishing to see a particular vehicle should make enquiries prior to their visit.

Registration	Date	Chassis	Body	New to	Fleet No	Status
BRS 37	1945	Daimler CWD6	Duple H30/26R	Aberdeen Corporation	155	R
JHT 802	1946	Bristol K6A	ECW H31/28R	Bristol Tramways	C3386	RP
AWG 623	1947	AEC Regal I O662	Alexander C31F	W Alexander & Sons	A36	R
AWG 639	1947	AEC Regal I O662	Alexander C35F	W Alexander & Sons	A52	R
CUH 859	1947	Leyland Tiger PS1	ECW B-R	Western Welsh Omnibus Co	859	A
HFO659	1947	Guy Arab III	(chassis only)	Blackburn Corporation	78	R
note o	1947	Albion Venturer CX19	Comeng H33/28R	DRTT of Sydney	1877	RP
XG 9304	1947	Leyland Titan PD1A	Northern Counties L27/26R	Middlesborough Corporation	52	A
AWG 393	1948	Guy Arab III	Cravens H30/26R	W Alexander & Sons	RO607	R
BMS 405	1948	Daimler CVD6	Burlingham C33F	W Alexander & Sons	D10	A
BWG 39	1948	Bedford OB	Scottish Motor Traction C25F	W Alexander & Sons	W218	RP
ESG 652	1948	Guy Arab III	Metro Cammell B35R	Edinburgh Corporation	739	R
FSC 182	1949	Daimler CVG6	Metro Cammell H31/25R	Edinburgh Corporation	135	R
CWG 283	1950	Leyland Tiger PS1	Alexander C35F	W Alexander & Sons	PA181	R
DCS 616	1950	Daimler CVD6	Massey O32/28RD	Hunter (A1) of Dreghorn	16A	R
EVA 324	1950	Guy Arab III	Guy B33R	Central SMT Co	K24	R
GVD 47	1950	Guy Arab III	Duple H31/26R	Hutchinson's Coaches of Overtown		R
SJ 1340	1950	Bedford OB	Duple C29F	Gordon of Lamlash		RP
SS 7486	1950	Bedford OB	Duple C29F	Stark's Motor Services of Dunbar		A
SS 7501	1950	Bedford OB	Duple C29F	Fairbairn of Haddington		R
AYJ 379	1951	Daimler CVD6	Croft H30/26R	Dundee Corporation	127	R
DGS 536	1951	Leyland Tiger PS1/1	McLennan C39F	A & C McLennan of Spittalfield		R
DGS 625	1951	Leyland Tiger PS1/1	McLennan C39F	A & C McLennan of Spittalfield		R
DMS 820	1951	Leyland Tiger OPS2/1	Alexander C35F	W Alexander & Sons	PB7	A
DMS 823	1951	Leyland Tiger OPS2/1	Alexander C35F	W Alexander & Sons	PB10	A
DWG 526	1951	Leyland Royal Tiger PSU1/15	Leyland C41C	W Alexander & Sons	PC30	R
MTE 639	1951	AEC Regent III 6812A	Weymann H33/26R	Morecambe & Heysham Corporation	77	R
BMS 222	1952	Leyland Royal Tiger PSU1/15	Alexander C41C	W Alexander & Sons	PC1	R
CYJ 252	1953	AEC Regent III 9613E	Alexander H32/26R	Dundee Corporation	137	R
FGS 59D	1953	Bedford SB	Mulliner B36F	Royal Navy		RP
NXP 506	1953	Bedford SB	Plaxton C33F	D Halley of Sauchie		R
CHG 541	1954	Leyland Tiger PS2/14	East Lancs B39F	Burnley Colne & Nelson	41	R
GM 6384	1954	Leyland Titan PD2/10	Leyland L27/28R	Central SMT Co	L484	A
LFS 480	1954	Leyland Titan PD2/20	Metro Cammell H34/29R	Edinburgh Corporation	480	R
ETS 964	1955	Daimler CVG6	Metro Cammell H36/28R	Dundee Corporation	184	RP
FWG 846	1955	Bristol LS6G	ECW B45F	W Alexander & Sons	E11	RP
HRG 209	1955	AEC Regent V D2RV6G	Crossley H35/29R	Aberdeen Corporation	209	A
TYD 888	1955	AEC Reliance MU3RV	Duple C43F	Wakes of Sparkford		R
UFF 178	1955	AEC Regent V D2RV6G	Crossley H35/29R	Aberdeen Corporation	207	A
OFS 777	1957	Leyland Titan PD2/20	Metro Cammell H34/29R	Edinburgh Corporation	777	R
OFS 798	1957	Leyland Titan PD2/20	Metro Cammell H34/29R	Edinburgh Corporation	798	RP
OWS 620	1957	Bristol Lodekka LD6G	ECW H33/27R	Scottish Omnibuses	AA620	A
FAS 982	1959	Albion Victor FT39KAN	Reading B35F	Jersey Motor Transport Co	5	R
SWS 671	1959	AEC Reliance 2MU3RV	Alexander C38F	Scottish Omnibuses	B671	R
SWS 715	1959	AEC Reliance 2MU3RV	Park Royal C41F	Scottish Omnibuses	B715	A
TFU 90	1959	Bedford SB1	Plaxton C41F	Paterson of Duffturn		R
EDS 320A	1960	AEC Routemaster R2RH	Park Royal H36/28R	London Transport	RM606	RP
NMS 366	1960	AEC Reliance 2MU3RV	Alexander C41F	W Alexander & Sons	AC155	RP
RAG 578	1960	Daimler CVG6LX-30	Northern Counties FH41/32F	T Hunter (A1) of Kilmarnock		R
VSC 86	1960	Leyland Tiger Cub PSUC1/3	Weymann B47F	Edinburgh Corporation	86	R
WAJ 112	1960	Albion Nimbus NS3N	Plaxton C29F	Watson of Huntingdon		A
XSL 945A	1960	Bristol MW6G	Alexander C41F	Western SMT Co	T1590	A
XSN 25A	1960	Bristol MW6G	Alexander C41F	Western SMT Co	T1591	A
EDS 288A	1961	AEC Routemaster R2RH	Park Royal H36/28R	London Transport	RM910	R
JVS 541	1961	Leyland Tiger Cub PSUC1/2	Alexander C41F	Alexander (Fife)	FPD225	R
RAG 411	1961	Bristol Lodekka LD6G	ECW H33/27RD	Western SMT Co	1645	R
RCS 382	1961	Leyland Titan PD3A/3	Alexander L35/32RD	Western SMT Co	1684	R

W2lou

50

Registration	Date	Chassis	Body	New to	Fleet No	Status
YSG 101	1961	Leyland Leopard PSU3/2R	Alexander B33T	Edinburgh Corporation	101	R
YYJ 914	1961	Leyland Tiger Cub PSUC1/2	Alexander C41F	Stark's Motor Services of Dunbar	H8	A
7424 SP	1962	AEC Reliance 2MU3RV	Alexander C41F	W Alexander & Sons (Fife) Ltd	FAC4	R
LDS 201A	1962	AEC Routemaster R2RH	Park Royal H36/28R	London Transport	RM1607	R
NSJ 502	1962	AEC Reliance 2MU3RV	Alexander C41F	W Alexander & Sons (Northern)	NAC205	R
UCS 659	1963	Albion Lowlander LR3	Northern Counties H40/31F	Western SMT Co	N1795	R
AFS 91B	1964	AEC Reliance 4MU3RA	Alexander B53F	Eastern Scottish	B91	R
ARG 17B	1964	AEC Reliance 2MU3RA	Alexander C41F	W Alexander & Sons (Northern) Ltd	NAC246	RP
ASC 665B	1964	Leyland Titan PD3/6	Alexander H41/29F	Edinburgh Corporation	665	R
AWA 124B	1964	Bedford SB13	Duple C41F	J O Andrew of Sheffield		R
BXA 464B	1964	Bristol Lodekka FS6G	ECW H33/27RD	W Alexander & Sons (Fife) Ltd	FRD199	R
CSG 29C	1965	Bristol Lodekka FLF6G	ECW -	Eastern Scottish		R
CSG 43C	1965	Bristol Lodekka FLF6G	ECW H38/32F	Scottish Omnibuses	AA43	RP
DMS 325C	1965	Leyland Leopard PSU3/3R	Alexander -	Alexander (Midland)	MPE40	R
DMS 359C	1965	Leyland Leopard PSU3/3R	Alexander -	Alexander (Midland)	MPE73	R
ESF 801C	1965	Leyland Atlantean PDR1/1	Alexander H43/31F	Edinburgh Corporation	801	R
EWS 130D	1966	AEC Reliance 2U3RA	Alexander C—F	Eastern Scottish	ZB130	A
EWS 168D	1966	Bristol RELH6G	Alexander C38Ft	Scottish Omnibuses (Eastern Scottish)	XA168	A
FFV 447D	1966	AEC Reliance 2U3RA	Plaxton C45F	J Abbott & Sons of Blackpool		R
WTE 155D	1966	Guy Arab V	Northern Counties H41/30F	Lancashire United Transport	232	R
GRS 343E	1967	Albion Viking VK43AL	Alexander DP40F	W Alexander & Sons (Northern) Ltd	NNV43	R
HDV 639E	1967	Bristol MW6G	ECW C39F	Western National Omnibus Co	1434	R
HGM 335E	1967	Bristol Lodekka FLF6G	ECW H44/34F	Central SMT Co	BL335	R
HGM 346E	1967	Bristol Lodekka FLF6G	ECW H44/34F	Central SMT Co	BL346	R
JSC 900E	1967	Leyland Atlantean PDR2/1	Alexander O47/35F	Edinburgh Corporation	900	R
LUS 524E	1967	AEC Reliance 2U3RA	Willowbrook C49F	David MacBrayne of Glasgow	150	R
NMY 636E	1967	AEC Routemaster	Park Royal H—/—F	British European Airways		R
KGM 664F	1968	Leyland Leopard PSU3/1R	Alexander B53F	Central SMT Co	T64	A
LFS 288F	1968	Bristol VRTLL/6LX	ECW O47/33F	Scottish Omnibuses	AA288	R
LFS 294F	1968	Bristol VRTLL/6LX	ECW H47/36F	Eastern Scottish	AA294	RP
LFS 303F	1968	Bristol VRTLL/6LX	ECW H-/-F	Scottish Omnibuses	AA303	RP
NTY 416F	1968	AEC Reliance 6MU3R	Plaxton C45F	J Rowell of Prudhoe		RP
VMP 8G	1968	Albion Viking VK43AL	Alexander DP40F	Road Transport Industry Training Board	16	RP
NAG 120G	1969	Bristol REMH6G	Alexander C42Ft	Western SMT Co	T2214	RP
XFM 42G	1969	Guy Arab V	Northern Counties H41/32F	Chester Corporation	42	R
SSF 237H	1970	Bedford VAL70	Duple C53F	Edinburgh Corporation	237	A
TMS 585H	1970	Leyland Leopard PSU3/1R	Alexander C49F	Road Transport Industry Training Board	84	A
TGM 214J	1971	Daimler Fleetline CRG6LX	ECW H43/34F	Central SMT Co	D14	R
XWS 165K	1971	Bedford J2	Plaxton C20F	Glass of Haddington		R
BFS 1L	1972	Leyland Atlantean AN68/1R	Alexander H45/30D	Edinburgh City Transport	1	R
BWG 833L	1972	Leyland Leopard PSU3/3R	Alexander B53F	W Alexander & Sons (Midland) Ltd	MPE133	A
YSD 350L	1972	Leyland Leopard PSU3/3R	Alexander B41F	Western SMT Co	L2390	R
BFS 463L	1973	Bedford YRQ	Alexander DP45F	Scottish Omnibuses (Eastern Scottish)	C463	A
BWS 105L	1973	Seddon Pennine IV-236	Seddon DP25F	Edinburgh Corporation	105	R
SCS 333M	1974	Leyland Leopard PSU3/3R	Alexander B53F	Western SMT Co	L2464	R
SCS 366M	1974	Leyland Leopard PSU3/3R	Alexander B53F	Western SMT Co	L2497	R
LSX 16P	1975	Volvo Ailsa B57	Alexander H44/35F	Alexander (Fife)	FRA16	A
MSF 750P	1976	Seddon Pennine VII	Alexander C42Ft	Scottish Omnibuses (Eastern Scottish)	XS750	R
SMS 120P	1976	Daimler Fleetline CRG6LXB	Alexander H44/31F	W Alexander & Sons (Midland)	MRF120	RP
NCS 16P	1976	Leyland Fleetline FE30AGR	Alexander H43/31F	Hill (A1) of Stevenston		RP
NDL 656R	1977	Bristol VRTSL3/6LXB	ECW H43/31F	Southern Vectis Omnibus Co	656	RP
ORS 60R	1977	Leyland Leopard PSU4C/4R	Alexander C45F	Grampian Regional Transport	60	R

Note: Please be aware that vehicles on display can vary from time to time as not all museums display their entire 'fleet'. Visitors wishing to see a particular vehicle should make enquiries prior to their visit.

Registration	Date	Chassis	Body	New to	Fleet No	Status
OSJ 629R	1977	Leyland Leopard PSU3C/3R	Alexander B53F	Western SMT Co	L2629	RP
RRS 46R	1977	Leyland Leopard PSU3E/4R	Duple C49F	W Alexander & Sons (Northern)	NPE46	R
XMS 252R	1977	Leyland Leopard PSU3C/4R	Alexander B53F	W Alexander & Sons (Midland)	MPE252	A
CSG 773S	1978	Volvo Ailsa B55-10	Alexander H43/32F	Scottish Omnibuses (Eastern Scottish)	VV773	RP
CSG 792S	1978	Seddon Pennine VII	Plaxton C45F	Scottish Omnibuses (Eastern Scottish)	S792	A
JSF 928T	1978	Seddon Pennine VII	Alexander DP49F	Scottish Omnibuses	S928	RP
JTU 588T	1978	Leyland National 10351B/1R	Leyland National B—F	Crosville Motor Services	SNG588	RP
XBO 121T	1978	Bristol VRT/SL3/6LXB	ECW O43/31F	National Welsh Omnibus Services	HR4878	R
JSX 595T	1979	Leyland Atlantean AN68A/1R	Alexander H45/30D	Lothian Regional Transport	595	R
LIL 9929	1979	Bedford VAS	Plaxton C29F	Blood Transfusion Service		RP
WTS 266T	1979	Volvo Ailsa B55-10	Alexander H44/31D	Tayside Regional Council	266	R
DSD 936V	1979	Seddon Pennine VII	Alexander C49F	Western SMT Co	S2936	RP
GSO 80V	1980	Leyland Leopard PSU3E/4R	Alexander C49F	W Alexander & Sons (Northern)	NPE80	RP
ESF 647W	1980	Guy Victory Mk 2	Alexander H60/24D	China Motor Bus	LV36	R
SSX 602V	1980	Seddon Pennine VII	Alexander B53F	Scottish Omnibuses (Eastern Scottish)	S602	RP
LMS 374W	1980	Leyland Leopard PSU3F/4R	Alexander B53F	W Alexander & Sons (Midland)	MPE374	A
RHS 400W	1980	Wales & Edwards	Wales & Edwards B12F	South of Scotland Electricity		R
FES 831W	1981	Volvo B58-61	Duple B59F	Stagecoach of Perth		RP
YFS 310W	1981	Leyland National 2 NL116L11/1R	Leyland National B48F	Scottish Omnibuses	N310	RP
HSC 173X	1981	Leyland Cub CU435	Duple B31F	Lothian Region Transport	173	RP
GSC 667X	1982	Leyland Olympian ONTL11/1R	Alexander H47/28D	Lothian Region Transport	667	R
KSX 102X	1982	Leyland National 2 NL116L11/2R	Leyland National B40D	Lothian Region Transport	102	R
ULS 716X	1982	Leyland Leopard PSU3G/4R	Alexander C49F	W Alexander & Sons (Midland)	MPE416	RP
ULS 717X	1982	Leyland Leopard PSU3G/4R	Alexander C49F	W Alexander & Sons (Midland)	MPE417	RP
NFS 176Y	1982	Leyland Leopard PSU3G/4R	Alexander C49F	W Alexander & Sons (Fife)	FPE176	RP
B349 LSO	1985	Leyland Olympian ON5LXCT/1R	Alexander H45/32F	W Alexander & Sons (Northern)	NLO49	A
C777 SFS	1985	Leyland Olympian ONTL11/2R	ECW H51/32D	Lothian Region Transport	777	R

Notes:

CD 7045	Rebodied 1928. On loan from Stagecoach South East
SO 3740	Passed to W Alexander & Sons in 1930; numbered P63 in 1932 and rebodied in 1934
VD 3433	Rebodied 1945
WG 3260	Rebodied 1945
WG 8107	Breakdown Vehicle. Originally C35F.
ETJ 108	Breakdown Vehicle
HF 9126	Originally H28/26R; acquired by Lancshire County Constabulary in 1952 and converted for use as mobile control post
DSG 169	Alexander body to Leyland design; converted to open-top in 1959 and restored in 1980/1
CDR 679	Orig Roe body converted to platform lorry in 1963. Present body from VV 9135.
JWS 594	Originally London Transport G77 (GLL577); rebuilt and rebodied 1953
JHT 802	1949 body fitted in 1957
note o	Not registered
HFO659	Originally registered ACB 907. Breakdown vehicle.
SS 7486	Passed to Scottish Omnibuses (C22) in 1964
DCS 616	Rebodied in 1958 as H32/28RD
GVD 47	Acquired by McGill's Bus Services of Barrhead in 1952
AYJ 379	On loan from Dundee Museums
FGS 59D	Originally registered 51 51 RN
UFF 178	Originally registered HRG 207
ETS 964	On loan from Travel Dundee
FAS 982	Originally registered J 1359

EDS 320A	Originally registered WLT 606; acquired by Kelvin Scottish Omnibuses (1919) in 1986
XSN 25A	Originally registered OCS 713
XSL 945A	Originally registered OCS 712
EDS 288A	Originally registered WLT 910; acquired by Kelvin Scottish Omnibuses (1929) in 1986
JVS 541	Originally registered RMS 714
YYJ 914	Originally registered ESS 989
NSJ 502	Originally registered SRS 117.
LDS 201A	Originally registered 607 DYE; acquired by Stagecoach at Perth in 1986
CSG 29C	Converted to breakdown vehicle
DMS 325C	Converted to Breakdown Vehicle
DMS 359C	Converted to Breakdown Vehicle
NMY 636E	Converted to mobile caravan
HDV 639E	First vehicle operated by Stagecoach
JSC 900E	Originally H47/35F
LFS 288F	Converted to open-top
YSD 350L	Originally C49F; rebuilt and shortened by Western SMT in 1980
XBO 121T	Converted to open-top by SVBM
NDL 656R	Acquired by Lowland Scottish Omnibuses (856) in 1991
LIL 9929	Originally registered CJU 998T
ESF 647W	Original Hong Kong registration was CH 9399
RHS 400W	Battery-electric bus
FES 831W	First new vehicle delivered to Stagecoach (as C50Ft)

Sheffield Bus Museum
Tinsley

Contact address: Tinsley Tram Sheds, Sheffield Road, Tinsley, Sheffield S9 2FY
Phone: 0114 255 3010
Website: www.sheffieldbusmuseum.com
Brief description: The display of over 25 vehicles is housed in part of a former tram shed.
Events planned: 12 June, 14 August, 11 September, 9 October, 11 December. Please see enthusiast press for details.
Opening days/times: Open days as advertised; also most Saturdays and Sundays (not Christmas) 12.00 to 16.00 (please telephone to check opening times before travelling especially to see specific vehicles).
Directions by car: From M1 Junction 34 take A6178
Directions by public transport: By Supertram to Carbrook (200yd from museum); also good bus links from Sheffield and Rotherham.
Charges: Adult £1.50, concession 75p, Family £3.
Facilities: A, B(e), D, F, H, G. S, R (open days)

Registration	Date	Chassis	Body	New to	Fleet No	Status
GWJ 724	1941	AEC Regent O661	Sheffield Transport Department -	Sheffield Corporation	G54	A
JWB 416	1947	Leyland Tiger PS1	Weymann B34R	Sheffield Corporation	216	A
HD 7905	1948	Leyland Tiger PS1	Brush B34F	Yorkshire Woollen District Transport Co	622	R
KWE 255	1948	AEC Regent III 9612E	Weymann -	Sheffield Corporation	G55	RP
MHY 765	1950	Leyland Comet ECPO/1R	Duple C32F	Orient Coaches of Bristol	-	RP
OWE 116	1952	AEC Regent III 9613A	Roe H33/25R	Sheffield Joint Omnibus Committee	116	RP
KET 220	1954	Daimler CVG6	Weymann H30/26R	Rotherham Corporation	220	RP
RWB 87	1954	Leyland Titan PD2/12	Weymann H32/26R	Sheffield Corporation	687	R
WRA 12	1955	AEC Monocoach MC3RV	Park Royal B45F	Booth & Fisher of Halfway	-	R
VDV 760	1958	Bristol Lodekka LD6G	ECW H33/27RD	Western National Omnibus Co	1943	R
TDK 322	1959	AEC Regent V D2RA	Weymann H33/28RD	Rochdale Corporation	322	R
TET 135	1959	Daimler CVG6-30	Roe -	Rotherham Corporation	135	A
6330 WJ	1960	AEC Regent V 2D3RA	Roe H39/30RD	Sheffield Joint Omnibus Committee	1330	A
7874 WJ	1960	AEC Regent V 2D3RA	Alexander H37/32R	Sheffield Corporation	874	R
TUJ 261	1960	Ford Trader	Burlingham C-F			A
1322 WA	1961	AEC Reliance 2MU3RA	Plaxton C36F	Sheffield United Tours	322	A
GHD 765	1962	Leyland Titan PD3A/1	Metro Cammell H39/31F	Yorkshire Woollen District Transport Co	893	R
449 CLT	1963	AEC Routemaster	Park Royal H36/28R	London Transport	RM1449	RP
DWB 54H	1970	AEC Swift 5P2R	Park Royal B50F	Sheffield Transport	54	RP
LWB 388P	1976	Volvo Ailsa B55-10	Van Hool McArdle H44/31D	South Yorkshire PTE	388	RP
PSJ 825R	1976	Volvo Ailsa B55-10	Van Hool McArdle H44/31F	J Hunter (A1) of Kilmarnock	-	RP
CWG 756V	1979	Leyland Atlantean AN68A/1R	Roe H45/29D	South Yorkshire PTE	1756	A
C53 HDT	1985	Dennis Domino SDA1202	Optare B33F	South Yorkshire PTE	53	A

Notes:

GWJ 724	Originally bus 462; converted to grit wagon
KWE 255	Originally bus 255; converted to grit wagon
TET 135	Originally H39/31F; converted to breakdown vehicle
PSJ 825R	Originally H44/31D

Note: Please be aware that vehicles on display can vary from time to time as not all museums display their entire 'fleet'. Visitors wishing to see a particular vehicle should make enquiries prior to their visit.

Tameside Transport Collection
Mossley

Contact address: Roaches Industrial Estate, Manchester Road, Mossley, Greater Manchester

Brief description: A working museum comprising a small but varied collection of vehicles ranging from 1929 to the1960s. There is in addition a display of transport-related items.

Opening days/times: Last weekend of each month (except December), 10.00 to 15.00; visits at other times by prior appointment.

Directions by car: From Ashton-under-Lyne take A635 (Huddersfield) through Mossley. Museum is 1 mile on right-hand side, adjacent to Claybank Terrace.

Directions by public transport:

Bus service 355 from Ashton-under-Lyne or Oldham.

By rail to Mossley station (approximately 1 mile walk towards Greenfield).

Charges: No charge but donations welcome.

Facilities: D S R T

Other information: Car parking is limited.

Registration	Date	Chassis	Body	New to	Fleet No	Status
LG 2637	1929	Crossley Arrow	Crossley B32R	S Jackson & Sons of Crewe		RP
DNF 204	1937	Crossley Mancunian	Metro Cammell/Crossley B32R	Manchester Corporation	129	RP
DBN 978	1949	Crossley SD42/7	Crossley B32R	Bolton Corporation	8	R
JND 728	1950	Daimler CVG6	Metro Cammell H32/26R	Manchester Corporation	4127	RP
CRC 911	1951	Crossley DD42/8A	Brush H30/26R	Derby Corporation	111	R
FRJ 511	1951	Daimler CVG6	Metro Cammell H30/24R	Salford City Transport	511	R
422 CAX	1961	AEC Regent V MD3RV	Massey L31/28R	Bedwas & Machen UDC	5	R
105 UTU	1962	Leyland Titan PD2/37	Northern Counties H36/28F	SHMD Board	5	RP
7209 PW	1962	Bedford J2SZ2	Plaxton C20F	H & I Jarvis of Downham Market	4	R
BWO 585B	1964	AEC Regent V 2MD3RA	Massey L31/28R	Bedwas & Machen UDC	8	A
NMA 328D	1966	Daimler Fleetline CRG6LX	Northern Counties H-/-F	SHMD Board	28	RP

Notes:

LG 2637	Passed to Crosville Motor Services (U2) in 1934
DNF 204	Open rear platform
422 CAX	Converted to trainer by Rhumney Valley UDC 1976
BWO 585B	Last AEC to receive lowbridge body
NMA 328D	Used as exhibition bus 1983 to1992

Transport Museum Society of Ireland
Howth

Contact address: Howth Castle Demesne, Howth, Dublin 13, Ireland

Phone: (00) 353 1 832 0427

Affiliation: NARTM

Brief description: The museum is run by a group of volunteers dedicated to the preservation and restoration of valuable road transport heritage. Exhibits include buses, trams and commercial, public utility, military, fire-appliance, electric and horse-drawn vehicles. Other displays include transport-associated memorabilia. The museum is a registered charity.

Opening days/times:

June to August: Monday to Saturday 10.00 to 17.00; Sunday 14.00 to 17.00.

September to May: Saturdays, Sundays and Bank Holidays 14.00 to 17.00.

Directions by car: Howth is 9 miles north of Dublin City Centre or 7 miles from the M1/M50 junction at Dublin Airport. Museum is located in grounds of Howth Castle Demesne.

Directions by public transport: Bus 31 from Dublin City Centre; Local DART rail service to Howth station, then short walk.

Charges: Please telephone for charges.

Facilities: E G P T

Other information: Limited access for disabled.
Note: No recent vehicle data received from this museum.

Registration	Date	Chassis	Body	New to	Fleet No	Status
TE 5110	1928	Leyland Lion PLSC3	(chassis only)	Colne Corporation	22	A
note i	1933	AEC Regal I	(chassis only)	(unknown)		A
ZI 9708	1933	Dennis Lancet I	Dublin United Tramways Co B32R	Dublin United Tramways Co	F21	A
ZC 714	1937	Leyland Titan TD4	Leyland H32/26R	Dublin United Tramways Co	R1	R
FRU 305	1945	Bristol K6A	Hants & Dorset FO31/28R	Hants & Dorset Motor Services	1108	A
GZ 7638	1947	Leyland Tiger PS1	Northern Ireland Road Transport Board B34R	Northern Ireland Road Transport Board B34R	A8570	A
IY 1940	1948	AEC Regent III 9621E	Park Royal O33/26R	Morecambe & Heysham Corporation	58	A
ZD 7163	1948	Leyland Tiger OPS3	(chassis only)	CIE	P23	A
ZH 3926	1948	AEC Regal III O962	Park Royal C35R	Great Northern Railway (Ireland)	427	A
ZH 3937	1948	AEC Regent III 9612E	Park Royal H30/26RD	Great Northern Railway (Ireland)	438	R
ZH 4538	1948	Leyland Titan PD2/3	Leyland H33/27R	CIE	R389	R
LTU 869	1949	Commer Avenger I	Plaxton C33F	Thornley of Woodley		A
MZ 7396	1950	Guy Arab III	Harkness B31F	Belfast Corporation	298	A
ZL 2718	1950	GNR Gardner	Park Royal/GNR	Great Northern Railway (Ireland)	387	A
GUX 188	1951	Bedford OB	Duple B31F	Lloyd of Oswestry		A
IY 7384	1951	GNR Gardner	Park Royal/GNR DP33R	Great Northern Railway (Ireland)	390	RP
ZJ 5933	1951	Leyland Tiger OPS3	CIE	CIE	P193	A
OZ 6686	1953	Daimler CVG6	Harkness H30/26R	Belfast Corporation	432	A
ZL 6816	1953	Leyland Titan OPD2/1	CIE H37/31R	CIE	R506	A
ZO 6819	1953	Leyland Tiger PS2/14	CIE B39R	CIE	P309	A
ZO 6857	1953	Leyland Tiger PS2/14	CIE B39R	CIE	P347	R
ZO 6881	1954	Leyland Royal Tiger PSU1/15	CIE C34C	CIE	U10	A
ZO 6949	1954	Leyland Royal Tiger PSU1/15	CIE B39D	CIE	U78	A
ZY 79	1954	AEC Regal IV 9822E	Park Royal/GNR B45R	Great Northern Railway (Ireland)	274	A
ZU 9241	1955	Leyland Titan OPD2/1	CIE H37/31RD	CIE	R567	A
CYI 621	1958	Leyland Titan OPD2/2	CIE	CIE	R819	A
HZA 230	1960	Leyland Titan PD3/2	CIE H41/33R	CIE	RA105	RP
HZA 279	1961	AEC Regent V 2D2RA	CIE H41/28RD	CIE	AA2	A
404 RIU	1963	Albion Lowlander LR1	Alexander H41/31F	W Alexander & Sons (Midland) Ltd	MRE38	A
HZD 593	1963	Leyland Worldmaster ERT2/1	Van Hool DP53F	CIE	WVH13	A
NZE 598	1964	Leyland Leopard L2	CIE B45F	CIE	E170	A
NZE 620	1964	Leyland Titan PD3A/6	Dundalk (Park Royal frame) H41/33R	CIE	R911	A
EZH 17	1965	Leyland Leopard PSU3/4R	CIE B45F	CIE	C17	A
EZH 64	1965	Leyland Leopard PSU3/4R	CIE/North East Health Board	CIE	C64	A
NZE 629	1965	Leyland Titan PD3A/3	Dundalk (Park Royal frame) O—/—R	CIE	R920	A
EZH 231	1966	Leyland Leopard PSU3/4R	CIE B53F	CIE	C231	A
VZL 179	1966	Bedford VAL14	Plaxton C53F	Wallace Arnold Tours of Leeds		A
EZL 1	1967	Bedford VAS5	CIE B33F	CIE	SS1	RP
VZI 44	1967	Leyland Atlantean PDR1/1	CIE H43/35F	CIE	D44	A
WZJ 724	1967	Bedford VAM14	Duffy C45F	P O'Grady of Santry		A
DIV 83	1971	Daimler Fleetline CRG6LX	Alexander H45/32F	Trent Motor Traction Co	550	A
AIT 934	1972	Mercedes 406D	Asco Clubman	Flagline of Athlone		A
note j	1972	Bedford VAL70	Duffy B40D	Aer Lingus	301	A
694 ZO	1975	Leyland Atlantean AN68/1R	Van Hool H45/29D	CIE	D694	A
GSI 353	1983	Bombardier	Bombardier H45/29D	CIE	KD353	A
UZG 100	1984	Bombardier GAC	Bombardier B44D	CIE	KC100	A

Note: Please be aware that vehicles on display can vary from time to time as not all museums display their entire 'fleet'. Visitors wishing to see a particular vehicle should make enquiries prior to their visit.

Notes:

The Transport Museum — Wythall

Contact address: The Transport Museum, Chapel Lane, Wythall, Worcestershire, B47 6JX
Phone: 01564 826471
E-mail: enquiries@bammot.org.uk
Web site: www.bammot.org.uk
Affiliations: AIM, NARTM, Transport Trust, MLA West Midlands
Brief description: The collection is based on buses built and/or operated locally, plus others of significant PSV history. In addition, there is a unique collection of battery-operated road vehicles and a miniature passenger-carrying steam railway on site. Museum developed and run by volunteers
Events planned:
Operating days 16/17, 30 April; 1, 28 May 2006
29 May 2006 — Two Museums Day, half hourly buses to Aston Manor Transport Museum
Major construction work commences in June thanks to a Heritage Lottery Fund grant. Access may be temporarily restricted. Check web site or enthusiast press for events later in season.
Opening days/times: Saturdays, Sundays and Bank Holidays 11.00 to 16.00 (17.00 on event days), Easter Sunday to end October.
Directions by car: Wythall is on the main A435 Birmingham-Evesham road. The museum is next to Wythall old church. From M42 use junction 3 and head towards Birmingham.
Directions by public transport: Museum services operate on event days (including ex-Hill St, Birmingham 11.30 on 17 April; 1, 29 May. Bus services serve Wythall from Birmingham and Solihull. Neither operates on Sundays
Wythall rail station is 25min walk from museum.
Charges: £2.00 (£4 on Bank Holiday Mondays, and Sunday operating days). Admission ticket can be upgraded to all-day riding ticket at additional charge of £3 — includes admission to Aston Manor Transport Museum on 29 May
Facilities: B(e) E P S T
Other information: Refreshments available on event days

Registration	Date	Chassis	Body	New to	Fleet No	Status
O 9926	1913	Tilling Stevens TTA2	Thomas Tilling O18/16RO	BMMO ('Midland Red')	26	RP
HA 3501	1925	SOS Standard	Ransomes Sims & Jefferies B32F	BMMO ('Midland Red')	501	A
CN 2870	1927	SOS Q	Brush B37F	Northern General Transport Co	321	RP
CC 7745	1928	SOS QL	Brush B37F	Royal Blue of Llandudno		A
OV 4090	1931	Morris Commercial Dictator	Metro Cammell B34F	Birmingham Corporation Tramways	90	A
OV 4486	1931	AEC Regent 661	Metro Cammell H27/21R	Birmingham Corporation Tramways	486	A
OC 527	1933	Morris Commercial Imperial	Metro Cammell H50R	Birmingham Corporation Tramways	527	A
AHA 582	1935	SOS DON	Brush B36F	BMMO ('Midland Red')	1703	A
CVP 207	1937	Daimler COG5	Metro Cammell H30/24R	Birmingham City Transport	1107	R
RC 4615	1937	AEC Regal O662	Willowbrook B34F	Trent Motor Traction Co	714	R
GHA 333	1940	SOS SON	(chassis only)	BMMO ('Midland Red')	2414	RP
GHA 337	1940	SOS SON	Brush B38F	BMMO ('Midland Red')	2418	RP
HHA 637	1946	BMMO S6	Metro Cammell B40F	BMMO ('Midland Red')	3036	A
FFY 402	1947	Leyland Titan PD2/3	Leyland O30/26R	Southport Corporation	85	RP
GUE 247	1948	Leyland Tiger PS1	Northern Coachbuilders B34F	Stratford-upon-Avon Blue Motors	41	A
HOV 685	1948	Leyland Titan PD2/1	Brush H30/24R	Birmingham City Transport	1685	R
JRR 404	1948	Leyland Titan PD1	Duple L29/26F	Barton Transport of Chilwell	473	RP
KAL 579	1948	Daimler CVD6	Massey H33/28RD	W Gash & Sons of Newark	DD2	R

Registration	Date	Chassis	Body	New to	Fleet No	Status
FDM 724	1949	Foden PVD6	Massey H30/26R	E H Phillips Motor Services of Holywell		A
FJW 616+	1949	Sunbeam F4	Park Royal H28/26R	Wolverhampton Corporation	616	A
HDG 448	1949	Albion Venturer CX19	Metro Cammell H30/26R	Cheltenham District Traction Co	72	R
HWO 334	1949	Guy Arab III	Duple L27/26R	Red & White Services	34	R
JOJ 245	1950	Leyland Tiger PS2/1	Weymann B34F	Birmingham City Transport	2245	R
JOJ 533	1950	Guy Arab III special	Metro Cammell H30/24R	Birmingham City Transport	2533	R
JUE 349	1950	Leyland Tiger PS2/3	Northern Counties H35/28F	Stratford-upon-Avon Blue Motors	33	RP
KFM 775	1950	Bristol L5G	ECW B35R	Crosville Motor Services	KG126	R
NHA 744	1950	BMMO S12	Brush B44F	BMMO ('Midland Red')	3744	RP
NHA 795	1950	BMMO D5B	Brush H30/26RD	BMMO ('Midland Red')	3795	A
ORB 277	1950	Daimler CVD6	Duple C35F	Tailby & George ('Blue Bus Services') Willington		R
MXX 23	1952	AEC Regal IV 9821LT RF	Metro Cammell B41F	London Transport	RF 381	R
JOJ 976	1953	Guy Arab IV	Metro Cammell H30/25R	Birmingham City Transport	2976	R
PDH 808	1953	Leyland Royal Tiger PSU1	Park Royal DP40F	Walsall Corporation	808	R
RDH 505	1953	Leyland Titan PD2/12	Roe FH33/23RD	Walsall Corporation	815	A
SHA 431	1953	Leyland Titan PD2/12 special	Leyland H30/26RD	BMMO ('Midland Red')	4031	RP
FRC 956	1954	Leyland Titan PD2/12	Leyland H32/26RD	Trent Motor Traction Co	1256	R
UHA 255	1955	BMMO S14	BMMO B44F	BMMO ('Midland Red')	4255	R
XHA 482	1956	BMMO D7	Metro Cammell H37/26RD	BMMO ('Midland Red')	4482	R
XHA 496	1956	BMMO D7	Metro Cammell	BMMO ('Midland Red')	4496	A
SUK 3	1957	Guy Arab IV	Metro Cammell H33/27R	Wolverhampton Corporation	3	RP
UTU 596J	1957	Guy Otter NLLODP	Mulliner B26F	Douglas Corporation	9	A
VVP 911	1958	Bedford SB3	Duple C41F	Sandwell Motor Co of Birmingham		R
WDF 569	1959	Leyland Tiger Cub PSUC1	Willowbrook DP41F	Soudley Valley Coaches of Cinderford		R
871 KHA	1960	BMMO D9	BMMO H40/32RD	BMMO ('Midland Red')	4871	RP
943 KHA	1960	BMMO D10	BMMO H43/35F	BMMO ('Midland Red')	4943	R
802 MHW	1961	Bristol Lodekka FSF6G	ECW H34/26F	Cheltenham District Traction Co	6037	R
3016 HA	1962	BMMO D9	BMMO/LPC O40/32RD	BMMO ('Midland Red')	5016	R
5073 HA	1962	BMMO S15	BMMO B40F	BMMO ('Midland Red')	5073	R
5212 HA	1962	Leyland Leopard PSU3/4R	Willowbrook B53F	BMMO ('Midland Red')	5212	A
SBF 233	1962	Leyland Titan PD2/28	Northern Counties -	Harper Bros of Heath Hayes	25	R
248 NEA	1963	Daimler CVG6-30	Metro Cammell H41/33R	West Bromwich Corporation	248	R
6545 HA	1964	BMMO S16	BMMO B52F	BMMO ('Midland Red')	5545	R
BHA 399C	1965	BMMO D9	BMMO H40/32RD	BMMO ('Midland Red')	5399	R
BHA 656C	1965	BMMO CM6T	BMMO C44Ft	BMMO ('Midland Red')	5656	R
BON 474C	1965	Daimler Fleetline CRG6LX	Marshall B37F	Birmingham City Transport	3474	R
CUV 219C	1965	AEC Routemaster R2RH/1	Park Royal CH36/29RD	London Transport	RCL2219	R
EHA 767D	1966	BMMO S17	BMMO/Plaxton B52F	BMMO ('Midland Red')	5767	R
GHA 415D	1966	Daimler Fleetline CRG6LX	Alexander H44/33F	BMMO ('Midland Red')	6015	RP
GRY 60D	1966	Leyland Titan PD3A/1	Park Royal H41/33R	Leicester City Transport	60	R
HBF 679D	1966	Leyland Titan PD2A/27	Metro Cammell H36/28RD	Harper Bros of Heath Hayes	27	R
Q124 VOE	1966	Leyland Leopard PSU4/4R	Plaxton -	Midland Red Omnibus Co	5826	A
JHA 868E	1967	BMMO S21	BMMO DP49F	BMMO ('Midland Red')	5868	R
KHW 306E	1967	Bristol RELL6L	ECW B53F	Cheltenham District Traction Co	1000	R
NJW 719E	1967	Daimler Roadliner SRC6	Strachan B54D	Wolverhampton Corporation	719	R
KOX 780F	1968	Daimler Fleetline CRG6LX	Park Royal H43/33F	Birmingham City Transport	3780	R
NEA 101F	1968	Daimler Fleetline CRG6LX	Metro Cammell H42/31F	West Bromwich Corporation	101	R
NOV 796G	1968	Daimler Fleetline CRG6LX	Park Royal H43/29D	Birmingham City Transport	3796	R
XDH 56G	1968	Daimler Fleetline CRC6-36	Northern Counties H51/34D	Walsall Corporation	56	RP
SHA 645G	1969	Leyland Leopard PSU4A/4R	Plaxton C36F	BMMO ('Midland Red')	6145	R
SOE 913H	1969	Daimler Fleetline CRG6LX-33	Park Royal H47/33D	West Midlands PTE	3913	RP
UHA 956H	1969	BMMO S23	BMMO/Plaxton B51F	BMMO ('Midland Red')	5956	R
XDH 516G	1969	Daimler Fleetline CRG6LX	Northern Counties H41/27D	Walsall Corporation	116	R
FRB 211H	1970	Bristol VRTSL6LX	ECW H39/31F	Midland General Omnibus Co	322	R
JHA 941H	1970	BMMO S23	BMMO B51F	BMMO ('Midland Red')	5941	A

Note: Please be aware that vehicles on display can vary from time to time as not all museums display their entire 'fleet'. Visitors wishing to see a particular vehicle should make enquiries prior to their visit.

Registration	Date	Chassis	Body	New to	Fleet No	Status
UHA 981H	1970	BMMO S23	BMMO/Plaxton B51F	BMMO ('Midland Red')	5981	R
WNG 864H	1970	Bristol RELL6G	ECW DP50F	Eastern Counties Omnibus Co	RLE864	R
AHA 451J	1971	Leyland Leopard PSU4B/4R	Plaxton C36F	BMMO ('Midland Red')	6451	R
OWE 271K	1972	Bristol VRTSL6LX	East Lancs H43/30F	Sheffield Transport	271	RP
PDU 135M	1973	Daimler Fleetline CRG6LX	East Lancs H44/30F	Coventry City Transport	135	RP
NOB 413M	1974	Bristol VRTSL6LX	MCW H43/33F	West Midlands PTE	4413	RP
PHA 370M	1974	Ford R1014	Plaxton/Midland Red DP23F	Midland Red Omnibus Co	370	R
JOV 613P	1975	Daimler Fleetline CRG6LX	Park Royal H43/33F	West Midlands PTE	4613	R
99-64-HB	1976	Den Oudsten LOK	Den Ousden B35D	VAD of Ermele (Netherlands)	5656	A
KON 311P	1976	Leyland Fleetline FE30ALR	Metro Cammell H43/33F	West Midlands PTE	6311	R
NOE 544R	1976	Leyland National 11351A/1R	Leyland National B49F	Midland Red Omnibus Co	544	R
WDA 835T	1978	MCW Metrobus DR102/1	MCW H43/30F	West Midlands PTE	6835	RP
BOK 1V	1979	MCW Metrobus DR102/12	MCW H43/30F	West Midlands PTE	2001	A

Notes:

RC 4615	Rebodied 1950
GHA 333	Converted to works tug with AEC engine by Midland Red c1960.
FFY 402	Originally H30/26R
KAL 579	Rebodied 1958
JUE 349	Rebodied 1963
PDH 808	Originally B42F
XHA 496	Converted to Breakdown Vehicle 1972
UTU 596J	Originally registered WMN 485
943 KHA	Entered service 1961
3016 HA	Originally H40/32RD; converted to open-top by Marshall ('Obsolete Fleet') London (OM5)
5073 HA	Reseated from DP40F in 1969
SBF 233	Rebuilt as towing tender 1981
Q124 VOE	Rebuilt as towing tender 1977
PHA 370M	Shortened to B27F by Midland Red in 1979. Reseated to DP23F in 1983
99-64-HB	Netherlands registration
KON 311P	Gardner engine fitted in 1981. Reverted to Leyland O680 Oct 2005
WDA 835T	Exhibited at 1978 Commercial Motor Show

Trolleybus Museum at Sandtoft

Contact address: Belton Road, Sandtoft, Doncaster DN8 5SX
Phone: 01724 711391
E-mail: enquiries@sandtoft.org.uk
Web site: www.sandtoft.org.uk
Affiliation: NARTM
Brief description: Home of the nation's trolleybuses
Events planned: 15-17 April 2006 — Easter Weekend;, 16 April 2006 — Morris Minor Club Rally; 17 April 2006 — A35 Club Rally; 29 April-1 May — North East Trolleybus Event; 11 June 2006 — Trolleyday; 25 June 2006 — Vintage Caravan Club Rally; 9 July 2006 — Vintage Bicycle Rally; 29/30 July 2006 — Sandtoft Gathering; 12/13 August 2006 — MG Owners Rally; 26-28 August 2006 — 6-wheeler Trolleybuses; 16/17 September 2006 — Model Weekend; 15 October 2006 — St Leger Rally and Yorkshire Day; 9/10 December 2006 — Santa Days (date to be confirmed).
Opening days/times: 11.00 to 17.00 on the above dates.
Except: 29 July — 11.00-22.00; 30 July — 10.00-18.00
Directions by car: From M180 junction 2, take A161 southbound to Belton. Turn right and museum is 2 miles on right-hand side.
Directions by public transport: Free bus from Doncaster station at 13.30 on 17 April, 1 May, 29 may, 30 July, 28 August and 15 October (please telephone to check operation)
Charges: Adult £4.50, Child/Senior Citizen £2.50, Family £12.
Except: 29/30 July — Adult £6.00, Child/Senior Citizen £4.00.
Facilities: A B(e) D E F G H L P R S T
Other information: Coach tours and private party visits can be accommodated at other times by prior arrangement

Registration	Date	Chassis	Body	New to	Fleet No	Status
KW 6052+	1929	English Electric A	English Electric B32F	Bradford Corporation	562	A
note t+	1929	Guy BTX	Ransomes B—C	Hastings Tramways Co		RP
TV 4484+	1931	Ransomes Sims & Jefferies D6	(chassis only)	Nottingham City Transport	346	R

Registration	Date	Chassis	Body	New to	Fleet No	Status
1425 P+	1932	Fabrique Nationale	Fabrique Nationale B26SD	Liege (Belgium)	425	R
TV 9333+	1934	Karrier E6	Brush H64R	Nottingham City Transport	367	A
FW 8990+	1937	AEC 661T	Park Royal H30/26R	Cleethorpes Corporation	54	RP
FTO 614	1939	AEC Regent O661		Nottingham City Transport	802	R
964 H87+	1943	Vetra CB60	CTL B17D	Limoges (France)	5	R
GHN 574+	1944	Karrier W	East Lancs H39/31F	Bradford Corporation	792	R
GKP 511+	1944	Sunbeam W	Roe H34/28R	Maidstone Corporation	56	R
CDT 636+	1945	Karrier W	Roe H34/28R	Doncaster Corporation	375	RP
DKY 703+	1945	Karrier W	East Lancs H37/29F	Bradford Corporation	703	RP W 2 12 11
DKY 706+	1945	Karrier W	East Lancs H37/29F	Bradford Corporation	706	R
GTV 666+	1945	Karrier W	Brush UH30/26R	Nottingham City Transport	466	RP
CVH 741+	1947	Karrier MS2	Park Royal H40/30R	Huddersfield Corporation	541	RP
EDT 703	1947	Leyland Titan PD2/1	Roe H34/28R	Doncaster Corporation	94	RP
HKR 11+	1947	Sunbeam W	Northern Coachbuilders H30/26R	Maidstone Corporation	72	R
JV 9901	1947	AEC Regent III O961 RT	Roe H31/25R	Grimsby Corporation	81	RP
JMN 727	1948	AEC Regent III O961	Northern Counties H30/26R	Douglas Corporation	63	R
KTV 493+	1948	BUT 9611T	Roe H31/25R	Nottingham City Transport	493	RP
BCK 939	1949	Leyland Titan PD1		Preston Corporation	6	RP
EKU 743+	1949	BUT 9611T	Roe H33/25R	Bradford Corporation	743	A
EKU 746+	1949	BUT 9611T	Roe H33/25R	Bradford Corporation	746	R
EKY 558	1949	Leyland Titan PD2/3	Leyland H33/26R	Bradford Corporation	558	RP
GDT 421	1949	Daimler CVD6	Roe L27/26R	Doncaster Corporation	112	A
LHN 784+	1949	BUT 9611T	East Lancs H37/29F	Bradford Corporation	834	R
ERD 152+	1950	Sunbeam S7	Park Royal H38/30RD	Reading Corporation	181	R
FET 618+	1950	Daimler CTE6	Roe H40/30R	Rotherham Corporation	44	R
GAJ 12+	1950	Sunbeam F4	Roe H35/26R	Tees-side Railless Traction Board	2	RP
GFU 692+	1950	BUT 9611T	Northern Coachbuilders H38/26R	Cleethorpes Corporation	59	A
JWW 375+	1950	Sunbeam F4	East Lancs H37/29F	Bradford Corporation	845	RP
JWW 376+	1950	Sunbeam F4	East Lancs H37/29F	Bradford Corporation	846	A
JWW 377+	1950	Sunbeam F4	East Lancs H37/29F	Bradford Corporation	847	A
KTV 506+	1950	BUT 9641T	Brush H38/32R	Nottingham City Transport	506	R
BDJ 87+	1951	BUT 9611T	East Lancs H30/26R	St Helens Corporation	387	RP
FKU 758+	1951	BUT 9611T	Weymann H33/26R	Bradford Corporation	758	RP
KDT 393	1951	AEC Regent III 9613A	Roe H31/25R	Doncaster Corporation	122	R
LYR 542	1952	AEC Regent III O961 RT	Park Royal H30/26R	London Transport	RT3323	RP
MDT 222	1953	AEC Regal III 9621A	Roe B39F	Doncaster Corporation	22	R
OTV 137	1953	AEC Regent III 9613E	Park Royal H30/26R	Nottingham City Transport	137	RP
JDN 668	1954	AEC Regent III 6812A	Roe H33/25RD	York Pullman Bus Co	64	R
KVH 219+	1956	BUT 9641T	East Lancs H40/32R	Huddersfield Corporation	619	R
XWX 795	1959	AEC Reliance 2MU3RV	Roe C41F	Felix Motors of Doncaster	40	RP
9629 WU	1960	AEC Reliance 2MU3RV	Roe DP41F	Felix Motors of Doncaster	41	R
VRD 193+	1961	Sunbeam F4A	Burlingham H38/30F	Reading Corporation	193	RP
657 BWB	1962	Leyland Atlantean PDR1/1	Park Royal H44/33F	Sheffield Joint Omnibus Committee	1357	R
433 MDT	1963	Leyland Tiger Cub PSUC1/11	Roe B45F	Doncaster Corporation	33	R
JTF 920B	1964	AEC Reliance 2MU3RV	East Lancs B—D	Reading Corporation	48	A
KDT 206D	1966	Daimler CVG6LX	Roe H34/28F	Doncaster Corporation	206	A
66+	1967	Lancia	Dalfa H43/25D	Oporto (Portugal)	140	R
UDT 455F	1968	Leyland Royal Tiger Cub RTC1/2	Roe B45D	Doncaster Corporation	55	R
WWJ 754M	1973	Daimler Fleetline CRG6LXB	Park Royal H43/27D	Sheffield Transport	754	R
C45 HDT+	1985	Dennis Dominator DTA1401	Alexander H47/33F	South Yorkshire PTE	2450	R

+ Trolleybus

Note: Please be aware that vehicles on display can vary from time to time as not all museums display their entire 'fleet'. Visitors wishing to see a particular vehicle should make enquiries prior to their visit.

Notes:

KW 6052	Caravan conversion to be restored.
cnote t	Possibly Hastings 57 - not yet proven
FTO 614	Converted to tower wagon
964 H87	French registration.
GHN 574	Originally single-decker; rebodied 1958
GKP 511	Rebodied 1960
DKY 706	Rebodied 1960
CDT 636	Rebodied 1955
DKY 703	Rebodied 1960
EDT 703	Originally Leyland body. Roe body 1955 ex-Trolleybus
HKR 11	On loan from Maidstone Borough Council
LHN 784	Rebodied 1962; chassis new to Darlington
BCK 939	Converted to breakdown vehicle
FET 618	Rebodied 1957 (formerly single-decker)
GAJ 12	Rebodied 1964
JWW 375	Rebodied 1962; chassis ex-Mexborough & Swinton
JWW 377	Rebodied 1962; chassis ex-Mexborough & Swinton
JWW 376	Rebodied 1962; chassis ex-Mexborough & Swinton
657 BWB	Rebodied 1968; renumbered 227 in 1970 following dissolution of JOC
JTF 920B	Caravan conversion; originally registered 5148 DP
66	Portuguese registration.
C45 HDT	Experimental vehicle; originally registered B450 CKW

Ulster Folk & Transport Museum
Cultra

Contact address: Cultra, Holywood, Co Down, BT18 OEU
Phone: 028 9042 8428
Brief description: A unique collection of wheeled vehicles from cycles to trams, railways, buses and cars. Interpretive exhibitions show the development of road transport. Not all the vehicles listed are always on display. Please enquire before your visit.
Opening days/times: All the year round but closing for a few days at Christmas time. From 10.00 on weekdays and 11.00 on Sundays (please 'phone for details)
Directions by car: On A2 Belfast-Bangor road
Directions by public transport: On main Belfast-Bangor railway and bus routes
Charges: £6.50 (discounts for groups)
Facilities: A D E F G L P R T

Registration	Date	Chassis	Body	New to	Fleet No	Status
CZ 7013	1935	Dennis Lancet I	Harkness B31F	Belfast Corporation	102	R
FZ 7897+	1948	Guy BTX	Harkness H36/32R	Belfast Corporation	112	R
EOI 4857	1973	Daimler Fleetline CRG6LX-33	Alexander (Belfast) H49/37F	Belfast Corporation	857	R
+ Trolleybus						

Notes:

EOI 4857	Passed to Citybus (2857) in 1973; rebodied 1976

Wirral Transport Museum
Birkenhead

Contact address: 1 Taylor Street, Birkenhead, Merseyside, L41 5HN
Phone: 0151 666 2756
Web site: www.wirraltransportmuseum.org
Affiliation: NARTM
Brief description: The museum houses a collection of buses, tramcars, motor cycles, cars and a model railway. Local enthusiast groups are restoring some of the trams and buses. Trams operate during weekends and some school holidays.
Opening days/times: Weekends 13.00-17.00. Please see web site for further details
Directions by car: Adjacent to Woodside ferry terminal
Directions by public transport: Bus or ferry to Woodside, or train to Hamilton Square station

Registration	Date	Chassis	Body	New to	Fleet No	Status
BG 8557	1944	Guy Arab II	Massey H31/26R	Birkenhead Corporation	242	RP
BG 9225	1946	Leyland Titan PD1A	Massey H30/26R	Birkenhead Corporation	105	RP
HLF 820	1949	AEC Regent III	Weymann H30/26R	Liverpool Corporation	A344	RP
AHF 850	1951	Leyland Titan PD2/1	Metro Cammell H30/26R	Wallasey Corporation	54	R
CHF 565	1956	Leyland Titan PD2/10	Burlingham H30/26R	Wallasey Corporation	106	RP
FBG 910	1958	Leyland Titan PD2/40	Massey H31/28R	Birkenhead Corporation	10	R
FHF 451	1958	Leyland Atlantean PDR1/1	Metro Cammell H44/33F	Wallasey Corporation	1	R
101 CLT	1962	AEC Routemaster R2RH	Park Royal H36/28R	London Transport	RM1101	R
RCM 493	1964	Leyland Leopard L1	Massey B42D	Birkenhead Corporation	93	R
GCM 152E	1967	Leyland Titan PD2/37	Massey H36/30R	Birkenhead Corporation	152	R
UFM 52F	1968	Bristol RELL6G	ECW DP50F	Crosville Motor Services	ERG52	R
OFM 957K	1972	Daimler Fleetline CRG6LX-30	Northern Counties O43/29F	Chester Corporation	57	R
THM 692M	1973	Daimler Fleetline CRL6-30	MCW H34/10Dt	London Transport	DMS1692	R
CWU 146T	1979	Leyland Fleetline FE30AGR	Roe H43/33F	West Yorkshire PTE	7146	R
B926 KWM	1984	Leyland Atlantean AN68D/1R	Alexander H43/32F	Merseyside PTE	1070	R

Notes:

BG 8557	Rebodied in 1953. Original body was Park Royal utility
CHF 565	Carries 1949 body
FHF 451	First production Atlantean
FBG 910	Driver trainer 1974-81
RCM 493	Former road safety unit
OFM 957K	Originally H43/29F; rebodied 1984 and converted to open-top (renumbered 75) in 1998
THM 692M	Mobile classroom.
CWU 146T	Promotional vehicle for The Hamilton Quarter. Currently H6/2FL
B926 KWM	Last production Atlantean

Left: New to Devon General in 1981 as no1215 (LFJ 862W), this Bristol VRTSL3 has been repainted into the short-lived cream and red livery adopted by Devon General immediately after deregulation. *Philip Lamb*

Below: Part of the Bristol Omnibus Vehicle Collection is Bristol LSX5G 2800 (NHU 2), new to Bristol Tramways in 1950. *Philip Lamb*

Right: Built in 1955, preserved ex-Thames Valley Bristol KSW 748 (JRX 823) rallied at Medstead.

Part 2

Aldershot & District Bus Interest Group

Contact address: 111 Park Barn Drive, Guildford, Surrey, GU2 6ER
Web site: www.geocities.com/adbigweb
Affiliation: NARTM, FBHVC.
Brief description: The group was formed in 1994 to consolidate the collection of ex-Aldershot & District preserved vehicles and other artefacts which had been saved over the years. The vehicles range from 1920s Dennis E types to Dennis, AEC and Bristol buses which entered service in the 1960s and 1970s at the very end of the company's existence. The vehicles in the collection are in the care of members of an associated group which also welcomes the owners of other preserved Dennis buses and coaches.
Event: 4 June 2006 — Running day at Aldershot to celebrate 100 years of Aldershot's buses.
Other information: Regular working parties; new members welcome.

Registration	Date	Chassis	Body	New to	Fleet No	Status
OT 8283	1928	Dennis E	(chassis only)	Aldershot & District Traction Co	D210	A
OT 8592	1928	Dennis E	Strachan & Brown	Aldershot & District Traction Co	D217	A
OT 8898	1928	Dennis E	Strachan & Brown	Aldershot & District Traction Co	D226	A
OT 8902	1928	Dennis E	Dennis B32R	Aldershot & District Traction Co	D235	A
RT 4539	1928	Dennis 30cwt	(chassis only)	Green Coaches of Ashfield cum Thorpe		RP
CC 8671	1929	Dennis GL	Roberts T19	Llandudno UDC	2	R
CC 9424	1930	Dennis GL	Roberts T20	Llandudno UDC	3	A
MJ 4549	1932	Dennis Lancet I	Short B32F	Smith of Westoning		R
YD 9533	1934	Dennis Ace	Dennis B20F	Southern National Omnibus Co	3560	RP
JG 8720	1937	Dennis Lancet II	Park Royal B35R	East Kent Road Car Co		RP
GAA 580	1948	Dennis Lancet J3	Strachan B32R	Aldershot & District Traction Co	944	A
GAA 616	1948	Dennis Lancet J3	Strachan C32R	Aldershot & District Traction Co	980	RP
GOU 845	1950	Dennis Lance K3	East Lancs L25/26R	Aldershot & District Traction Co	145	RP
HOU 904	1950	Dennis Lancet J10	Strachan B38R	Aldershot & District Traction Co	178	R
LAA 231	1953	Dennis Lancet J10C	Strachan FC38R	Aldershot & District Traction Co	196	RP
LOU 48	1954	Dennis Lance K4	East Lancs L28/28R	Aldershot & District Traction Co	220	R
MOR 581	1954	AEC Reliance MU3RV	Metro Cammell B40F	Aldershot & District Traction Co	543	R
POR 428	1956	Dennis Falcon P5	Strachan B30F	Aldershot & District Traction Co	282	R
SOU 456	1958	Dennis Loline	East Lancs H37/31RD	Aldershot & District Traction Co	348	RP
SOU 465	1958	Dennis Loline	East Lancs H37/31RD	Aldershot & District Traction Co	357	R
XHO 370	1960	AEC Reliance 2MU3RV	Weymann DP40F	Aldershot & District Traction Co	370	R
462 EOT	1962	Dennis Loline III	Alexander H39/29F	Aldershot & District Traction Co	462	RP
488 KOT	1964	Dennis Loline III	Weymann H39/29F	Aldershot & District Traction Co	488	R
AAA 503C	1965	Dennis Loline III	Weymann H39/29F	Aldershot & District Traction Co	503	R
AAA 506C	1965	Dennis Loline III	Weymann H39/29F	Aldershot & District Traction Co	506	R
AAA 508C	1965	Dennis Loline III	Weymann H39/29F	Aldershot & District Traction Co	508	RP
CCG 296K	1971	Bristol RESL6G	ECW B40D	Aldershot & District Traction Co	651	RP
KCG 627L	1973	Leyland National 1151/1R/0402	Leyland National B49F	Alder Valley	127	R

Notes:

OT 8283	Originally Dennis F converted to E type
JG 8720	Rebodied 1949
MOR 581	Rebodied 1967

Aycliffe & District Bus Preservation Society

Contact address: 35 Lowther Drive, Newton Aycliffe, Co Durham, DL5 4UL
Affiliation: NARTM
Brief description: A collection of Darlington area service buses, the majority fully restored and in running order.
Opening days/times: Viewing by prior appointment only.

Registration	Date	Chassis	Body	New to	Fleet No	Status
GHN 189	1942	Bristol K5G	ECW L27/26R	United Automobile Services	BGL29	R
LHN 860	1950	Bristol L5G	ECW B35F	United Automobile Services	BG413	R
304 GHN	1958	Bristol LS6B	ECW C39F	United Automobile Services	BUC4	RP
AHN 451B	1964	Daimler CCG5	Roe H33/28R	Darlington Corporation	7	R
NDL 769G	1969	Bristol LHS6L	Marshall B35F	Southern Vectis Omnibus Co	833	R

Notes:

GHN 189	1949 body fitted in 1954
LHN 860	Converted to OMO c1957
304 GHN	Now fitted with Gardner engine. Was C34F when new.
NDL 769G	Acquired by United Automobile Services (1452) in 1977

Barrow Transport Group

Phone: 01229 870336
Web site: http://website.lineone.net/~barrow_transport
Brief Description: A brief collection of ex-Barrow in Furness vehicles. Restored examples can be seen at rallies. The group plans a museum in the future.

Registration	Date	Chassis	Body	New to	Fleet No	Status
EO 9051	1949	Leyland Titan PD2/3	Park Royal	Barrow in Furness Corporation	124	
EO 9177	1950	Leyland Titan PD2/3	Roe H31/28RD	Barrow in Furness Corporation	147	A
CEO 956	1958	Leyland Titan PD2/40	Park Royal H33/28R	Barrow in Furness Corporation	169	R
CEO 957	1958	Leyland Titan PD2/40	Park Royal H33/28R	Barrow in Furness Corporation	170	R
SEO 209M	1974	Leyland National 10351/1R	Leyland National B48F	Barrow in Furness Corporation	9	R
UEO 478T	1974	Leyland National 11351A/1R	Leyland National B49F	Barrow in Furness Corporation	16	RP
CEO 720W	1981	Leyland National NL116L11/1R	Leyland National B45F	Barrow in Furness Corporation	20	A
CEO 723W	1981	Leyland National NL116L11/1R	Leyland National B49F	Barrow in Furness Corporation	23	A
LEO 734Y	1983	Leyland Atlantean AN68D/1R	Northern Counties H43/32F	Barrow in Furness Corporation	104	RP
LEO 735Y	1983	Leyland Atlantean AN68D/1R	Northern Counties H43/32F	Barrow in Furness Corporation	105	A
E570 MAC	1988	Talbot Pullman	Talbot B20F	Barrow Borough Transport	99	RP

Notes:

EO 9051	Converted to recovery vehicle

Bohemia-Buses Transport Museum

Contact address: Zamek Borec, 41002 Borec, Near Lovoisice, Czech Republic
Phone: 00420 6062 89770
Brief description: The Heritage Park is currently closed for development. Vehicles in the collection may be viewed by arrangement. Please contact the address given
E-mail: heritage.collection@bohemiabuses.com
Web site: www.bohemiabuses.com
Opening days/times: Daily 10.00-18.00. Please phone to confirm
Directions by car: Two miles from end of D8 motorway/E55 direction Teplice
Directions by public transport: 550010 Lovosice–Borec–Velemin–Milesov
Facilities: B, D, E, L, P, R, S, T

Registration	Date	Chassis	Body	New to	Fleet No	Status
NRH 802A	1961	AEC Routemaster R2RH	Park Royal H36/28R	London Transport	RM798	R
AED 31B	1964	Leyland Titan PD2/40	East Lancs H37/28R	Warrington Corporation	149	A
LJF 31F	1968	Leyland Titan PD3A/12	MCW H41/31R	Leicester City Transport	31	RP
LHC 919P	1976	Bedford YLQ	Duple C45F	Warrens Coaches, Ticehurst	-	A
SDX 33R	1977	Leyland Atlantean AN68A/1R	Roe H43/29D	Ipswich Corporation	33	R
WYW 82T	1979	MCW Metrobus DR101/9	Metro Cammell H43/26D	London Transport	M82	R
OTB 26W	1981	Leyland Atlantean AN68C/1R	East Lancs H45/33F	Warrington Corporation	26	R
C386 XFD	1986	Bedford CF250	Bedford	Birmingham City Council		
D176 NON	1987	Freight Rover Sherpa 350	Carlyle B18F	Bee Line Buzz Co, Manchester		
L674 UKF	1993	Leyland-DAF 400	C19F	Powells Bus, Rotherham		

Notes:
NRH 802A   Originally registered WLT 798
C386 XFD   Fitted with long side bench seating for 12

Bolton Bus Group

Contact address: 12 Arundale, Westhoughton, Bolton BL5 3YB
Brief description: A small group of enthusiasts formed to preserve examples of Bolton's buses. Some of the vehicles are displayed at Bury Transport Museum, which can be visited by prior arrangement.
Opening days/times: Please write to the above address to arrange a visit

Registration	Date	Chassis	Body	New to	Fleet No	Status
NBN 436	1959	Leyland Titan PD3/4	East Lancs H41/32F	Bolton Corporation	128	RP
UBN 902	1962	Leyland Titan PD3A/2	East Lancs FH41/32F	Bolton Corporation	169	R
UWH 185	1963	Leyland Atlantean PDR1/1	East Lancs H45/33F	Bolton Corporation	185	RP
FBN 232C	1965	Leyland Atlantean PDR1/1	East Lancs H45/33F	Bolton Corporation	232	R
KUS 607E	1967	Leyland Atlantean PDR1/1	Alexander H44/34F	Glasgow Corporation	LA352	RP
TWH 807K	1971	Leyland Atlantean PDR2/1	East Lancs H49/37F	SELNEC PTE	6807	A
TWH 809K	1971	Leyland Atlantean PDR2/1	East Lancs H49/37F	SELNEC PTE	6809	R

Notes:
TWH 807K   Playbus

Bournemouth Heritage Transport Collection

Phone: 01202 658333

Brief description: The collection comprises vehicles, mainly from Bournemouth Corporation or the Bournemouth area, built between the years 1928 and 1980. Most are owned by the Bournemouth Passenger Transport Association Ltd, which is a registered charity.

Events planned: Please see the enthusiast press for details

Opening days/times: Owing to storage relocation, the collection is not currently open to the public.

Registration	Date	Chassis	Body	New to	Fleet No	Status
RU 2266	1925	Shelvoke & Drewery Tramocar	(chassis only)	Bournemouth Corporation	9	A
LJ 500	1929	Karrier WL6/1	Hall Lewis B40D	Bournemouth Corporation	33	RP
VH 6188	1934	AEC Regent O661	Hall Lewis H26/24R	Huddersfield Corporation	119	A
VH 6217	1934	AEC Regent 661	Lee Motors -	Huddersfield Corporation	120	R W2·10·11
BOW 162	1938	Bristol L5G	Hants & Dorset -	Hants & Dorset Motor Services	9081	RP
DKY 712+	1944	Karrier W	East Lancs H37/29F	Bradford Corporation	712	A
FRU 224	1944	Guy Arab		Bournemouth Corporation	40	A
JLJ 403	1949	Leyland Tiger PS2/3	Burlingham FDP35F	Bournemouth Corporation	46	R W2·10·11
KEL 110	1949	Leyland Titan PD2/3	Weymann FH33/25D	Bournemouth Corporation	110	R
NNU 234+	1949	BUT 9611T	Weymann H32/26R	Nottinghamshire & Derbyshire Traction Co	353	RP
KEL 133	1950	Leyland Titan PD2/3	Weymann FH27/21D	Bournemouth Corporation	247	R
KLJ 346+	1950	BUT 9641T	Weymann H31/25D	Bournemouth Corporation	212	R
MOD 978	1952	Bristol LS6G	ECW C41F	Southern National Omnibus Co (Royal Blue)	1291	A
NLJ 268	1953	Leyland Royal Tiger PSU1/13	Burlingham B42F	Bournemouth Corporation	258	R W2·10·11
NLJ 272	1953	Leyland Royal Tiger PSU1/13	Burlingham B42F	Bournemouth Corporation	262	R W2·10·11
RRU 901	1955	Leyland Tiger Cub PSUC1/1	Park Royal B42F	Bournemouth Corporation	264	R
RRU 904	1955	Leyland Tiger Cub PSUC1/1	Park Royal B42F	Bournemouth Corporation	267	R W2·10·11
YLJ 147	1959	Leyland Titan PD3/1	Weymann H37/25D	Bournemouth Corporation	147	R W2·10·11
8154 EL	1960	Leyland Titan PD3/1	Weymann H37/25D	Bournemouth Corporation	154	R W2·10·11
8156 EL	1960	Leyland Titan PD3/1	Weymann O37/25D	Bournemouth Corporation	156	R W2·10·11
297 LJ+	1962	Sunbeam MF2B	Weymann H37/28D	Bournemouth Corporation	297	R
6167 RU	1963	Leyland Titan PD3A/1	Weymann H39/30F	Bournemouth Corporation	167	R
AEL 170B	1964	Leyland Atlantean PDR1/1	Weymann H43/31F	Bournemouth Corporation	170	R W2·10·11
ALJ 340B	1964	Daimler Fleetline CRG6LX	M H Cars H44/33F	Bournemouth Corporation	40	R W2·10·11
CRU 103C	1965	Leyland Leopard PSU3/2R	Weymann DP45F	Bournemouth Corporation	103	R W2·10·11
CRU 180C	1965	Daimler Fleetline CRG6LX	Weymann CO43/31F	Bournemouth Corporation	180	R
CRU 187C	1965	Daimler Fleetline CRG6LX	Weymann CO43/31F	Bournemouth Corporation	187	R
CRU 197C	1965	Daimler Fleetline CRG6LX	Weymann H43/31F	Bournemouth Corporation	197	R
ERV 252D	1966	Leyland Atlantean PDR1/1	MCW O43/33F	Portsmouth Corporation	252	R
KRU 55F	1967	Daimler Roadliner SRC6	Willowbrook B49F	Bournemouth Corporation	55	R W2·10·11
ORU 230G	1969	Leyland Atlantean PDR1A/1	Alexander H43/31F	Bournemouth Corporation	230	R W2·10·11
VRU 124J	1971	Daimler Fleetline CRG6LXB	Roe H43/31F	Hants & Dorset Motor Services	1901	R
XRU 277K	1972	Leyland Atlantean PDR1A/1	Alexander H43/31F	Bournemouth Corporation	277	RP W2·10·11
DLJ 111L	1973	Daimler Fleetline CRL6	Alexander O43/31F	Bournemouth Corporation	111	R
FEL 105L	1973	Leyland Leopard PSU3B/4R	Plaxton C47F	Bournemouth Corporation	105	RP
FEL 209V	1979	Dodge KCSK6055	Rootes B18F	Bournemouth Transport	M9	A

+ Trolleybus

Notes:

RU 2266	Believed only chassis & axles are from RU 2266	NLJ 268	Originally B42F; used as canteen at Chesterfield 1970-81. Now mobile museum display vehicle
VH 6217	Converted to tower wagon in 1948		
VH 6188	Chassis new 1934; fitted with 1928 body	8156 EL	Converted to open-top in 1991
BOW 162	New with Beadle body; converted to breakdown vehicle	DLJ 111L	Originally H43/31F
FRU 224	Converted to breakdown vehicle	FEL 209V	Battery-powered bus
DKY 712	Rebodied 1960		

Bristol Omnibus Vehicle Collection

Contact address: 'Combe Barton', High Street, Dinder, Wells BA5 3PL
e-mail: drmichaelwalker@hotmail.com
Brief description: A collection of former of Bristol Omnibus Company vehicles.
Events planned: The vehicles will be attending rallies during the season

Registration	Date	Chassis	Body	New to	Fleet No	Status
LHY 976	1949	Bristol L5G	ECW B33D	Bristol Tramways	C2736	R
NHU 2	1950	Bristol LSX5G	ECW B42D	Bristol Tramways	2800	R
OHY 938	1952	Bristol KSW6B	ECW L27/28RD	Bristol Tramways	L8089	R
UHY 360	1955	Bristol KSW6B	ECW H32/28R	Bristol Tramways	C8320	R
UHY 384	1955	Bristol KSW6G	ECW H32/28RD	Bristol Tramways	8336	R
924 AHY	1958	Bristol MW5G	ECW B45F	Bristol Omnibus Co	2934	R
969 EHW	1959	Bristol Lodekka LD6G	ECW H33/25RD	Bristol Omnibus Co	L8515	R
972 EHW	1959	Bristol Lodekka LD6B	ECW H33/25R	Bristol Omnibus Co	LC8518	RP
869 NHT	1961	Bristol Lodekka FS6G	ECW CO33/27R	Bristol Omnibus Co	L8579	RP
BHU 92C	1965	Bristol MW6G	ECW C39F	Bristol Omnibus Co	2138	R
OAE 954M	1973	Bristol RELL6L	ECW B50F	Bristol Omnibus Co	1332	A
AFB 592V	1980	Bristol LH6L	ECW B43F	Bristol Omnibus Co	461	R

Notes:

NHU 2	Prototype Bristol LS
OHY 938	Named Peter Davey after previous owner

Bristol Road Transport Collection

Contact address: 'The Nook', Water Lane, Walls Quarry, Brinscombe, Stroud GL5 2SS
E-mail: william.staniforth@virgin.net
Brief Description: Collection not currently on public display. For enquiries or an appointment to view a particular vehicle, please write to the address shown, enclosing a stamped self-addressed envelope.

Registration	Date	Chassis	Body	New to	Fleet No	Status
FAE 60	1938	Bristol L5G	-	Bristol Omnibus Co	W75	RP
KHU 28	1948	Bedford OB	Duple C29F	Wessex Coaches		A
KHW 630	1948	Leyland Titan PD1	ECW H30/26R	Bristol Tramways	C4019	A
FAM 2	1949	Bristol L6B	Beadle C32R	Wilts & Dorset Motor Services	285	RP
HPW 108	1949	Bristol K6B	ECW H30/26A	Eastern Counties Omnibus Co	LKH 108	A
JEL 257	1949	Bristol K5G	ECW L27/28R	Hants & Dorset Motor Services	1238	A
LHW 918	1949	Bristol L5G	ECW B35R	Bristol Tramways	2410	A
MHU 49	1949	Bedford OB	Duple B30F	Bristol Tramways	207	RP
LFM 753	1950	Bristol L6B	ECW DP31R	Crosville Motor Services	KW172	R
CNH 699	1952	Bristol KSW6B	ECW L27/28R	United Counties Omnibus Co	860	A
UHY 359	1955	Bristol KSW6B	ECW H32/28R	Bristol Tramways	C8319	A
YHT 958	1958	Bristol Lodekka LD6B	ECW O33/25RD	Bristol Omnibus Co	L8462	R
980 DAE	1959	Bristol MW5G	ECW B45F	Bristol Omnibus Co	2960	A
904 OFM	1960	Bristol SC4LK	ECW C33F	Crosville Motor Services	CSG655	R
57 GUO	1961	Bristol MW6G	ECW C39F	Western National Omnibus Co (Royal Blue)	2268	A
Q507 OHR	1961	Bristol MW6G	ECW	Bristol Omnibus Co	W151	RP
507 OHU	1962	Bristol Lodekka FLF6G	ECW H38/32F	Bristol Omnibus Co	7062	RP

Registration	Date	Chassis	Body	New to	Fleet No	Status
862 RAE	1962	Bristol SUS4A	ECW B30F	Bristol Omnibus Co	301	R
RDB 872	1964	Dennis Loline III	Alexander H39/32F	North Western Road Car Co	872	RP
DFE 963D	1966	Bristol Lodekka FS5G	ECW H33/27RD	Lincolnshire Road Car Co	2537	R
OHU 770F	1968	Bristol RELL6L	ECW B50F	Bristol Omnibus Co	1071	R
LRN 60J	1970	Bristol VRLLH/6L	ECW CH42/18Ct	W C Standerwick	60	R
GYC 160K	1971	Bristol LH6L	ECW B45F	Hutchings & Cornelius Services of South Petherton		RP
HAX 399N	1975	Bristol LHS6L	Duple C35F	R I Davies & Son of Tredegar		RP
KHU 326P	1976	Bristol LH6L	ECW B43F	Bristol Omnibus Co	376	RP
KOU 791P	1976	Bristol VRTSL3/6LXB	ECW H39/31F	Bristol Omnibus Co	5505	A
EWS 746W	1981	Bristol VRTSL3/680	ECW H43/31F	Bristol Omnibus Co	5538	RP
C416 AHT	1986	Ford Transit 190D	Carlyle B16F	Bristol Omnibus Co	7416	A

Notes:

FAE 60	Originally bus 2086, converted to tower wagon in 1956.
YHT 958	Originally H33/25RD
Q507 OHR	Originally coach 2111 registered 404 LHT; converted to breakdown vehicle in 1974

Bristol Vintage Bus Group

Contact address: 74 Ridgeway Lane, Whitchurch, Bristol BS14 9PJ
Location: Unit G, Flowers Hill Road, Brislington, Bristol
Affiliation: NARTM
Brief description: A small group of enthusiasts formed to preserve examples of Bristol's buses.
Events planned: Please see enthusiast press for details
Opening days/times: At any time by prior arrangement if someone is available
Directions by car: Flowers Hill Road is off the A4 Bath road, right on the City boundary near the Park & Ride
Directions by public transport: Main bus service to Bath from the Bus Station and Temple Meads railway station stops near Flowers Hill
Charges: No admission charge for viewing or special events

Registration	Date	Chassis	Body	New to	Fleet No	Status
AHU 803	1934	Bristol J5G	Brislington Body Works B35R	Bristol Tramways	2355	R
GHT 154	1940	Bristol K5G	Brislington Body Works H30/26R	Bristol Tramways	C3336	R
GHT 127	1941	Bristol K5G	ECW O30/26R	Bristol Tramways	C3315	R
FTT 704	1945	Bristol K6A	ECW L27/28R	Western National Omnibus Co	353	R
LAE 13	1948	Leyland Titan PD1A	ECW H30/26R	Bristol Tramways	C4044	R
JXC 323	1949	Leyland Tiger PS1	Mann Egerton B30F	London Transport	TD130	A
KLB 721	1950	AEC Regent III O961 RT	Park Royal H30/26R	London Transport	RT1599	R
YHY 80	1957	Bristol LS6G	ECW B43F	Bristol Omnibus Co	3004	RP
363 CLT	1962	AEC Routemaster R2RH	Park Royal H36/28R	London Transport	RM1363	RP
CWN 629C	1965	Bristol MW6G	ECW B45F	United Welsh Services	134	A

Notes:

AHU 803	Rebodied 1947. Originally a petrol-engined coach
GHT 127	Restored in Brighton Hove & District livery
FTT 704	Original Strachans body replaced in 1955
YHY 80	Rebuilt 1972.

British Trolleybus Society

Contact address: 8 Riding Lane, Hildenborough, Tonbridge, Kent, TN11 9HX
Affiliation: NARTM
Brief description: The British Trolleybus Society is a contributor society to the Trolleybus Museum at Sandtoft. Vehicles from the collection of trolleybuses can be seen from time to time at Sandtoft on display.
Events planned: Details given in the section on Sandtoft Transport Centre

Registration	Date	Chassis	Body	New to	Fleet No	Status
note h	1902	Rob Blackwell & Co	Horse-drawn tower wagon	Reading Corporation	'William'	A
WW 4688+	1927	Garrett O type	Garrett B32C	Mexborough & Swinton Traction Co	34	A
ALJ 973+	1935	Sunbeam MS2	Park Royal H31/25D	Bournemouth Corporation	99	R
RD 7127	1935	AEC Regent O661	Park Royal L26/26R	Reading Corporation	47	R
CU 3593+	1937	Karrier E4	Weymann H29/26R	South Shields Corporation	204	R
ARD 676+	1939	AEC 661T	Park Royal H30/26R	Reading Corporation	113	R
CKG 193+	1942	AEC 664T	Northern Counties H38/32R	Cardiff Corporation	203	R
HYM 812+	1948	BUT 9641T	Metro Cammell H40/30R	London Transport	1812	R
NDH 959+	1951	Sunbeam F4	Brush H34/31R	Walsall Corporation	342	R
AC-L 379+	1956	Henschel 562E	Ludewig RB17/44T	Aachen (Germany)	22	R
XDH 72+	1956	Sunbeam F4A	Willowbrook H36/34RD	Walsall Corporation	872	RP
FYS 839+	1958	BUT 9613T	Crossley H37/34R	Glasgow Corporation	TB78	R
PVH 931+	1959	Sunbeam S7A	East Lancs H40/32R	Huddersfield Corporation	631	R

+ Trolleybus

Notes:

note h.	Unregistered wooden bodied tower wagon
NDH 959	Rebuilt/lengthened 1965
AC-L 379	German registration
XDH 72	Last Walsall trolleybus; on display at Aston Manor Road Transport Museum

Cardiff & South Wales Trolleybus Project

Contact address: 211 Hillrise, Llanedeyrn, Cardiff CF23 6UQ
Affiliation: NARTM
Brief description: The only trolleybus preservation group in the principality of Wales. A regular newsletter is issued, and new members are always welcome.

Registration	Date	Chassis	Body	New to	Fleet No	Status
DKY 704+	1945	Karrier W	East Lancs H37/29F	Bradford Corporation	704	RP
EBO 919+	1949	BUT 9641T	Bruce H38/29D	Cardiff Corporation	262	RP
KBO 961+	1955	BUT 9641T	East Lancs B40R	Cardiff Corporation	243	RP
DHW 293K	1972	Bristol LH6L	ECW B42F	Bristol Omnibus Co	353	R

+ Trolleybus

Notes:

DKY 704	Rebodied 1959
EBO 919	Body built on East Lancs frames
DHW 293K	Support vehicle

Chelveston Preservation Society

Contact address: 36 Moor Road, Rushden, Northants, NN10 9SP
Affiliation: NARTM
Brief description: A private collection owned by a few members has evolved to represent most types of Bristol chassis from a range of former Tilling Group companies.

Registration	Date	Chassis	Body	New to	Fleet No	Status
VV 5696	1937	Bristol JO5G	ECW B35R	United Counties Omnibus Co	450	R
MPU 21	1948	Bristol K6B	ECW L27/28R	Eastern National Omnibus Co	3960	RP
FRP 692	1950	Bristol KS5G	ECW L27/28R	United Counties Omnibus Co	692	R
FRP 828	1950	Bristol LL5G	ECW B39R	United Counties Omnibus Co	828	A
NAE 3	1950	Bristol L6B	ECW FC31F	Bristol Tramways	2467	RP
CNH 860	1952	Bristol LWL6B	ECW B39R	United Counties Omnibus Co	426	R
CNH 862	1952	Bristol LWL6B	ECW DP33R	United Counties Omnibus Co	428	R
HWV 294	1952	Bristol KSW5G	ECW L27/28R	Wilts & Dorset Motor Services	365	A
JBD 975	1953	Bristol KSW6B	ECW L27/28R	United Counties Omnibus Co	938	A
KNV 337	1954	Bristol KSW6B	ECW L27/28R	United Counties Omnibus Co	964	R
RFM 408	1954	Bristol Lodekka LD6B	ECW H33/25R	Crosville Motor Services	ML663	A
TUO 497	1956	Bristol LS6G	ECW B45F	Southern National Omnibus Co	1781	RP
604 JPU	1957	Bristol SC4LK	ECW B35F	Eastern National Omnibus Co	427	A
ONU 425	1957	Bristol SC4LK	ECW B35F	United Counties Omnibus Co	125	RP W 2.10.4
RFU 689	1958	Bristol SC4LK	ECW DP33F	Lincolnshire Road Car Co	2611	R
TFF 251	1958	Bristol MW6G	ECW -	Crosville Motor Services	G341	A
566 JFM	1959	Bristol SC4LK	ECW B35F	Crosville Motor Services	SSG626	A
675 COD	1960	Bristol SUS4A	ECW B30F	Western National Omnibus Co	603	A
264 KTA	1962	Bristol MW6G	ECW C39F	Western National Omnibus Co	1395	A
268 KTA	1962	Bristol SUL4A	ECW C37F	Western National Omnibus Co	434	A
675 AAM	1962	Bristol MW6G	ECW C34F	Wilts & Dorset Motor Services	717	A
891 XFM	1962	Bristol FS5G	ECW H36/26F	Crosville Motor Services	DFG81	A
375 GWN	1964	Bristol RELL6G	ECW C47F	United Welsh Services	52	RP
ABD 253B	1964	Bristol RELH6G	ECW C47F	United Counties Omnibus Co	253	A
CHY 419C	1965	Bristol Lodekka FLF6G	ECW H38/32F	Bristol Omnibus Co	C7201	RP
GAX 2C	1965	Bristol RELL6G	ECW B54F	Red & White Services	R2 65	RP
EDV 555D	1966	Bristol SUL4A	ECW B36F	Southern National Omnibus Co	692	RP
HFM 561D	1966	Bristol MW6G	ECW C39F	Crosville Motor Services	CMG561	R
OWC 182D	1966	Bristol MW6G	ECW C34F	Tillings Transport	182	R
UFM 53F	1968	Bristol RELL6G	ECW DP50F	Crosville Motor Services	ERG53	RP
MMW 354G	1969	Bristol RELL6G	ECW B45D	Wilts & Dorset Motor Services	824	R
TBD 279G	1969	Bristol RELH6G	ECW DP49F	United Counties Omnibus Co	279	A
HAH 537L	1972	Bristol LH6P	ECW B45F	Eastern Counties Omnibus Co	LH537	RP
YFM 283L	1973	Bristol RELL6G	ECW DP50F	Crosville Motor Services	ERG283	R
JFJ 506N	1975	Bristol LH6L	Plaxton C43F	Greenslades Tours	326	R
HBD 919T	1977	Bristol VRTSL3/6LXB	ECW CH41/25F	United Counties Omnibus Co	919	R
ARP 601X	1981	Leyland Olympian ONLXB/1R	ECW H45/32F	United Counties Omnibus Co	601	R

Notes:

VV 5696	Rebodied 1949
CNH 862	Gardner 5LW engine fitted in 1956. Reverted to Bristol AVW in 1996.
CNH 860	Renumbered 426 in 1952; Gardner 5LW engine fitted 1956
RFM 408	Eighth production Lodekka. Currently has no engine or gearbox
TFF 251	Converted to towing vehicle
OWC 182D	Passed to Eastern National (392) in 1968 and to Tilling's Travel (9392) in 1971

Cherwell Bus Preservation Group

Contact address: 32 Mill Street, Kidlington OX5 2EF
Brief description: A collection of mainly ex-City of Oxford vehicles housed under cover.
Events planned: The operational vehicles will attend a few events during the rally season.

Registration	Date	Chassis	Body	New to	Fleet No	Status
OJO 727	1950	AEC Regal III 9621A	Willowbrook B32F	City of Oxford Motor Services	727	R
191 AWL	1956	AEC Regent V MD3RV	Weymann L30/26R	City of Oxford Motor Services	L191	R
975 CWL	1958	AEC Regent V LD3RA	Park Royal H37/28R	City of Oxford Motor Services	H975	RP
312 MFC	1961	AEC Bridgemaster 2B3RA	Park Royal H43/29F	City of Oxford Motor Services	312	R
332 RJO	1963	AEC Renown 3B3RA	Park Royal H38/27F	City of Oxford Motor Services	332	R
OFC 902H	1970	Bristol VRTSL/6LX	ECW H39/31F	City of Oxford Motor Services	902	RP
AUD 310J	1971	Leyland Leopard PSU3B/4R	Plaxton C51F	O A Slatter & Sons of Long Hanborough	40	A
TJO 56K	1971	AEC Reliance 6MU4R	Marshall DP49F	City of Oxford Motor Services	56	A
YWL 134K	1972	Leyland Leopard PSU3B/4R	Plaxton C53F	R Jarvis & Sons of Middle Barton		A
NUD 105L	1973	Bristol VRTSL/6LX	ECW CH41/27F	City of Oxford Motor Services	105	A
RBW 87M	1974	Bristol RELH6L	ECW DP49F	City of Oxford Motor Services	87	A
PWL 999W	1980	Leyland Olympian B45 ONTL11/2R	Alexander H50/32D	Leyland (prototype)		A
VJO 201X	1982	Leyland Olympian ONLXB/1R	ECW H47/28D	City of Oxford Motor Services	201	A
VUD 30X	1982	Leyland Leopard PSU3G/4R	ECW C49F	City of Oxford Motor Services	30	R
C729 JJO	1986	Ford Transit 190D	Carlyle DP20F	City of Oxford Motor Services	729	RP

Notes:
PWL 999W   Prototype operated by Singapore Bus Services, registered SBS 5396B. Acquired by COMS (999) in 1987.

City of Portsmouth Preserved Transport Depot

Contact address: Friends of CPPTD, 58 South View Gardens, Andover, Hampshire SP10 2AQ
Affiliation: NARTM
Brief description: A collection comprising a range of veteran and vintage buses, most of which spent their working lives in the South of England. Suitable premises in the Portsmouth area are being sought for the Museum following closure of the Broad Street site, but the collection's vehicles (currently in storage at two locations) still operate free bus services and attend rallies, carnivals and other events. Please see the enthusiast press for the latest developments.

Registration	Date	Chassis	Body	New to	Fleet No	Status
note a	1876	Horse bus		G Wheeler of Fawley		A
RV 6367	1935	Leyland Titan TD4	English Electric O26/24R	Portsmouth Corporation	7	R
CTP 200	1944	Bedford OWB	Duple (replica) UB32F	Portsmouth Corporation	170	R
DTP 823	1947	Leyland Titan PD1	Weymann H30/26R	Portsmouth Corporation	189	RP
AHC 442	1951	AEC Regent III 9613A	Bruce H30/26R	Eastbourne Corporation	42	R
EHV 65	1951	Bedford OB	Duple B29F	East Ham Borough Council		R
LRV 996	1956	Leyland Titan PD2/12	Metro Cammell O33/26R	Portsmouth Corporation	4	R
ORV 989	1958	Leyland Titan PD2/40	Metro Cammell H30/26R	Portsmouth Corporation	112	RP
BBK 236B	1964	Leyland Atlantean PDR1/1	Metro Cammell H43/33F	Portsmouth Corporation	236	R
BTR 361B	1964	AEC Regent V 2D3RA	East Lancs Neepsend H37/29R	Southampton Corporation	361	R
GTP 175F	1967	Leyland Panther Cub PSURC1/1	MCW B42D	Portsmouth Corporation	175	R

Registration	Date	Chassis	Body	New to	Fleet No	Status
TBK 190K	1971	Leyland Atlantean PDR2/1	Seddon Pennine B40D	Portsmouth Corporation	190	R
XTP 287L	1973	Leyland Atlantean AN68/1R	Alexander H45/30D	Portsmouth Corporation	287	RP
+ Trolleybus						

Notes:

note a	Not registered		EHV 65	Preserved in Hants & Sussex livery
RV 6367	Originally H26/24R		LRV 996	Originally H33/26R
CTP 200	Replica body; wartime livery			

Classic Southdown Onmibuses

Contact address: Dormy Cottage, 2 Alan Road, Wimbledon Village, London SW19 7PT
Affiliation: NARTM
Brief description: One of the largest single privately owned collections of Southdown Vehicles in the country, ranging from 1939 Leyland Titan TD4 to the last Bristol VR delivered new to Southdown.
Events planned: The operational vehicles will attend events in the south of England during the rally season as well as being used for private hire work.

Registration	Date	Chassis	Body	New to	Fleet No	Status
GCD 48	1939	Leyland Titan TD5	Park Royal H28/26R	Southdown Motor Services	248	R
RUF 186	1956	Leyland Titan PD2/12	Beadle H33/26R	Southdown Motor Services	786	R
410 DCD	1964	Leyland Titan PD3/4	Northern Counties FCO39/30F	Southdown Motor Services	410	R
422 DCD	1964	Leyland Titan PD3/4	Northern Counties FCO39/30F	Southdown Motor Services	422	R
HCD 347E	1967	Leyland Titan PD3/4	Northern Counties FH39/30F	Southdown Motor Services	347	R
UUF 110J	1971	Bristol VRT Series II	ECW H39/31F	Southdown Motor Services	510	RP
JWV 976W	1981	Bristol VRTSL3/6LXB	ECW H43/31F	Southdown Motor Services	276	R

Notes:

GCD 48	Rebodied 1950
RUF 186	Body built on Park Royal frames

County Durham Bus Preservation Group

Contact address: 38 Lambton Drive, Hetton-le-Hole, Houghton-le-Spring, Tyne & Wear DH5 0EW
E-mail: fonzypop@hotmail.com
Affiliation: NARTM
Brief description: The group comprises individuals who own a number of restored vehicles and are in the process of restoring others. The collection is not normally open to the public but may be viewed by prior arrangement

Registration	Date	Chassis	Body	New to	Fleet No	Status
BTN 113	1934	Daimler COS4	Northern Coachbuilders B34R	Newcastle Corporation	173	A
BGA 97	1938	Daimler COG6	(chassis only)	Glasgow Corporation	531	A
HHN 202	1947	Bristol L5G	ECW B35R	United Automobile Services	DB216	R
HUP 236	1948	Albion Valiant CX39N	ACB C33F	Economic Bus Services of Whitburn	W7	R
LVK 123	1948	Leyland Titan PD2/1	Leyland H30/26R	Newcastle Corporation	123	A
NVK 341	1950	AEC Regent III 9612A	Northern Coachbuilders H30/26R	Newcastle Corporation	341	R
TUG 20	1954	AEC Reliance MU3RV	Roe C41C	Roe demonstrator		RP

Registration	Date	Chassis	Body	New to	Fleet No	Status
TUP 859	1956	AEC Regent V MD3RV	Roe H35/28R	Hartlepool Corporation	4	RP
VUP 328	1957	Leyland Tiger Cub PSUC1/1	Crossley B44F	Economic Bus Services of Whitburn	A2	A
YPT 796	1958	AEC Reliance MU3RV	Roe C41C	Economic Bus Services of Whitburn	W3	R
221 JVK	1962	Leyland Atlantean PDR1/1	Alexander H44/34F	Newcastle Corporation	221	R
WNL 259A	1962	AEC Reliance 4MU3RA	Plaxton B55F	Economic Bus Services of Whitburn	W5	R
EUP 405B	1964	AEC Routemaster 3R2RH	Park Royal H41/31F	Northern General Transport Co	2105	R
GGR 103N	1974	Leyland Atlantean AN68/2R	Northern Counties H47/36F	OK Motor Services		RP
VPT 598R	1977	Leyland National 11351A/1R	Leyland National B49F	Northern General Transport Co	4598	RP
JPT 906T	1979	Bristol VRTSL3/501	ECW CH41/29F	Northern General Transport Co	3406	RP
SGR 935V	1979	Bristol VRTSL3/501	ECW H43/31F	Northern General Transport Co	3435	RP
AUP 369W	1980	Leyland Atlantean AN68B/1R	Roe H43/30F	Northern General Transport Co	3469	RP
SPT 963V	1980	Leyland Leopard PSU3E/4R	Plaxton C53F	OK Motor Services		RP
UTN 501Y	1983	MCW Metrobus DR102/37	MCW H46/31F	Northern General Transport Co	3501	RP

Notes:

BGA 97	Chassis only
HHN 202	Rebodied 1957 with 1946 body; passed to Durham District Services (DB216) in 1959
WNL 259A	Originally registered 8031 PT
JPT 906T	Has been re-registered twice and now retains original number.

The Devon General Society

Contact address: Membership Secretary, Greenfields, The Rowe, Stableford, Newcastle-under-Lyme, Staffs ST5 4EN
Web site: www.devongeneral.org.uk
Brief description: The Devon General Society was formed in 1982 to promote interest in the former Devon General company and its successors, also to stimulate the preservation of all aspects of the company's past for the benefit of future generations. Approximately 35 former Devon General vehicles are currently preserved privately by society members, The society actively assists them and regularly stages events in Devon whereby these vehicles can be enjoyed.
Events planned: Please see web site

Registration	Date	Chassis	Body	New to	Fleet No	Status
OD 7497	1934	AEC Regent O661	Short O31/24R	Devon General	DR210	R
HTT 487	1946	AEC Regal I O662	Weymann B35F	Devon General	SR487	R
KOD 585	1949	AEC Regent III 9612E	Weymann H30/26R	Devon General	DR585	R
NTT 661	1952	AEC Regent III 9613A	Weymann H30/26R	Devon General	DR661	R
NTT 679	1952	AEC Regent III 9613S	Weymann H30/26R	Devon General	DR679	R
UFJ 296	1957	Guy Arab IV	Park Royal H31/26R	Exeter Corporation	56	R
VDV 798	1957	AEC Reliance MU3RA	Weymann B41F	Devon General	SR798	A
VDV 817	1957	AEC Regent V MD3RV	Metro Cammell H33/26R	Devon General	DR817	R
XTA 839	1958	Albion Nimbus NS3N	Willowbrook B31F	Devon General	SN839	R
XUO 721	1958	Bristol MW6G	ECW B41F	Western National Omnibus Co (Royal Blue)	2238	R
872 ATA	1959	Leyland Atlantean PDR1/1	Metro Cammell H44/32F	Devon General	DL872	RP
913 DTT	1960	Leyland Atlantean PDR1/1	Roe H43/31F	Devon General	DL913	R
928 GTA	1961	Leyland Atlantean PDR1/1	Metro Cammell CO44/31F	Devon General	DL928	RP
931 GTA	1961	Leyland Atlantean PDR1/1	Metro Cammell CO44/31F	Devon General	DL931	R
932 GTA	1961	Leyland Atlantean PDR1/1	Metro Cammell CO44/31F	Devon General	DL932	R
935 GTA	1961	AEC Reliance 2MU3RV	Willowbrook C41F	Devon General (Grey Cars)	TCR935	R W

Registration	Date	Chassis	Body	New to	Fleet No	Status
960 HTT	1962	AEC Reliance 2MU3RV	Willowbrook C41F	Devon General (Grey Cars)	TCR960	R
503 RUO	1964	AEC Regent V 2D3RA	Willowbrook H39/30F	Devon General	503	RP
9 RDV	1964	AEC Reliance 2U3RA	Marshall B49F	Devon General	9	R
CTT 23C	1965	AEC Reliance 2MU3RA	Park Royal B39F	Devon General	23	R
NDV 537G	1968	Leyland Atlantean PDR1A/1	MCW H44/31F	Devon General	537	R
TUO 74J	1970	AEC Reliance 6MU3R	Willowbrook B41F	Devon General	74	R
VOD 550K	1971	Bristol VRTSL/6LX	ECW H43/31F	Western National Omnibus Co (Devon General)	550	RP
VOD 88K	1972	Bristol LHS6L	Marshall B33F	Western National Omnibus Co	88	RP
ATA 563L	1973	Bristol VRTSL/6LX	ECW H43/31F	Devon General	563	R
KTT 42P	1975	Bristol LH6L	ECW B43F	Western National Omnibus Co	112	R
FDV 829V	1979	Leyland National 2 NL116L11/1R	Leyland National B50F	Western National Omnibus Co (Devon General)	2883	R
LFJ 862W	1980	Bristol VRT SL3/6LX	ECW H43/31F	Western National Omnibus Co	1215	R
C526 FFJ	1986	Ford Transit 160D	Carlyle B16F	Devon General (Bayline) Ltd	526	R

Notes:

OD 7497	Converted to open top in 1955
XUO 721	Originally C39F Royal Blue coach. Rebuilt 1973 as bus numbered 2902 in Devon General fleet.
FDV 829V	First production National 2 to enter service in UK

Dewsbury Bus Museum

Contact address: 5 Oakenshaw Street, Agbrigg, Wakefield WF1 5BT
Phone: 01924 258314
Affiliation: NARTM
Brief description: The group was formed in the early 1970s and concentrated on ex-West Riding vehicles. By 1989 the collection had grown and, to provide covered accommodation, a new, 14-vehicle shed was erected. Vehicles can be seen at local events, or on site by appointment.
Opening days/times: Open only on rally days and when work is being done on vehicles (please enquire before visiting).
Transport Collectors Fairs 12 March and 12 November 2004.
7 May 2006 — museum open day in association with West Yorkshire Transport Society spring rally in Dewsbury town centre.
Other information: Other events are being planned — please see enthusiast press for details.

Registration	Date	Chassis	Body	New to	Fleet No	Status
Y 9608	1932	AEC Regal 662	Strachan C28R	Orange Bros of Bedlington	42	A
DHN 475	1939	Bristol L5G	ECW B35R	United Automobile Services	BLO11	A
BHL 682	1948	Leyland Titan PD2/1	Leyland L27/26R	West Riding Automobile Co	640	RP
TWY 8	1950	Albion CX39N	Roe L27/26RD	South Yorkshire Motors	81	RP
EHL 344	1952	Leyland Tiger PS2/12A	Roe B39F	West Riding Automobile Co	733	R
OWX 167	1955	Bristol Lodekka LD6B	ECW H33/27RD	West Yorkshire Road Car Co	DX23	RP
JHL 708	1956	AEC Reliance MU3RV	Roe B44F	West Riding Automobile Co	808	RP
KHL 855	1957	Guy Arab IV	Roe L29/26RD	West Riding Automobile Co	855	RP
TWT 123	1958	Bristol MW5G	ECW DP41F	West Yorkshire Road Car Co	EUG 71	RP
VLT 188	1959	AEC Routemaster R2RH	Park Royal H36/28R	London Transport	RM 188	RP
LEN 101	1960	Guy Wulfrunian	(chassis only)	Bury Corporation	101	A
574 CNW	1962	Daimler CVG6	Roe H39/31F	Leeds City Transport	574	RP
PJX 35	1962	Leyland Leopard L1	Weymann B44F	Halifax Corporation	35	R
827 BWY	1963	Bristol MW6G	ECW B45F	West Yorkshire Road Car Co	SMG19	RP
WHL 970	1963	Guy Wulfrunian	Roe H43/32F	West Riding Automobile Co	970	RP
CUV 208C	1965	AEC Routemaster R2RH	Park Royal H36/28R	London Transport	RM2208	R
EHT 108C	1965	Bristol Lodekka FLF6G	ECW H38/32F	Bristol Omnibus Co	C7219	RP
JJD 524D	1966	AEC Routemaster R2RH1	Park Royal H40/32R	London Transport	RML2524	RP
MWW 114D	1966	Bristol Lodekka FS6B	ECW H33/27RD	York - West Yorkshire Services	YDX233	RP
LHL 164F	1967	Leyland Panther PSUR1/1	Roe B51F	West Riding Automobile Co	164	R
NWW 89E	1967	Leyland Leopard L1	Willowbrook B45F	Todmorden Joint Omnibus Committee	9	R

Above: The Bristol Omnibus Vehicle Collection comprises, amongst others, KSW6B L8089 (OHY 938) and L5G C2736 (LHY 976). On the occasion of the Gloucester and Cheltenham Running Day in 2004 they are seen in the Gloucester depot of Stagecoach.

Below: The Three Counties Bus and Commercial Vehicle Museum hold United Counties 587 (SVV 587W), a Leyland National 2 of 1980. *Philip Lamb*

Above: Affiliated with the Southdown Historical Vehicle group is LFS 296F, a Bristol VR that was new to Eastern Scottish and was subsequently operated by Alder Valley, while Southdown 786 (RUF 186) is a Beadle-bodied Leyland Titan PD2 that is now part of the Classic Southdown Omnibuses collection. *Philip Lamb*

Below: Many of Ensignbus's and Blue Triangle's classic former London Transport buses hold Class VI tickets for use on special stage services. RT3232 (KYY 961) and RT3062 (KXW 171) are seen at Wisley Airfield on 3 April 2005 on the service linking this display site with the main rally held at Cobham Bus Museum. *Matthew Wharmby*

Registration	Date	Chassis	Body	New to	Fleet No	Status
XWW 474G	1968	Bristol VRTSL6LX	ECW H39/31F	West Yorkshire Road Car Co	VR4	A
THL 261H	1970	Bristol RELL6G	ECW B53F	West Riding Automobile Co	261	RP
MCK 229J	1971	Leyland Panther PSUR1B/1R	Pennine B47D	Preston Corporation	229	RP
OWY 750K	1972	Bristol RESL6G	ECW B47F	Keighley-West Yorkshire Services	2109	RP
WEX 685M	1973	AEC Swift 3MP2R	ECW B43D	Great Yarmouth Corporation	85	R
GNJ 583N	1975	Bristol VRTSL3/510	ECW H43/31F	Southdown Motor Services	583	A
JWW 227N	1975	Bristol VRTSL6LX	ECW H47/31F	York West Yorkshire Services	3968	RP
MUA 865P	1976	Leyland Atlantean AN68/1R	Roe H43/30F	Yorkshire Woollen District Transport Co	768	R
OWW 905P	1976	Bristol VRTSL3/6LX	ECW H43/31F	West Riding Automobile Co	761	RP
PUM 149W	1980	Bristol VRTSL3/6LXB	ECW H43/31F	West Yorkshire Road Car Co	1746	RP
XUA 73X	1982	Leyland National 2 NL116AL11/1R	Leyland National B49F	West Riding Automobile Co	73	RP

Notes:

DHN 475	Rebodied 1947 with 1938 body
TWY 8	New in 1950 registered JWT 112; rebodied and reregistered in 1958
MWW 114D	Latterly driver trainer 4068
OWY 750K	Originally B44F
MUA 865P	Rebodied 1981
XUA 73X	Gardner engine fitted c12/87

East Kent Road Car Heritage Trust

Contact address: 33 Alfred Road, Dover, Kent, CT16 2AD
Phone/Fax: 01304 204612
Brief Description: Between the trust and Friends of the East Kent members have around 18 former East Kent vehicles, based at various locations. A museum is planned but until then, the vehicles are taken to the public at various locations and some are available for stage carriage and hire work

Registration	Date	Chassis	Body	New to	Fleet No	Status
CJG 959	1947	Leyland Titan PD1A	Leyland L27/26R	East Kent Road Car Co		A
EFN 592	1950	Dennis Lancet J3	Park Royal C32F	East Kent Road Car Co		R
FFN 399	1951	Guy Arab III	Park Royal H32/26R	East Kent Road Car Co		R
GFN 273	1952	Beadle-Leyland	Beadle C35F	East Kent Road Car Co		R
KFN 239	1955	AEC Reliance MU3RV	Weymann DP41F	East Kent Road Car Co		RP
MFN 898	1956	Guy Arab IV	Park Royal H33/28RD	East Kent Road Car Co		RP
PFN 867	1959	AEC Regent V 2LD3RA	Park Royal FH40/32F	East Kent Road Car Co		R
YJG 807	1962	AEC Bridgemaster 2B3RA	Park Royal H43/29F	East Kent Road Car Co		R
6801 FN	1963	AEC Regent V 2D3RA	Park Royal H40/32F	East Kent Road Car Co		R
AFN 488B	1964	AEC Reliance 2MU4RA	Duple C34F	East Kent Road Car Co		RP
AFN 780B	1964	AEC Regent V 2D3RA	Park Royal H40/30F	East Kent Road Car Co		R
DJG 619C	1965	AEC Reliance 2U3RA	Park Royal C49F	East Kent Road Car Co		A
GJG 739D	1966	AEC Regent V 2D3RA	Park Royal H40/32F	East Kent Road Car Co		RP
OFN 721F	1968	AEC Reliance 6U3ZR	Marshall B53F	East Kent Road Car Co		RP
VJG 187J	1970	AEC Swift 5P2R	Marshall B51F	East Kent Road Car Co		R
EFN 178L	1973	Leyland National 1151/1R	Leyland National B49F	East Kent Road Car Co		R
PFN 788M	1974	AEC Reliance 6U3ZR	Duple C42F	East Kent Road Car Co		A
JJG 1P	1976	Leyland Atlantean AN68/1R	ECW H43/30F	East Kent Road Car Co		RP
NFN 84R	1977	Leyland National 11351A/1R	Leyland National DP48F	East Kent Road Car Co		RP
TFN 980T	1978	Bristol VRTSL3/6LXB	Willowbrook H43/31F	East Kent Road Car Co		RP

Notes:

GFN 273	Running units are ex-AJG 30, 1939 Leyland Titan TD5
PFN 867	Driver-training vehicle from 1976
EFN 178L	Fitted with wheelchair lift

Eastern Transport Collection Society
Attleborough

Phone: 01603 744794 or 891284

Affiliation: NARTM

Brief description: The collection includes a number of vehicles owned by the society and members, together with a range of bus memorabilia bequeathed by the late Tony Powell together with other items added by the society. Viewing is by appointment only.

Events planned: Norwich Bus Rally - please see enthusiast press for date.

Opening days/times: By appointment only.

Charges: Free admission but donations welcome.

Registration	Date	Chassis	Body	New to	Fleet No	Status
KNG 718	1950	Bristol LL5G	ECW B39F	Eastern Counties Omnibus Co	LL718	R
NAH 941	1952	Bristol KSW5G	ECW H32/28R	Eastern Counties Omnibus Co	LKH341	RP
MXX 481	1953	AEC Regal IV 9821LT RF	Metro Cammell B41F	London Transport	RF504	R
OVF 229	1954	Bristol Lodekka LD5G	ECW H33/25RD	Eastern Counties Omnibus Co	LKD229	R
KDB 696	1957	Leyland Tiger Cub PSUC1/1	Weymann B44F	North Western Road Car Co	696	RP
5789 AH	1959	Bristol MW5G	ECW C39F	Eastern Counties Omnibus Co	LS789	R
675 OCV	1962	Bedford SB3	Duple C41F	Crimson Tours		R
MOO 177	1962	Bristol MW6G	ECW B45F	Eastern National Omnibus Co	556	RP
KVF 658E	1967	Bristol RESL6G	ECW B46F	Eastern Counties Omnibus Co	RS658	R
PBJ 2F	1967	Leyland Titan PD2/47	Massey H34/28R	Lowestoft Corporation	12	RP
EPW 516K	1972	Bristol RELL6G	ECW B53F	Eastern Counties Omnibus Co	RL516	RP
OCK 988K	1972	Bristol VRTSL/6LX	ECW H39/31F	Ribble Motor Services	1988	RP
WNO 556L	1972	Leyland National 1151/1R/0401	Leyland National B50F	Eastern National Omnibus Co	1707	RP
RRM 148M	1974	Leyland National 1151/1R/2308	Leyland National DP51F	Leyland demonstrator		R
NAH 135P	1976	Bristol VRTSL3/501	ECW H43/31F	Eastern Counties Omnibus Co	VR172	RP
RGS 598R	1976	Bedford YMT	Duple C57F	Eagre Coaches		RP
WAD 640S	1978	Ford R1114	Plaxton C53F	Ladvale of Dursley		RP
H74 ANG	1990	Dennis Condor	Duple Metsec H69/41D	China Motor Bus		R

Notes

RRM 148M   Suburban Express Demonstrator

Ensign Transport Museum

Contact address: Ensignbus, Jubilee Close, Purfleet, RM15 4YF

Telephone: 01708 865656

Affiliation: NARTM

Brief description: The collection is based on ex-London types, the emphasis being to keep vehicles to Class VI condition, enabling regular operation on heritage services. A number of buses have been successfully repatriated from overseas and Ensign continue to seek rare or unusual ex-London types

Registration	Date	Chassis	Body	New to	Fleet No	Status
ELP 223	1938	AEC Regal 0662	LPTB C33F	London Transport	T499	RP
HLJ 44	1948	Bristol K6A	ECW L27/28R	Hants & Dorset Motor Services	TD895	R
JXC 194	1949	AEC Regent III O961 RT	Cravens H30/26R	London Transport	RT1431	R
KGK 758	1949	AEC Regent III O961 RT	Cravens H30/26R	London Transport	RT1499	R
KYY 961	1950	AEC Regent III O961 RT	Weymann H30/26R	London Transport	RT3232	R
MLL 952	1952	AEC Regal IV 9821LT RF	Metro Cammell B39F	London Transport	RF315	R

Registration	Date	Chassis	Body	New to	Fleet No	Status
MXX 261	1952	AEC Regent III	Weymann L27/26R	London Transport	RLH61	R
NLE 603	1953	AEC Regal IV 9821LT RF	Metro Cammell B39F	London Transport	RF603	A
NLE 882	1953	AEC Regent III O961 RT	Park Royal H30/26R	London Transport	RT3775	R
NXP 775	1954	AEC Regent III O961 RT	Weymann H30/26R	London Transport	RT4421	R
348 CLT	1962	AEC Routemaster	Park Royal H36/28R	London Transport	RM1348	R
799 DYE	1963	AEC Routemaster	Park Royal H36/28R	London Transport	RM1799	R
CRU 184C	1965	Daimler Fleetline CRG6LX	Weymann O43/31F	Bournemouth Corporation	184	A
CUV 220C	1965	AEC Routemaster	Park Royal H36/29RD	London Country Bus Services	RCL2220	R
JJD 405D	1966	AEC Routemaster	Park Royal H36/28R	London Transport	RML2405	R
NMY 658E	1967	AEC Routemaster R2RH/2	Park Royal H32/24F	British European Airways	RMA58	R
SMM 90F	1968	AEC Merlin	MCW B45D	London Transport	MB90	A
GHV 2N	1974	Daimler Fleetline CRL6	Park Royal H44/27D	London Transport	DM1002	A
THX 646S	1978	Leyland Fleetline FE30ALR	Park Royal H44/28D	London Transport	DM2646	A
A250 SVW	1983	Leyland Tiger TRCTL11/3R	Duple C57F	Southend Transport	250	A

Notes:

THX 646S   Fitted with Iveco engine 1988 to 1996

Friends of King Alfred Buses

Contact address: 27 White Dirt Lane, Catherington, Waterlooville, Hampshire, PO8 ONB
E-mail: info@fokab.org.uk
Web site: www.fokab.org.uk
Affiliation: NARTM
Brief description: The collection includes 12 former King Alfred Motor Services vehicles that have been rescued from around the world and restored. A charitable trust, FoKAB aims eventually to establish a museum. In the meantime, the vehicles can be viewed at the annual running day and other events.
Events planned:
1 Jan 2007 — Annual running day at Winchester.

Registration	Date	Chassis	Body	New to	Fleet No	Status
OU 9286	1931	Dennis 30cwt	Short B18F	King Alfred Motor Services		R
JAA 708	1950	Leyland Olympic HR40	Weymann B40F	King Alfred Motor Services		RP
POU 494	1956	Leyland Titan PD2/24	East Lancs L27/28R	King Alfred Motor Services		R
WCG 104	1959	Leyland Tiger Cub PSUC1/1	Weymann B45F	King Alfred Motor Services		R
326 CAA	1961	Bedford SB3	Harrington C41F	King Alfred Motor Services		R
595 LCG	1964	AEC Renown 3B2RA	Park Royal H43/31F	King Alfred Motor Services		R
596 LCG	1964	AEC Renown 3B2RA	Park Royal H43/31F	King Alfred Motor Services		R
BHO 543C	1965	Bedford CAL230	Martyn Walker B11	H. R. Richmond of Epsom		A
CCG 704C	1965	Bedford VAL14	Plaxton C49F	King Alfred Motor Services		R
HOR 590E	1967	Leyland Atlantean PDR1/2	Roe O43/31F	King Alfred Motor Services		R
HOR 592E	1967	Leyland Atlantean PDR1/2	Roe H43/33F	King Alfred Motor Services		R
UOU 417H	1970	Leyland Panther PSUR1A/1R	Plaxton B52F	King Alfred Motor Services		RP
UOU 419H	1970	Leyland Panther PSUR1A/1R	Plaxton B52F	King Alfred Motor Services		R
NKJ 849P	1976	Commer Karrier KC6055	Rootes B22F	Enham Village Disabled Transport		R

Notes:

POU 494   Repatriated from the USA in 1993
596 LCG   Repatriated from the USA in 1988
BHO 543C   To be restored to King Alfred condition
CCG 704C   Restoration involved body-swap
HOR 590E   Originally H43/33F; acquired by Bristol Omnibus Co (8602) and converted to open-top in 1979
HOR 592E   Acquired by Bristol Omnibus Co (8600) and converted to open-top in 1979; restored using roof from vehicle HOR 591E
NKJ 849P   Mobile display vehicle

Glasgow Vintage Vehicle Trust

Contact address: 17 Balmedie, Erskine, PA8 6EW
Museum address: Fordneuk Street, Glasgow G40 3AH
Phone: 0141 587 0418
E-mail: info@gvvt.org
Affiliation: NARTM
Brief description: Established in a former Glasgow Corporation bus depot.
Opening days/times: Telephone for access information. Prior arrangement only.
Directions by car: From City centre follow London Road eastbound.
Directions by public transport: First Glasgow 43 or 64 from City centre. SPT rail network to Bridgeton station
Events planned: 8 October 2006 — Open Day. Please see enthusiast press or telephone for details
Facilities: B(e), D, T

Registration	Date	Chassis	Body	New to	Fleet No	Status
DBY 001	1932	Fordson ET7	Barbara B31F	Malta		RP
WG 2373	1934	Leyland Lion LT5B	Burlingham B35F	W Alexander & Sons (Midland)	P169	R
WG 4445	1937	Leyland Tiger TS7	Alexander C35F	W Alexander & Sons	P331	A
CRG 811	1947	Daimler CVD6	Alexander C35F	Aberdeen Corporation	41	A
GUS 926	1949	Maudslay Marathon III	Park Royal C35F	David MacBrayne of Glasgow	136	R
CHL 772	1950	Daimler CVD6	Willowbrook DP35F	Bullock of Featherstone		R
FVA 854	1950	Albion Valiant CX39N	Duple C33F	Hutchinsons of Overtown		R
HGG 359	1950	Thornycroft HF/ER4	Croft B20F	MacBrayne	149	R
6769	1955	Albion Victor FT39AN	Heaver B35F	Guernsey Railway Co	55	RP
NSF 757	1956	Leyland Titan PD2/20	Metro Cammell H34/29R	Edinburgh Corporation	757	A
KAG 856	1957	Leyland Titan PD2/20	Alexander L31/28R	Western SMT Co	D1375	RP
TVS 367	1958	Bristol Lodekka LD6G	ECW H33/27R	Central SMT Co	B87	A
MSD 407	1959	Leyland Titan PD3/6	Alexander L35/32RD	Western SMT Co	D1543	RP
MSD 408	1959	Leyland Titan PD3/3	Alexander L35/32RD	Western SMT Co	D1544	R
NMS 358	1960	AEC Reliance 2MU3RV	Alexander C41F	W Alexander & Sons	AC147	R
YYS 174	1960	Bedford C5Z1	Duple C21FM	David MacBrayne of Glasgow	54	R
198 CUS	1961	AEC Reliance 2MU3RA	Duple (Midland) C41F	David MacBrayne of Glasgow	63	RP
RAG 400	1961	Bristol Lodekka LD6G	ECW H33/27RD	Western SMT Co	B1634	A
SGD 500	1961	AEC Regent V 2D2RA	Alexander H41/31F	Glasgow Corporation	A350	RP
TCK 821	1963	Leyland Titan PD3/5	Metro Cammell FH41/31F	Ribble Motor Services	1821	R
828 SHW	1964	Bristol Lodekka FLF6B	ECW H38/32F	Bristol Omnibus Co	C7135	A
NGE 172P	1964	AEC Reliance 2U3RA	Plaxton C46F	World Wide of Lanark		A
BJX 848C	1965	Bedford VAS1	Duple C29F	Abbeyways of Halifax		A
CUV 121C	1965	AEC Routemaster	Park Royal H36/28R	London Transport	RM2121	R
DMS 348C	1965	Leyland Leopard PSU3/3R	Alexander	W Alexander & Sons (Midland)	MPE62	R
GYS 896D	1966	Leyland Atlantean PDR1/1	Alexander H44/34F	Glasgow Corporation	LA320	R
HGA 983D	1966	Bedford VAS1	Willowbrook B24FM	David MacBrayne of Glasgow	210	R
GRS 334E	1967	Albion Viking VK43AL	Alexander DP40F	W Alexander & Sons (Northern)	NNV34	A
HFR 501E	1967	Leyland Titan PD3A/1	MCW H41/30R	Blackpool Corporation	501	A
JMS 452E	1967	Albion Viking VK43AL	Alexander DP40F	W Alexander & Sons (Midland)	MNV37	RP
NRG 26H	1969	AEC Swift 2MP2R	Alexander B43D	Aberdeen Corporation	26	A
VMP 10G	1969	AEC Reliance 6U3ZR	Alexander DP57F	Road Transport Industry Training Board		R
XTC 530H	1970	Bedford VAL70	Plaxton			A
WSD 756K	1972	Leyland Leopard PSU3/3R	Alexander -	Western SMT Co	L2366	R
XGM 450L	1972	Leyland Leopard PSU3/3R	Alexander B53F	Central SMT Co	T150	R
VSS 158M	1974	Ford R1014	Plaxton C45F	Wiles of Port Seaton		A
MSF 122P	1975	Leyland Leopard PSU3C/4R	Alexander C49F	Lothian Region Transport	122	A
MSF 465P	1976	Leyland Atlantean AN68A/1R	Alexander H-/-D	Lothian Region Transport	465	RP
PRA 109R	1976	Leyland Leopard PSU3C/4R	Alexander C49F	Trent Motor Traction Co		A
OJD 903R	1977	Leyland National 10351A/1R	Leyland National B36D	London Transport	LS103	R
PAU 204R	1977	Daimler Fleetline CRG6LX	Northern Counties H-/-D	Nottingham City Transport	204	RP

Registration	Date	Chassis	Body	New to	Fleet No	Status
RSD 973R	1977	Seddon Pennine VII	Alexander C49F	Western SMT Co	S2670	RP
SSN 248S	1977	Volvo Ailsa B55-10	Alexander H44/35F	Tayside Regional Council	248	RP
XUS 575S	1977	Leyland Atlantean AN68A/1R	Alexander H-/-F	Greater Glasgow PTE	LA1204	A
TSJ 47S	1978	Leyland Leopard PSU3D/4R	Alexander B53F	Western SMT Co	L2747	RP
VHB 678S	1978	Bristol VRT/SL3/501	ECW O43/31F	National Welsh Omnibus Services	HR4378	A
WTS 270T	1979	Volvo Ailsa B55-10	Alexander H44/31D	Tayside Regional Council	270	RP
DDW 431V	1980	Leyland National 10351A/1R	Leyland National B41F	Cynon Valley	31	A
EMS 362V	1980	Leyland Leopard PSU3E/4R	Alexander C49F	W Alexander & Sons (Midland)	MPE362	A
FSL 615W	1980	Bedford YMQ	Plaxton C45F	Henderson Coaltown of Markinch		R
HSD 86V	1980	Leyland Fleetline FE30AGR	Alexander H44/31F	Western SMT Co	R86	R
LMS 168W	1980	Leyland Fleetline FE30AGR	Alexander H44/31F	W Alexander & Sons (Midland)	MRF168	RP
RSG 825V	1980	Leyland National 2 NL116L11/1R	Leyland National B52F	W Alexander & Sons (Fife)	FPN25	RP
UHG 141V	1980	Leyland Atlantean AN68A/2R	Alexander H49/36F	Preston Borough Transport	141	R
WDS 112V	1980	Leyland Fleetline FE30AGR	Alexander H44/31F	Western SMT Co	R73	RP
RMS 400W	1981	Leyland Leopard PSU3F/4R	Alexander C49F	W Alexander & Sons (Midland)	MPE400	R
RRM 386X	1981	Leyland National 2 NL116AL11/1R	Leyland National B52F	Cumberland Motor Services	386	RP
SSA 5X	1981	Leyland Olympian ONLXB/1R	Alexander H45/32R	W Alexander & Sons (Northern)	NL05	R
UGB 196W	1981	Leyland Atlantean AN68A/1R	Alexander H45/33F	Strathclyde PTE	LA1443	RP
FLD 447Y	1982	Bedford YMP	Plaxton C35F	Bonas of Coventry		RP
RSC 194Y	1982	Leyland Leopard PSU3G/4R	Alexander C49F	W Alexander & Sons (Fife)	FPE194	R
TMS 403X	1982	Leyland Leopard PSU3G/4R	Alexander DP49F	W Alexander & Sons (Midland)	MPE403	RP
TSO 16X	1982	Leyland Olympian ONLXB/1R	ECW H45/32F	W Alexander & Sons (Northern)	NLO16	R
ALS 102Y	1983	Leyland Tiger	Alexander C49F	W Alexander & Sons (Midland)	MPT102	RP
MNS 10Y	1983	Leyland Tiger TRBTL11/2R	Alexander C49F	Central SMT Co	LT10	A
XMS 422Y	1983	Leyland Leopard PSU3G/4R	Alexander B53F	W Alexander & Sons (Midland)	MPE422	A
47638	1984	Ford R1015	Wadham Stringer B45F	Jersey Motor Transport Co	23	RP
B177 FFS	1985	Volvo Citybus B10M-50	Alexander H47/37F	W Alexander & Sons (Fife)	FRA77	A
C177 VSF	1986	Leyland-DAB Lion LDTL11/1R	Alexander CH45/37F	Eastern Scottish	ZLL177	RP
F300 SSX	1989	Renault G10	Wadham Stringer DP29F	Blood Transfusion Service		A

Notes:

WG 2373	Rebodied 1947.
WG 4445	Rebodied 1949
CRG 811	Rebodied 1958
6769	Guernsey registration
NGE 172P	Chassis originally registered AAG 651B. Rebodied and reregistered 1976
DMS 348C	Converted to recovery vehicle 1982
VMP 10G	Restored in Baxters livery
WSD 756K	Converted to recovery vehicle 1982
XUS 575S	Exhibition unit
VHB 678S	Converted to open top
WDS 112V	Originally registered HSD 73V
FLD 447Y	Originally registered BAC 551Y
47638	Original registration Jersey J 43063. Currently carries Guernsey registration

Golcar Transport Collection

Contact address: 45 Cowlersley Lane, Cowlersley, Huddersfield HD4 5TZ
Affiliation: NARTM
Brief description: A unique collection of Karrier vehicles, most of which are long-term restoration projects. The collection includes two WL6 six-wheeled saloons.
Opening days/times: Collection opens to coincide with craft weekends at the Colne Valley Museum; can be opened at other times by prior arrangement.

Registration	Date	Chassis	Body	New to	Fleet No	Status
note v	1922	Karrier	(unknown) B20F	(unknown)		A
WT 9156	1925	Karrier JH	Strachan & Brown B26F	Premier Transport of Keighley		RP
DY 5029	1928	Karrier JKL	London Lorries C26D	A Timpson & Son of Catford	117	A
KD 3185	1928	Karrier WL6	Liverpool Corporation B38R	Liverpool Corporation		A
TE 5780	1928	Karrier WL6	English Electric B32F	Ashton-under-Lyne Corporation	8	RP
VH 2088	1929	Karrier ZA	(unknown) B14F			RP
RB 4757	1932	Commer Centaur	Reeve & Kenning B14D	H G Fox of Alfreton		R
JC 5313	1938	Guy Wolf	Waveney C20F	Llandudno UDC		R
14 PKR	1961	Karrier BFD	Plaxton C14F	W Davis & Sons of Sevenoaks		A

Notes:

note v	Unregistered solid-tyred disc-wheeled chassis.
WT 9156	Body originally on EH 4960
VH 2088	Period body acquired from Anglesey
RB 4757	Carries 1929 body from Ford AA chassis

Halifax Bus Museum

Contact address: 1 Vicar Park Road, Norton Tower, Halifax HX2 ONL
Brief description: A collection of privately-owned vehicles, most of which operated originally in West Yorkshire.
Events planned: Please see enthusiast press for details.
Opening days/times: The collection is not normally open to the
public, but an appointment to view can be arranged by contacting the above address.

Registration	Date	Chassis	Body	New to	Fleet No	Status
JUB 29	1932	Leyland Titan TD2	Eastern Counties L27/26R	Keighley-West Yorkshire Services	K451	A
JX 7046	1939	AEC Regent O661	Park Royal H30/26R	Halifax Corporation	80	A
JX 9106	1946	AEC Regal O662	Weymann	Hebble Motor Services	181	A
GTJ 694	1947	AEC Regent II O661	Park Royal	Morecambe & Heysham Corporation	10	RP
HHP 755	1948	Maudslay Regal III	Duple FC33F	Greenslades Tours of Exeter		A
AJX 369	1949	AEC Regent III 9612E	Park Royal H33/26R	Halifax Joint Omnibus Committee	243	A
ECX 425	1949	AEC Regent III 9612E	Northern Coachbuilders L29/26R	Huddersfield Joint Omnibus Committee	225	RP
BCP 671	1950	AEC Regent III 9612E	Park Royal H33/26R	Halifax Joint Omnibus Committee	277	R
LTF 254	1950	AEC Regent III 9612E	Park Royal H33/26R	Morecambe & Heysham Corporation	69	R
ODK 705	1956	AEC Regent V D2RA6G	Weymann H3328R	Rochdale Corporation	305	
ROD 765	1956	AEC Regent V MD3RV	Metro Cammell H33/26RD	Devon General Omnibus & Touring Co	DRD765	R
TTT 781	1956	AEC Regent V MD3RV	Metro Cammell H33/26RD	Devon General Omnibus & Touring Co	DRD781	RP
UTV 229	1956	AEC Regent V D3RV	Park Royal H33/28R	Nottingham City Transport	229	RP
3916 UB	1959	AEC Regent V 2D3RA	Metro Cammell H38/32R	Leeds City Transport	916	R
LJX 198	1959	AEC Regent V 2D3RA	Metro Cammell H39/32F	Hebble Motor Services	307	R
LJX 215	1960	AEC Regent V 2D3RA	Metro Cammell H40/32F	Halifax Joint Omnibus Committee	215	RP
1925 WA	1961	AEC Bridgemaster 2B3RA	Park Royal H43/29F	Sheffield Corporation	525	R
214 CLT	1962	AEC Routemaster R2RH	Park Royal H36/28R	London Transport	RM1214	R
TSJ 272	1962	AEC Bridgemaster 2B3RA	Park Royal	East Yorkshire Motor Services		RP
CTT 518C	1965	AEC Regent V 2MD3RA	Willowbrook H33/28F	Devon General Omnibus & Touring Co	518	RP

Notes:

JUB 29	Rebodied in 1951 using 1932 body
JX 9106	Converted to tow lorry in 1956 and renumbered L4
GTJ 694	Breakdown Vehicle
HHP 755	Exhibited at the 1948 Commercial Motor Show
TSJ 272	Originally registered 9725 AT
214 CLT	In Halifax Joint Omnibus livery.

Huddersfield District Transport Museum Society

Contact address: 20 Alma Drive, Dalton, Huddersfield HD5 9EF
Affiliation: NARTM
Brief description: The collection is based in Huddersfield and comprises nearly 20 vehicles, including commercial vehicles and trams.
Opening days/times: Please contact the above address for an appointment to view.

Registration	Date	Chassis	Body	New to	Fleet No	Status
LHN 785+	1949	BUT 9611T	East Lancs H37/29F	Bradford Corporation	835	R
JVH 373	1955	AEC Regent III 9613E	East Lancs L30/28R	Huddersfield Corporation	243	R
JVH 378	1955	AEC Regent III 9613E	East Lancs H33/28R	Huddersfield Joint Omnibus Committee	178	R
GHD 215	1961	Ford 570E	Duple C41F	Yorkshire Woollen District Transport Co	871	R
RWU 534R	1977	Leyland Leopard PSU4D/4R	Plaxton DP43F	West Yorkshire PTE	8534	R
+ Trolleybus						

Notes:
LHN 785   Rebodied 1962. Chassis originally Darlington

Irish Transport Trust

Contact address: 14 Mayfields, Lisburn, Co Antrim, Northern Ireland BT28 3RP
Affiliation: NARTM
Website: www.irishtransporttrust.freeserve.co.uk
Brief description: Formed in 1969, the Trust provides for the preservation, recording and information exchange on all aspects pertaining to road transport history, current and future matters. A number of vehicles both pre- and postwar have been restored by Trust members and the Trust itself has six vehicles from more recent times which are under-represented in preservation. It is planned to obtain limited company status in the near future, and ultimately charitable status with a view to establishing a museum dedicated to road passenger transport in Northern Ireland.
Events planned: 22 April 2006. Annual bus and coach rally at Cultra, Co Down, at the site of the Ulster Folk & Transport Museum. For other events, please refer to the enthusiast press.

Registration	Date	Chassis	Body	New to	Fleet No	Status
FOI 1629	1973	Bristol LH6L	Alexander (Belfast) B45F	Ulsterbus	1629	R
OSJ 620R	1977	Leyland Leopard PSU3C/3R	Alexander (Falkirk) B53F	Western SMT Co	1886	R
SOI 3591	1978	Leyland Leopard PSU3A/4R	Alexander (Belfast) B53F	Ulsterbus	1591	R
VOI 8415	1980	Bristol RELL6G	Alexander (Belfast) B43D	Belfast Citybus	2415	R
AXI 2259	1982	Leyland Leopard PSU3E/4R	Wright Royale C49F	Ulsterbus	259	R
BXI 2583	1982	Bristol RELL6G	Alexander (Belfast) B51F	Ulsterbus	2583	R

Notes
FOI 1629   First of batch of 100 LH
SOI 3591   Chassis originally AOI 1347 of 1969. Rebuilt 1974-8
VOI 8415   B32D + 47 standing when new
AXI 2259   Wright Royal body

John Shearman Collection
Tunbridge Wells

Phone: 01892 534067
Brief description: A private collection which includes vehicles representing traditional British double deckers designed for export markets.
Opening days/times: Vehicles attend rallies every summer.

Registration	Date	Chassis	Body	New to	Fleet No	Status
LEV 917	1946	Leyland Titan PD1/1	Alexander O33/26R	City Coach Company of Brentwood	LD1	R
KSV 102	1954	AEC Regent III 9631E	Weymann H37/28R	Carris of Lisbon	255	R
AD 7156	1966	AEC Regent V 2D2RA	Metal Sections H51/39D	Kowloon Motor Bus	A165	RP

Notes:
LEV 917   Converted to open top by Eastern National in 1958. Originally H30/26R. Restored as Eastern National 2102 with support of Springhill Vehicle Preservation Group.
KSV 102   Left hand drive. Portugese registration GB-21-07. Originally H32/26R. Restored with support of Carris AEC Preservation Group.
AD 7156   34ft 3in long Hong Kong registration.Originally H50/28D. On loan to at the Oxford Bus Museum Trust. Restored with support of KMB.

Kelvin Amos Collection

Contact address: 30 Blandford Close, Nailsea, Bristol BS48 2QQ
Brief description: The vehicles in the collection are regularly shown and run on free bus services.

Registration	Date	Chassis	Body	New to	Fleet No	Status
LHT 911	1948	Bristol L5G	Brislington Body Works B35R	Bristol Tramways	2388	R
KED 546F	1968	Leyland Panther Cub PSURC1	East Lancs B41D	Warrington Corporation	92	R
PWS 492S	1977	Leyland Leopard PSU3E/4R	Plaxton C49F	Bristol Omnibus Co	2098	R

Notes:
LHT 911   Rebodied 1958 with 1950 body
PWS 492S   Rebodied 1983 with Paramount body after a fire

Lancastrian Transport Trust

Contact address: Apt. 11, Admiral Heights, 164 Queens Promenade, Blackpool FY2 9GJ
E-mail: philip@ltt.org.uk
Web site: www.ltt.org.uk
Brief description: The Trust is dedicated to preserving historic buses from Fylde Coast. Vehicles can often be seen at local rallies and other events. Open days held at Blackpool based vehicle restoration workshops. The Lancashire Transport trust also has a growing tramcar collection
Membership details: Support organisation is TransSupport with a £12 annual membership fee. Quarterly magazine published *In Trust*.

Registration	Date	Chassis	Body	New to	Fleet No	Status
GTB 903	1946	Leyland Titan PD1	Leyland H30/26R	Lytham St Annes Corporation	19	R
CCK 663	1949	Leyland Titan PD2/3	Brush L27/26R	Ribble Motor Services	2687	A
DFV 146	1949	Leyland Titan PD2/5	Burlingham FH31/23C	Blackpool Corporation	246	A

Registration	Date	Chassis	Body	New to	Fleet No	Status
JCK 530	1956	Leyland Titan PD2/12	Burlingham H33/28RD	Ribble Motor Services	1455	R
760 CTD	1957	Leyland Titan PD2/20	Northern Counties H30/28R	Lytham St Annes Corporation	61	A
PFR 346	1959	Leyland Titan PD2/27	Metro Cammell FH35/28RD	Blackpool Corporation	346	A
534 RTB	1961	Guy Arab IV	Metro Cammell H41/32R	Lancashire United Transport	43	R
561 TD	1962	Daimler Fleetline CRG6LX	Northern Counties H43/33F	Lancashire United Transport	97	R
583 CLT	1962	AEC Routemaster 2R2RH	Park Royal H36/28R	London Transport	RM1583	R
RRN 405	1962	Leyland Atlantean PDR1/1	Weymann L38/33F	Ribble Motor Services	1805	R
YFR 351	1962	Leyland Titan PD3/1	Metro Cammell FH41/32R	Blackpool Corporation	351	A
AAO 771A	1963	Leyland Titan PD3/5	Metro Cammell FH41/31F	Ribble Motor Services	1841	R
CTF 627B	1964	Leyland Titan PD2A/27	Massey H37/27F	Lytham St Annes Corporation	70	R
HFR 512E	1967	Leyland Titan PD3A/1	MCW H41/30R	Blackpool Corporation	512	R
HFR 516E	1967	Leyland Titan PD3A/1	MCW H41/30R	Blackpool Corporation	516	R W2.10
LFR 529F	1968	Leyland Titan PD3/11	MCW H41/30R	Blackpool Corporation	529	RP
LFR 540G	1968	Leyland Titan PD3/11	MCW H41/30R	Blackpool Corporation	540	A
PFR 554H	1970	AEC Swift MP2R	Marshall B47D	Blackpool Corporation	554	R
ATD 281J	1971	Leyland Atlantean PDR1A/1	Northern Counties H44/33F	Lytham St Annes Corporation	77	R
OCK 997K	1972	Bristol VRTSL6G	ECW H43/31F	Ribble Motor Services	1997	A
RTJ 422L	1972	Daimler Fleetline CRG6LXB-33	Northern Counties H47/32F	Lancashire United Transport	394	A
STJ 847L	1972	Seddon RU	Pennine B51F	Lytham St Annes Corporation	47	A
OFR 970M	1974	AEC Swift 3MP2R	Marshall B47D	Blackpool Corporation	570	R
HRN 99N	1975	Leyland Atlantean AN68/1R	Northern Counties H43/31F	Fylde Borough Transport	79	A
OJI 4371	1977	Leyland Atlantean	Northern Counties H74F	Fylde Borough Transport	71	R
AHG 334V	1980	Leyland Atlantean AN68/2R	East Lancs H50/36F	Blackpool Transport	331	A
F575 RCW	1988	Optare City Pacer	Optare B21F	Blackpool Transport	575	R

Notes:

583 CLT	Restored to Blackpool livery.
AAO 771A	Driver training vehicle 1981-98. Originally registered TCK 841
CTF 627B	On loan from North West Museum of Road Transport
HFR 516E	Preserved as driver training bus

Legionnaire Group

Contact address: 66 Montfort Road, Strood, Rochester, Kent ME2 3EX
E-mail: bob.wingrove@btinternet.com
Brief description: The group aims to restore at least one of each combination of chassis/Legionnaire so that Harrington's last body style is represented in preservation.

Registration	Date	Chassis	Body	New to	Fleet No	Status
SPU 985	1951	Leyland Olympic HR44	Weymann DP44F	Jennings Coaches of Ashen		RP
72 MMJ	1964	Bedford VAL14	Harrington C52F	Reliance Coaches of Meppershall	72	RP
CDK 409C	1965	Bedford VAL14	Harrington C52F	Yelloway Motor Services of Rochdale		A
JNK 681C	1965	Ford Thames 36 676E	Harrington C52F	SP Coaches of Sutton		RP

Notes:

SPU 985	Engine is O600 horizontal No 2.
JNK 681C	Used as Harrington demonstrator when new

Leicester Corporation Bus Preservation Group

Phone: 01872 552616
Affiliation: NARTM
Brief description: Formed in 2002, the group has been set up to bring together those owning buses formerly operated by 'The Corpo'. Vehicles are mostly stored in the Leicester area and may be viewed by appointment.
Opening days/times: By appointment only.
Charges: Free admission but donations welcome.

Registration	Date	Chassis	Body	New to	Fleet No	Status
OJF 191	1956	Leyland Tiger Cub PSUC1/1	Weymann B44F	Leicester City Transport	191	RP
217 AJF	1961	AEC Bridgemaster B3RA	Park Royal H76R	Leicester City Transport	217	RP
90 HBC	1964	Leyland Titan PD3A/1	East Lancs H41/33R	Leicester City Transport	90	RP
DBC 190C	1965	AEC Renown 3B3RA	East Lancs H44/31F	Leicester City Transport	190	R
FJF 40D	1966	AEC Renown 3B3RA	East Lancs H43/31R	Leicester City Transport	40	RP
GRY 48D	1966	Leyland Titan PD3A/1	MCW H41/33R	Leicester City Transport	48	A
PBC 98G	1968	Leyland Atlantean PDR1A/1	ECW H43/31F	Leicester City Transport	98	RP
PBC 113G	1969	Leyland Atlantean PDR1A/1	Park Royal H43/31F	Leicester City Transport	113	RP
TRY 122H	1969	Bristol RELL6L	ECW B47D	Leicester City Transport	122	RP
ARY 225K	1972	Scania BR111MH	MCW B46D	Leicester City Transport	225	R
GJF 301N	1975	Scania BR111DH	MCW H45/28D	Leicester City Transport	301	R
UFP 233S	1977	Dennis Dominator DD101	East Lancs H43/31F	Leicester City Transport	233	RP
MUT 253W	1980	Dennis Dominator	East Lancs H43/31F	Leicester City Transport	253	RP
TBC 50X	1982	Dennis Dominator	East Lancs H76F	Leicester City Transport	50	RP

Notes:
ARY 225K   Exhibited Earls Court 1972.

Medstead Depot Omnibus Group

Contact Address: Hon Secretary, Medstead Depot Omnibus Group, c/o InterPower House, Windsor Way, Aldershot, Hants GU11 1JG.
Affiliation: NARTM, WOMP, Aldershot & District Bus Interest Group, Aldershot & District Omnibuses Rescue & Restoration Society, Southampton & District Transport Heritage Trust.. MDOG is a part of the Working Omnibus Museum Project, which is a registered charity.
Brief Description: Vehicles from the Medstead Depot Omnibus Group are regularly to be seen at shows and rallies throughout the season. In addition to the vehicles listed, others belonging to members of the Aldershot & District Bus Interest Groups and the Southampton & District Transport Heritage Trust are associated with the Group and stored on site mfrom time to time. There is an open day once per year, associated with the Mid-Hants Railway Alton Bus Rally, usually held in July.
Events Planned: Free bus services between Medstead & Four Marks station and Alton station and Medstead & Four Marks station and Petersfield station usually operated on the first Sunday of each month between April and October, in association with the City of Portsmouth Preserved Transport organisation.

Registration	Date	Chassis	Body	New to	Fleet No	Status
JRX 823	1955	Bristol KSW6B	ECW L27/28R	Thames Valley Traction Co	748	R
TDL 998	1960	Bristol Lodekka FS6G	ECW H33/27R	Southern Vectis Omnibus Co	565	R
RCP 237	1962	AEC Regent V 2D3RA	Northern Counties H39/32F	Hebble Motor Services	619	RP
YDL 315	1962	Bristol Lodekka FS6G	ECW H33/27RD	Southern Vectis Omnibus Co	570	R
KHC 367	1963	AEC Regent V 2D3RV	East Lancs H32/28R	Eastbourne Corporation	67	R

Merseyside Transport Trust

Contact address: The Secretary, Merseyside Transport Trust, Carlton House, 17-19 Carlton Street, Liverpool L3 7ED
E-mail: info@mttrust,co,uk
Web site: www.mttrust.co.uk
Affiliation: AEC Society; Leyland Society
Brief description: A collection of around 35 vehicles, mostly from the Merseyside area but including others of special interest.

Registration	Date	Chassis	Body	New to	Fleet No	Status
GKD 434	1946	AEC Regent II O661	Weymann/LCPT H30/26R	Liverpool Corporation	A233	RP
JKC 178	1949	Daimler CVA6	Northern Counties H30/26R	Liverpool Corporation	D553	A
KMN 519	1950	Leyland Comet CP01	Park Royal B30F	Douglas Corporation	21	R
LFM 756	1951	Bristol LL6B	ECW B39R	Crosville Motor Services	SLB175	R
MKB 994	1952	AEC Regent III 9613A	Crossley H30/26R	Liverpool Corporation	A801	A
NKD 536	1953	AEC Regent III 9613S	Crossley H30/26R	Liverpool Corporation	A36	RP
NKD 540	1954	AEC Regent III 9613S	Saunders Roe H32/26R	Liverpool Corporation	A40	RP
RKC 262	1955	Leyland Titan PD2/20	Alexander H32/26R	Liverpool Corporation	L161	RP
SKB 168	1956	Leyland Royal Tiger PSU1/13	Crossley/MCW RC23/21F	Liverpool Corporation	XL171	A
SKB 224	1956	Leyland Titan PD2/20	Crossley/LCPT H32/26R	Liverpool Corporation	L227	RP
VKB 711	1956	Leyland Titan PD2/20	Crossley H33/29R	Liverpool Corporation	L255	RP
VKB 841	1957	Leyland Titan PD2/20	Crossley H33/29R	Liverpool Corporation	L320	A
VKB 900	1957	AEC Regent V D3RV	Metro Cammell H33/29R	Liverpool Corporation	A267	R
116 TMD	1958	AEC Bridgemaster B3RA	Park Royal H43/33R	Liverpool Corporation	E3	A
371 BKA	1959	AEC Regent V LD3RA	Park Royal FH40/32F	Liverpool Corporation	E1	R
372 BKA	1959	Leyland Atlantean PDR1/1	Metro Cammell H43/35F	Liverpool Corporation	E2	RP
HHF 15	1960	Leyland Atlantean PDR1	Metro Cammell	Wallasey Corporation	15	A
256 SFM	1961	Bristol Lodekka FLF6B	ECW H38/22F	Crosville Motor Services	DFB43	A
875 VFM	1961	Bristol Lodekka FSF6G	ECW H34/26F	Crosville Motor Services	DFG65	A
501 KD	1962	Leyland Atlantean PDR1/1	Metro Cammell H43/35F	Liverpool Corporation	L501	R
FKF 801D	1966	Leyland Atlantean PDR1/1	MCW H43/35F	Liverpool City Transport	L801	A
FKF 835E	1967	Leyland Atlantean PDR1/1	MCW H43/28D	Liverpool City Transport	L835	RP
FKF 933G	1968	Leyland Panther PSUR1A/1R	MCW B47D	Liverpool City Transport	1054	RP
SKB 695G	1969	Bristol RELL6G	Park Royal B45D	Liverpool City Transport	2025	R
UKA 562H	1969	Leyland Atlantean PDR2/1	Alexander H47/32D	Liverpool City Transport	1111	R
XKC 789J	1971	Leyland Atlantean PDR2/1	Alexander H47/32D	Merseyside PTE	1162	RP
BKC 236K	1972	Leyland Atlantean PDR1A/1	Alexander H43/32F	Merseyside PTE	1236	R
BKC 276K	1972	Leyland Atlantean PDR1A/1	Alexander H43/32F	Merseyside PTE	1276	A
VWM 83L	1973	Leyland Atlantean AN68/1R	Alexander H45/29D	Southport Corporation	83	R
GKA 74N	1975	Bristol VRTSL6LX	East Lancs H43/32F	Merseyside PTE	2122	A
MTJ 771S	1977	Leyland National 11351A/1R	Leyland National B49F	Merseyside PTE	1771	RP
OEM 788S	1978	Leyland Atlantean AN68A/1R	MCW H43/32F	Merseyside PTE	1788	RP
TWM 220V	1979	Leyland Atlantean AN68A/1R	East Lancs H45/33F	Merseyside PTE	1836	R
UKA 23V	1980	MCW Metrobus DR103/2	MCW H43/30F	Merseyside PTE	0023	RP
WWM 904W	1980	Dennis Dominator DD120B	Willowbrook H45/33F	Merseyside PTE	0027	RP
AFY 187X	1982	Leyland Atlantean AN68B/1R	Willowbrook H45/33F	Merseyside PTE	1867	RP
EKA 220Y	1982	Leyland Tiger TRCTL11/1R	Duple C49F	Merseyside PTE	7020	RP
A323 GLV	1983	Leyland Atlantean AN68D/1R	Alexander H43/32F	Merseyside PTE	1003	R
A112 HLV	1984	Leyland Atlantean AN68D/1R	Alexander H43/32F	Merseyside PTE	1032	R

Notes

KMN 519	On loan to British Commercial Vehicle Museum at Leyland
SKB 168	Originally B40D numbered SL171; rebuilt by Metro Cammell in 1961
116 TMD	Former AEC demonstrator; acquired by Liverpool Corporation (E3) in 1959
FKF 835E	Originally H43/35F. Rebuilt by Pennine Coachcraft 1969.
XKC 789J	Private ownership - on loan to MTT
OEM 788S	Private ownership - on loan to MTT
A112 HLV	Private ownership - on loan to MTT

The Mike Sutcliffe Collection

Phone: 01525 221676
E-mail: sutcliffes@leylandman.co.uk
Affiliation: NARTM; Leyland Society member; HCVS member
Brief description: A collection of 15 vehicles, mainly buses of Leyland manufacture from the period 1908 to 1934, this is the most significant collection of of early motorbuses in the world, and includes the oldest British-built motorbus. Mike Sutcliffe was recently awarded the MBE 'for his services to Motor Heritage'
Opening days/times: Viewing can be arranged by prior appointment only. There is no charge, but donations are welcome.

Registration	Date	Chassis	Body	New to	Fleet No	Status
LN 7270	1908	Leyland X2	Thomas Tilling O18/16RO	London Central Motor Omnibus Co	14	R
HE 12	1913	Leyland S3.30.T	Brush B27F	Barnsley & District Electric Traction Co	5	R
LF 9967	1913	Leyland S3.30.T	Birch O20/16RO	Wellingborough Motor Omnibus Co	H	R
CC 1087	1914	Leyland S4.36.T3	Leyland Ch32	London & North Western Railway	59	R
BD 209	1921	Leyland G7	Dodson Ch/B32D	United Counties Omnibus Co	B15	R
C 2367	1921	Leyland G	Phoenix O23/20RO	Todmorden Corporation	14	R
DM 2583	1923	Leyland SG7	Leyland FB40D	Brookes Bros ('White Rose') of Rhyl	27	R
XU 7498	1924	Leyland LB5	Dodson O26/22RO	Chocolate Express Omnibus Co	B6	R
PW 8605	1926	ADC 415	United B35F	United Automobile Services	E61	A
YG 7831	1934	Leyland Tiger TS6	Northern Counties B36R	Todmorden Joint Omnibus Committee	15	RP

Notes:

LN 7270	Body new 1906 Bought second hand by LCMOC 1908. Orig on Milnes Daimler chassis of Thomas Tilling
LF 9967	On loan to British Commercial Vehicle Museum at Leyland
CC 1087	Requisitioned by War Office in 1915. Re-registered XA 8086 in 1919; reverted to CC 1087 in 1980
C 2367	On loan to Manchester Museum of Transport
BD 209	Formerly a Dodson demonstrator and Olympia Commercial Motor Show exhibit 1921
YG 7831	Rebuilt to recovery vehicle; being restored back to a bus

North East Bus Preservation Trust Ltd

Contact address: The Secretary. 8 Seaburn Hill, Sunderland SR6 8BS
Phone: 0191 548 7369
E-mail: northbritish@supanet.com
Affiliation: NARTM
Brief description: The collection is displayed at an 1826 former locomotive shed on the Bowes Railway, Gateshead. This accommodates up to 10 vehicles, and so vehicles rotate between this and other locations. If you wish to view a particular vehicle, you will need to mention this when making arrangements to view.
Opening days/times: Viewing by prior arrangement only.

Registration	Date	Chassis	Body	New to	Fleet No	Status
CN 4740	1931	SOS IM4	Short B34F	Northern General Transport Co	540	A
CN 6100	1934	Northern General Transport SE6 (LSE4)	Short B44F	Northern General Transport Co	604	RP
DPT 848	1939	Leyland Tiger TS8	Roe B32F	Sunderland District	159	R
EF 7380	1942	Leyland Titan TD7	Roe H26/22C	West Hartlepool Corporation	36	R
GSR 244	1943	Commer Q4	Scottish Aviation C29F	Meffan of Kirriemuir		RP
AHL 694	1947	Leyland Tiger PS1/1	Barnaby C33F	J Bullock & Sons of Featherstone	284	R
JRA 635	1947	Leyland Tiger PS1	Crossley B35R	Chesterfield Corporation	48	R
KTJ 502	1947	Leyland Tiger PS1	Burlingham B35F	Haslingden Corporation	2	RP

Above: Reeve & Kenning-bodied 1932 Commer Centaur RB 4757 is part of the Golcar Transport Collection. *Geoff Lumb*

Below: Part of the Kelvin Amos Collection in Bristol are ex-Warrington Corporation 92 (KED 546F), a Leyland Panther Cub dating from 1968, and Bristol L5G 2388 (LHT 911) new to Bristol Tramways in 1948.

Right: Eastbourne Corporation 67 (KHC 367), a 1963 East Lancs-bodied AEC Regent V, is part of the Medstead Depot Omnibus Group, and can be seen on summer Sunday services linking Medstead & Four Marks and Alton stations.

Below right: The Mike Sutcliffe Collection of early motor buses includes this 1923 Leyland SG7, new to Brookes Bros (White Rose) of Rhyl as their No 27 (DM 2583). *Mike Sutcliffe*

Registration	Date	Chassis	Body	New to	Fleet No	Status
ABR 433	1949	Crossley DD42/7C	Crossley H56R	Sunderland Corporation	100	RP
CFK 340	1949	AEC Regal III 6821A	Burlingham C33F	H & E Burnham of Worcester		R
LYM 729	1951	AEC Regal IV	ECW C—F	Tillings Transport		RP
CBR 539	1952	Guy Arab III	Roe H33/25R	Sunderland Corporation	139	RP
PHN 831	1952	Bristol LS5G	ECW B45F	United Automobile Services	BU2	A
SHN 301	1952	AEC Regal IV 9821E	Burlingham C41C	Scotts Greys of Darlington	5	R
DCN 83	1953	AEC Beadle	Beadle C35F	Northern General Transport Co	1483	A
SPT 65	1955	Guy Arab LUF	Weymann B44F	Northern General Transport Co	1665	RP
UUA 212	1955	Leyland Titan PD2/11	Roe H33/25R	Leeds City Transport	212	R
JHL 701	1956	Bedford SBG	Plaxton C41F	Swan of Berwick		RP
UFJ 292	1957	Guy Arab IV	Massey H30/26R	Exeter Corporation	52	R
WTS 708A	1957	Bristol LS5G	ECW B45F	United Automobile Services	BU250	A
AFT 930	1958	Leyland Titan PD3/4	Metro Cammell H41/32R	Tynemouth & District	230	RP
OSK 831	1958	Karrier BFD3023	Plaxton C14F	Brocksbank of Leeds		RP
RSL 905	1958	AEC Reliance MU3RV	Roe C41C	Essex County Coaches of Stratford		R
TCO 537	1960	Leyland Atlantean PDR1/1	Metro Cammell H44/33F	Plymouth Corporation	137	R
6249 UP	1963	Leyland Leopard PSU3/3RT	Alexander DP51F	Venture Transport Co of Consett	249	R
ACU 304B	1963	Leyland Leopard PSU3/3R	Plaxton B55F	Stanhope Motor Services		R
PCN 762	1964	AEC Routemaster 3R2RH	Park Royal H41/31F	Northern General Transport Co	2099	R
WBR 248	1964	Atkinson Alpha PM746HL	Marshall B45D	Sunderland Corporation	48	R
FBR 53D	1966	Leyland Panther PSUR1/1R	Strachan B47D	Sunderland Corporation	53	R
ECU 201E	1967	Bristol RESL6L	ECW B45D	South Shields Corporation	1	R
VVK 149G	1969	Bedford J6	Nicolou B33D	Cyprus		R
WHN 411G	1969	Bristol VRTSL6LX	ECW H39/31F	United Automobile Services	601	A
VTY 543J	1970	Leyland Leopard PSU3A/4R	Plaxton C45F	Tyne Valley of Acomb		A
WHA 237H	1970	Leyland Leopard PSU3A/4R	Plaxton C49F	BMMO ('Midland Red')	6237	RP
GAN 744J	1971	Leyland Leopard PSU5/4RT	Plaxton C57F	Banfield Coaches		RP
PCW 203J	1971	Bristol RESL6L	Pennine B45F	Burnley Colne & Nelson	103	R
SWV 155J	1971	Daimler Fleetline CRG6LX	Northern Counties	Swindon Corporation		RP
GBB 524K	1972	Leyland Atlantean PDR2/1	Alexander H48/30D	Tyneside PTE	688	RP
MCN 30K	1972	Leyland/NGT Tynesider	Weymann/Northern General H39/29F	Northern General Transport Co	3000	R
NHN 250K	1972	Daimler Fleetline SRG6LX-36	Roe B48D	Darlington Corporation	50	R
E901 DRG	1973	Bedford YRQ	Plaxton C45F	Smith of Durham		RP
E903 DRG	1975	Ford R1114	Plaxton C53F	Smith of Durham		RP
GUP 907N	1975	Bristol LH6L	ECW B43F	United Automobile Services	1623	R
OCU 769R	1977	Scania BR111DH	MCW H45/29D	Tyne & Wear PTE	769	RP
OCU 807R	1977	Leyland Fleetline FE30AGR	Alexander H44/30F	Tyne & Wear PTE	807	RP
RCU 588S	1977	Leyland Atlantean AN68/2R	Willowbrook H48/34F	Tyne & Wear PTE	588	RP
JPT 901T	1978	Bristol VRTSL3/501	ECW H43/31F	Northern General Transport Co	3401	R
RCU 838S	1978	Leyland Fleetline FE30AGR	Alexander H44/30F	Tyne & Wear PTE	838	R
SCN 268S	1978	Leyland Atlantean AN68A/2R	Alexander H49/37F	Tyne & Wear PTE	268	RP
PAJ 829X	1981	Bristol VRTSl3/6LXB	ECW H43/31F	United Automobile Services	829	RP
JFT 413X	1982	Scania BR112DH	Alexander H47/31F	Tyne & Wear PTE	413	RP
VCW 597Y	1982	Dennis Lancet SD505	Marshall B51F	Blackpool Transport	597	A

Notes:

GSR 244	1943 military chassis lengthened and body fitted 1950
ABR 433	Fitted with Gardner 5LW engine
WTS 708A	Originally registered 650 CHN
RSL 905	Originally registered MJD 759
OSK 831	Originally registered 6666 U
ACU 304B	Originally registered 6 MPT
PCN 762	Originally registered RCN 699
VVK 149G	Original Cyprus registration TEC 598. Replica body constructed 2003
WHA 237H	Towing vehicle
MCN 30K	Rebuilt from 1958 Leyland Titan PD3/4 new to Tyneside Tramways & Tramroads Co (49) registered NNL 49
E901 DRG	Built 1973, stored until 1988
E903 DRG	Built 1975, stored until 1988
RCU 838S	Originally H44/27D

Peter Stanier Collection

Phone: 01474 814476
Brief description: A collection of preserved Leyland petrol-engined vehicles with their origins in the island of Jersey
Opening days/times: Not normally open for viewing. Arrangements to visit can be made, strictly by appointment, telephoning first for details

Registration	Date	Chassis	Body	New to	Fleet No	Status
DM 6228	1929	Leyland Lioness LTB1	Burlingham C26D	Brooks Bros of Rhyl	7	
SV 6107	1929	Leyland Titan TD1	Leyland L24/24R	Jersey Motor Transport Co	24	

Notes:
SV 6107   1931 body fitted in 1934. Chassis new to Jersey originally registered J 1199

Ribble Vehicle Preservation Trust

Contact address: 34 Greystoke Park, Gosforth, Newxastle upon Tyne NE3 2DZ
Affiliation: NARTM
Brief description: The Trust promotes the preservation and restoration of vehicles from Ribble and associated companies.

Registration	Date	Chassis	Body	New to	Fleet No	Status
CK 4474	1931	Leyland Tiger TS3	Leyland C26F	Ribble Motor Services	1117	A
RN 7588	1935	Leyland Tiger TS7	Burlingham B35F	Ribble Motor Services	209	R
TJ 6760	1935	Leyland Lion LT5A	Leyland B32R	Lytham St Annes Corporation	24	RP
BTF 25	1937	Leyland Titan TD4c	Leyland FH30/24R	Lytham St Annes Corporation	45	A
RN 8622	1939	Leyland Titan TD5	Alexander L27/26R	Ribble Motor Services	2057	R
ACK 796	1944	Guy Arab II	Northern Counties / Bond UL27/26R	Ribble Motor Services	2413	A
ACB 904	1947	Guy Arab II	Northern Coachbuilders	Blackburn Corporation	502	A
CCK 359	1948	Leyland Titan PD2/3	Leyland L27/26R	Ribble Motor Services	2584	A
DRN 289	1950	Leyland Titan PD2/3	Leyland L27/26RD	Ribble Motor Services	1349	A
MTC 540	1950	AEC Regent III 9613E	Park Royal H30/26R	Morecambe & Heysham Corporation	72	RP
ERN 700	1952	Leyland Royal Tiger PSU1/13	Leyland B44F	Ribble Motor Services	377	R
FCK 884	1954	Leyland Tiger Cub PSUC1/1T	Saunders Roe B44F	Ribble Motor Services	452	R
HRN 31	1955	Leyland Titan PD2/13	Metro Cammell H33/28RD	Ribble Motor Services	1391	A
HRN 39	1955	Leyland Titan PD2/13	Metro Cammell H33/28RD	Ribble Motor Services	1399	A
JFV 527	1955	Commer TS3	Harrington C41C	Abbott of Blackpool		RP
JCK 542	1956	Leyland Titan PD2/12	Burlingham H33/28RD	Ribble Motor Services	1467	RP
JRN 41	1956	Leyland Tiger Cub PSUC1/2T	Burlingham C41F	Ribble Motor Services	975	A
528 CTF	1957	Leyland Titan PD2/40	Weymann L29/28RD	J Fishwick & Sons of Leyland	5	R
881 BTF	1958	Leyland Titan PD2/41	East Lancs H35/28R	Lancaster City Transport	881	A
KCK 869	1958	Leyland Titan PD3/4	Burlingham FH41/31F	Ribble Motor Services	1523	A
KCK 914	1958	Leyland Titan PD3/4	Burlingham FH41/31F	Ribble Motor Services	1553	A
MBN 177	1958	Leyland Titan PD3/5	East Lancs H41/33R	Bolton Corporation	122	RP
NRN 586	1960	Leyland Atlantean PDR1/1	Metro Cammell H44/33F	Ribble Motor Services	1686	R
SFV 421	1960	Leyland Atlantean PDR1/1	Weymann CH34/16Ft	W C Standerwick	25	A
PCK 618	1961	Leyland Leopard L2	Harrington C32F	Ribble Motor Services	1036	R
PRN 145	1961	Leyland Atlantean PDR1/1	Metro Cammell H44/33F	Scout Motor Services of Preston	5	RP
PRN 906	1961	Leyland Titan PD3/4	Metro Cammell H39/31F	Preston Corporation	14	RP
RRN 428	1962	Leyland Atlantean PDR1/1	Weymann CH39/20F	Ribble Motor Services	1279	R
TCK 465	1963	Leyland Leopard PSU3/1R	Marshall B53F	Ribble Motor Services	465	A

Registration	Date	Chassis	Body	New to	Fleet No	Status
TCK 726	1963	Leyland Leopard PSU3/3RT	Harrington C49F	Ribble Motor Services	726	RP
TRN 731	1964	Leyland Leopard PSU3/3R	Plaxton C49F	W C Standerwick	731S	R
ARN 811C	1965	Leyland Leopard PSU3/3RT	Weymann DP49F	Ribble Motor Services	811	RP
FPT 6G	1969	Leyland Leopard PSU3/3RT	Plaxton C51F	Weardale Motor Services of Frosterley		A
HRN 249G	1969	Bristol RELL6G	ECW B41D	Ribble Motor Services	249	A
LRN 321J	1970	Bristol RESL6L	Marshall B47F	Ribble Motor Services	321	A
NCK 106J	1971	Leyland Leopard PSU4	Plaxton C43F	Ribble Motor Services	1006	RP
NCK 338J	1971	Bristol RESL6L	ECW B47F	Ribble Motor Services	338	R
PRN 79K	1972	Bristol VRL/LH/6L	ECW CH42/18Ct	W C Standerwick	79	A
PTF 718L	1972	Leyland National 1151/2R/0401	Leyland National B48D	Ribble Motor Services	372	RP
PTF 727L	1972	Leyland National 1151/2R/0401	Leyland National B48D	Ribble Motor Services	386	R
UTF 732M	1974	Leyland Leopard PSU3B/4R	Duple C49F	Ribble Motor Services	1052	A
MFR 306P	1976	Leyland Leopard PSU3C/2R	Alexander B53F	Lancaster City Transport	306	R
XCW 955R	1978	Leyland National 11351A/1R	Leyland National B49F	J Fishwick & Sons of Leyland	24	R
TRN 481V	1979	Leyland Atlantean AN68A/1R	ECW H43/31F	Ribble Motor Services	1481	R
DBV 100W	1980	Leyland Olympian B45	ECW H45/33F	Ribble Motor Services	2100	
DBV 831W	1980	Leyland National 2 NL106L11/1R	Leyland National B44F	Ribble Motor Services	831	R

Notes:

RN 7588	Rebodied 1949
RN 8622	Chassis refurbished and rebodied in 1949
ACB 904	Breakdown vehicle
ERN 700	Originally B44F
SFV 421	Gay Hostess double-deck motorway coach
NCK 106J	In Ireland 1982-2005, registered 411 LIP
PTF 727L	Used as exhibition bus

The Roger Burdett Collection

Contact Address: 2 Pennyfields Boulevard, Long Eaton, NG10 3QS
E-mail: rogerrbctc@aol.com
Affiliation: NARTM
Brief Description: A collection of distinctive coaches supplemented by four double deckers of interest to the collection owner. All vehicles with the exception of the Bristol RE are either unique or one of a small number of survivors.
Opening days/times: Vehicles regularly attend rallies and events and the collection can be viewed by appointment. Please write to the address given.

Registration	Date	Chassis	Body	New to	Fleet No	Status
VG 5541	1933	Bristol GJW	Weymann O28/26R	Norwich Electric Tramways		RP
JYC 855	1948	Leyland Tiger PS1	Harrington C33F	Scarlet Motors of Minehead		R
GOU 732	1949	Tilling Stevens K6LA7	Scottish Aviation C33F	Altonian Coaches of Alton		R
GKV 94	1950	Daimler CVA6	Metro Cammell H31/29R	Coventry City Transport	94	RP
LTA 813	1950	Bristol KS5G	ECW L27/28R	Western National Omnibus Co	994	R
NTU 125	1951	Foden PVRF6	Metalcraft C41C	Hollinshead of Biddulph		RP
NXL 874	1953	AEC Regal III	Duple C39F	Eastern Belle of Bow London		R
OTT 43	1953	Bristol LS6G	ECW C39F	Western National Omnibus Co (Royal Blue)	2200	R
WKJ 787	1956	Beadle-Commer	Beadle C41C	Beadle Demonstrator		R
780 GHA	1959	BMMO C5	BMMO C41F	BMMO ('Midland Red')	4780	RP
56 GUO	1961	Bristol MW6G	ECW C39F	Western National Omnibus Co (Royal Blue)	2267	RP
5056 HA	1962	BMMO S15	BMMO B40F	BMMO ('Midland Red')	5056	R
EHA 424D	1966	BMMO D9	BMMO/Willowbrook H40/32RD	BMMO ('Midland Red')	5424	R
OTA 640G	1969	Bristol RELH6G	ECW C45F	Southern National Omnibus Co (Royal Blue)	2380	R

Notes:

VG 5541	Converted to diesel 1938 and open top 1950

Rotherham Trolleybus Group

Contact address: 113 Tinker Lane, Walkley, Sheffield S6 5EA
Phone: 0114 266 3173
Affiliation: Trolleybus Museum at Sandtoft
Brief description: This group is open to all with an interest in Rotherham area trolleys, the vehicles and the system. Active restoration of the vehicles takes place and the group works closely with the Trolleybus Museum at Sandtoft. A video *Remember the Trackless* is sold to raise funds for restoration. Vehicles can be viewed by contacting the group.

Registration	Date	Chassis	Body	New to	Fleet No	Status
CET 613+	1942	Sunbeam MS2c	East Lancs B39C	Rotherham Corporation	88	RP
FET 617+	1950	Daimler CTE6	Roe H40/30R	Rotherham Corporation	37	R
- Trolleybus						

Notes:

FET 617   Rebodied 1956 (formerly single-decker). On display at the Trolleybus Museum at Sandtoft

RTW Bus Group

Contact address: 7 Oldbury Close, St Mary Cray BR5 3TH
Affiliation: RT/RF Register, Cobham Bus Museum, HCVS
Brief description: The group was formed in 1999 and comprises the owners of the preserved RTW vehicles and those interested in the type. The vehicles appear at rallies from time to time. A video on the history of the RTW is available from the group.

Registration	Date	Chassis	Body	New to	Fleet No	Status
KGK 529	1949	Leyland Titan PD2/3 6RT	Leyland H30/26R	London Transport	RTW29	R
KGK 575	1949	Leyland Titan PD2/3 6RT	Leyland H30/26R	London Transport	RTW75	R
KLB 908	1949	Leyland Titan PD2/3 6RT	Leyland H30/26RD	London Transport	RTW178	R
KLB 915	1949	Leyland Titan PD2/3 6RT	Leyland H30/26R	London Transport	RTW185	R
KXW 435	1949	Leyland Titan PD2/3 6RT	Leyland H30/26RD	London Transport	RTW335	RP
LLU 957	1950	Leyland Titan PD2/3 6RT	Leyland H30/26R	London Transport	RTW467	R
LLU 987	1950	Leyland Titan PD2/3 6RT	Leyland H30/26R	London Transport	RTW497	R

Notes:

KLB 908   Originally H30/26R. Acquired by Stevensons of Spath in 1966 and fitted with platform doors and saloon heaters
KGK 575   Owned by Blue Triangle and operated as a PSV
KGK 529   On display at Bristol Vintage Bus Group

SELNEC Preservation Society

Contact address: 16 Thurleigh Road, Didsbury, Manchester M20 2DF
Affiliation: NARTM
Brief description: A collection of buses from the SELNEC era including SELNEC Standards, the trail-blazing 'Mancunian' and other vehicles from the Greater Manchester area.
Events planned: The operational vehicles will appear at a range of local rallies and shows.

Registration	Date	Chassis	Body	New to	Fleet No	Status
EN 9965	1950	Leyland Titan PD2/4	Weymann	Bury Corporation	165	RP
DNF 708C	1965	Daimler Fleetline CRG6LX	Metro Cammell O43/29C	Manchester Corporation	4708	A
END 832D	1966	Leyland Atlantean PDR1/2	Metro Cammell H43/32F	Manchester Corporation	3832	RP
GNB 518D	1966	Bedford VAL14	Plaxton C47F	Manchester Corporation	205	A
LNA 166G	1968	Leyland Atlantean PDR2/1	Park Royal H26/7D	Manchester City Transport	1066	R
NNB 547H	1969	Leyland Atlantean PDR2/1	East Lancs H47/32F	Manchester City Transport	1142	A
NNB 589H	1970	Daimler Fleetline CRG6LXB	Park Royal H47/28D	SELNEC PTE	2130	A
ONF 865H	1970	Leyland Atlantean PDR2/1	Park Royal H47/28D	SELNEC PTE	1177	A
PNF 941J	1971	Leyland Atlantean PDR1A/1	Northern Counties H43/32F	SELNEC PTE	EX1	R
RNA 220J	1971	Daimler Fleetline CRG6LXB	Park Royal H47/29D	SELNEC PTE	2220	A
TNB 759K	1972	Daimler Fleetline CRG6LXB	Northern Counties H45/27D	SELNEC PTE	EX19	A
VNB 132L	1972	Leyland Atlantean AN68/1R	Park Royal O43/32F	SELNEC PTE	7032	R
VNB 173L	1972	Leyland Atlantean AN68/1R	Northern Counties H43/32F	SELNEC PTE	7147	A
VNB 177L	1972	Daimler Fleetline CRG6LXB	Northern Counties H45/27D	SELNEC PTE	7206	R
VNB 203L	1972	Daimler Fleetline CRG6LXB	Northern Counties H31/4D	SELNEC PTE	7232	R
WBN 955L	1972	Leyland Atlantean AN68/1R	Park Royal O43/32F	SELNEC PTE	7077	R
YDB 453L	1972	Seddon Pennine IV-236	Seddon DP25F	SELNEC PTE	1700	RP
AJA 408L	1973	Bristol VRTSL/6LXB	ECW H43/32F	SELNEC Cheshire Bus Co	408	R
WWH 43L	1973	Daimler Fleetline CRG6LXB	Park Royal H43/32F	SELNEC PTE	7185	R
XJA 534L	1973	Leyland Atlantean AN68/1R	Park Royal H43/32F	SELNEC PTE	7143	A
XVU 341M	1973	Seddon Pennine IV-236	Seddon B23F	SELNEC PTE	1711	A
YNA 321M	1973	Daimler Fleetline CRG6LXB	Northern Counties H43/32F	SELNEC PTE	7366	A
BNE 729N	1974	Seddon Pennine IV-236	Seddon B19F	Greater Manchester PTE	1735	A
BNE 751N	1974	Leyland Atlantean AN68/1R	Northern Counties H43/32F	Greater Manchester PTE	7501	A
BNE 764N	1974	Bristol LH6L	ECW B43F	Greater Manchester PTE	1321	A
XVU 363M	1974	Seddon Pennine IV-236	Seddon B19F	Greater Manchester PTE	1733	A
HJA 121N	1975	Seddon Pennine IV-236	Seddon B19F	Greater Manchester PTE	1737	A
HNB 24N	1975	Leyland National 10351/1R	Leyland National B41F	Greater Manchester PTE	105	R
OBN 502R	1977	Leyland Fleetline FE30AGR	Northern Counties H43/32F	Lancashire United Transport	485	A
PTD 640S	1977	Leyland Fleetline FE30AGR	Northern Counties H43/32F	Lancashire United Transport	496	A
XBU 1S	1978	Leyland Fleetline FE30AGR	Northern Counties H43/32F	Greater Manchester PTE	8001	R
ANE 2T	1979	Leyland Titan TNLXB1RF	Park Royal H47/26F	Greater Manchester PTE	4002	A
BNC 960T	1979	Leyland Atlantean AN68A/1R	Park Royal H43/32F	Greater Manchester PTE	7960	RP
GBU 1V	1979	MCW Metrobus DR101/6	MCW H43/30F	Greater Manchester PTE	5001	R
GNF 15V	1980	Leyland Titan TNTL11/1RF	Park Royal H47/26F	Greater Manchester PTE	4015	A
GNF 16V	1980	Leyland Fleetline FE30AGR	Northern Counties H43/32F	Greater Manchester PTE	8141	RP
MNC 525W	1980	Leyland Atlantean AN68A/1R	Northern Counties H43/32F	Greater Manchester PTE	8325	A
NJA 568W	1980	Bristol Olympian B45/TL11/1R	Northern Counties H43/30F	Greater Manchester PTE	1451	RP
DWH 706W	1981	Leyland Fleetline FE30AGR	Northern Counties H43/32F	Lancashire United Transport	613	R
SND 455X	1981	Leyland Atlantean AN68B/1R	Northern Counties H43/32F	Greater Manchester PTE	8455	A
SND 460X	1981	Leyland Atlantean AN68B/1R	Northern Counties H43/32F	Greater Manchester PTE	8460	R
MIL 8338	1982	Volvo Ailsa B55-10	Northern Counties H44/35F	Greater Manchester PTE	1448	A
ANA 1Y	1982	Leyland Olympian ONTL11/1R	Northern Counties H43/30F	Greater Manchester PTE	3001	R
ANA 601Y	1983	Leyland Atlantean AN68D/1R	Northern Counties H43/32F	Greater Manchester PTE	8601	A
ANA 645Y	1983	Leyland Atlantean AN68D/1R	Northern Counties H43/32F	Greater Manchester PTE	8645	RP
FWH 461Y	1983	Scania BR112DH	Northern Counties H43/32F	Greater Manchester PTE	1461	A
A472 HNC	1984	Dennis Falcon V DD405	Northern Counties H43/37F	Greater Manchester PTE	1472	A
A701 LNC	1984	Leyland Atlantean AN68D/1R	Northern Counties H43/32F	Greater Manchester PTE	8701	A
A765 NNA	1984	Leyland Atlantean AN68D/1R	Northern Counties H43/32F	Greater Manchester PTE	8765	RP
A30 ORJ	1984	Leyland Olympian ONLXB/1R	Northern Counties H43/30F	Greater Manchester PTE	3030	A
B101 SJA	1985	Leyland Olympian ONLXB/1R	Northern Counties H44/30F	Greater Manchester PTE	3101	A
B901 TVR	1985	Dennis Dominator DDA1003	Northern Counties H43/32F	Greater Manchester PTE	2001	RP
C751 YBA	1985	Dennis Domino SDA 1201	Northern Counties B24F	Greater Manchester PTE	1751	R
C201 CBU	1986	Leyland Olympian ONLXB/1R	Northern Counties H43/30F	Greater Manchester PTE	3201	A
C225 CBU	1986	Leyland Olympian ONLXB/1R	Northern Counties H43/30F	Greater Manchester PTE	3225	A
C823 CBU	1986	Dodge S 56	Northern Counties B18F	Greater Manchester PTE	1823	RP
D302 JVR	1986	MCW Metrobus DR102/51	Northern Counties CH43/29F	Greater Manchester Buses	5302	A
D501 LNA	1986	Leyland Lynx LX5636LXCT2R1	Leyland B48F	Greater Manchester Buses	501	A
D320 LNB	1987	MCW Metrobus DR102/51	Northern Counties CH43/29F	Greater Manchester Buses	5320	R
D509 MJA	1987	Iveco 49-10	Robin Hood B21F	Greater Manchester Buses	1509	A
F305 DRJ	1989	Leyland Olympian ONLXB/1RZ	Northern Counties H43/30F	Greater Manchester Buses	3305	A

Notes:

EN 9965	Converted to Breakdown Vehicle
DNF 708C	Originally H43/32F
LNA 166G	Originally H47/29D; converted by Greater Manchester PTE for use as 'Exhibus' exhibition vehicle - restored in this condition
NNB 547H	Mancunian
NNB 589H	Mancunian
ONF 865H	Mancunian
RNA 220J	Mancunian
PNF 941J	Exhibited at 1970 Commercial Motor Show as prototype SELNEC Standard
VNB 203L	Originally H45/27D. Used as exhibition vehice.
VNB 177L	Exhibited at 1972 Commercial Motor Show
WBN 955L	Converted to open-top
VNB 132L	Converted to open-top
PTD 640S	Passed to GMPTE in 1981 as 6912. Rebodied 1983.
OBN 502R	Passed to Greater Manchester PTE (6901) in 1981
XBU 1S	First GMT Leyand Fleetline Standard
BNC 960T	Last Park Royal Bodied Standard
GBU 1V	GM First Metrobus
GNF 15V	GM Last Titan
NJA 568W	Exhibited at 1980 Commercial Motor Show. GM First Olympian
DWH 706W	Passed to Greater Manchester PTE (6990) in 1981. GM Last Fleetline
MIL 8338	Originally registered WRJ 448X
SND 455X	Seating reduced - converted to driver training vehicle
ANA 1Y	Exhibited at 1982 Commercial Motor Show
A472 HNC	One of only six built
A765 NNA	Greater Manchesters last Atlantean
C751 YBA	Exhibited at 1984 Commercial Motor Show
D320 LNB	Greater Manchesters last Metrobus

Southampton & District Transport Heritage Trust

Contact address: 104 Oak Tree Road, Southampton SO18 1PH

Affiliation: NARTM; WOMP

Brief description: The collection includes a selection of Southampton's fleet from the early 1970s. The small membership carries out restoration work. Several of the vehicles are privately owned by Trust members.

Registration	Date	Chassis	Body	New to	Fleet No	Status
FTR 511	1949	Guy Arab III	Park Royal O30/26R	Southampton Corporation	64	R
LOW 217	1954	Guy Arab III	Park Royal H30/26R	Southampton Corporation	71	R
JOW 928	1955	Guy Arab UF	Park Royal B39F	Southampton Corporation	255	RP
318 AOW	1962	AEC Regent V 2D3RA	Park Royal H37/29R	Southampton Corporation	318	RP
335 AOW	1963	Leyland Titan PD2A/27	Park Royal H37/29R	Southampton Corporation	335	RP
370 FCR	1963	AEC Regent V 2D3RA	East Lancs H37/29R	Southampton Corporation	350	R
BTR 361B	1964	AEC Regent V 2D3RA	East Lancs Neepsend H37/29R	Southampton Corporation	361	R
BOW 507C	1965	AEC Regent V 2D3RA	East Lancs Neepsend H37/29R	Southampton Corporation	371	RP
JOW 499E	1967	AEC Swift MP2R	Strachan B47D	Southampton Corporation	1	RP
KOW 909F	1967	AEC Regent V 3D2RA	East Lancs Neepsend H40/30R	Southampton Corporation	401	RP
KOW 910F	1967	AEC Regent V 3D2RA	East Lancs Neepsend H40/30R	Southampton Corporation	402	RP
PCG 888G	1968	AEC Reliance 6U3ZR	Plaxton C55F	Coliseum Coaches of Southampton		A
PCG 889G	1968	AEC Reliance 6MU3R	Plaxton C45F	Coliseum Coaches of Southampton		A
TTR 167H	1970	Leyland Atlantean PDR1A/1	East Lancs H45/31F	Southampton Corporation	133	RP
HNP 989J	1971	Leyland Atlantean PDR1A/1	East Lancs O45/31F	Southampton Corporation	139	RP
BCR 379K	1972	Seddon Pennine RU	Pennine B44F	Southampton Corporation	15	RP

Notes:

FTR 511	Converted to open-top. Owned by Southampton City Museums
LOW 217	Owned by Southampton City Museums
JOW 928	Originally B36D
PCG 888G	Originally C57F
HNP 989J	Preserved in Guide Friday livery. Originally registered WOW 531J

Southdown Historic Vehicle Group

Contact address: 173 Cuckfield Crescent, Worthing, West Sussex
E-mail: pd3@btinternet.com
Website: http://home.fastnet.co.uk/gerrycork/worthingbusrally/worthingbusrally.htm
Brief description: A private collection of vehicles, most of which operated for Southdown Motor Services or which have south coast connections or have taken our fancy. The collection is not on public view but vehicles are rallied and often appear in service at running days.
Event planned: 30 July 2006 — Worthing Bus Rally and Running Day.

Registration	Date	Chassis	Body	New to	Fleet No	Status
GUF 191	1945	Guy Arab II	Northern Counties O30/26R	Southdown Motor Services	451	RP
LRV 992	1956	Leyland Titan PD2/12	Metro Cammell O33/26R	Portsmouth Corporation	2	R
XUF 141	1960	Leyland Tiger Cub PSUC1/2	Weymann C41F	Southdown Motor Services	1141	R
70 AUF	1962	Commer Avenger IV	Harrington C—F	Southdown Motor Services	70	A
416 DCD	1964	Leyland Titan PD3/4	Northern Counties FCO39/30F	Southdown Motor Services	416	R
419 DCD	1964	Leyland Titan PD3/4	Northern Counties FCO39/30F	Southdown Motor Services	419	R
972 CUF	1964	Leyland Titan PD3/4	Northern Counties FH39/30F	Southdown Motor Services	972	RP
AOR 158B	1964	Leyland Titan PD3/4	Northern Counties FCO39/30F	Southdown Motor Services	412	R
PRX 187B	1964	Leyland Titan PD3/4	Northern Counties FCO39/30F	Southdown Motor Services	415	RP
PRX 200B	1964	Leyland Titan PD3/4	Northern Counties FCO39/30F	Southdown Motor Services	418	R
PRX 206B	1964	Leyland Titan PD3/4	Northern Counties FCO39/30F	Southdown Motor Services	401	R
BUF 122C	1965	Leyland Leopard PSU3/1RT	Marshall B45F	Southdown Motor Services	122	RP
BUF 260C	1965	Leyland Titan PD3/4	Northern Counties FC39/30F	Southdown Motor Services	260	R
BUF 277C	1965	Leyland Titan PD3/4	Northern Counties FC39/30F	Southdown Motor Services	277	R
BUF 426C	1965	Leyland Titan PD3/4	Northern Counties FCO39/30F	Southdown Motor Services	426	R
BUF 427C	1965	Leyland Titan PD3/4	Northern Counties FCO39/30F	Southdown Motor Services	427	R
BJK 672D	1966	Leyland Titan PD2A/30	East Lancs H32/28R	Eastbourne Corporation	72	RP
FCD 294D	1966	Leyland Titan PD3/4	Northern Counties FH39/29F	Southdown Motor Services	294	R
DHC 784E	1967	Leyland Titan PD2A/30	East Lancs O32/28R	Eastbourne Corporation	84	R
KUF 199F	1968	Leyland Leopard PSU3/1RT	Willowbrook B45F	Southdown Motor Services	199	R
LFS 296F	1968	Bristol VRTLL/6LX	ECW O41/36F	Scottish Omnibuses (Eastern Scottish)	AA296	R
SYK 569F	1968	Leyland Leopard PSU4/4R	Duple C41F	Grey Green Coaches of London		A
PUF 165H	1969	Leyland Leopard PSU3/1RT	Northern Counties DP49F	Southdown Motor Services	465	R
TCD 374J	1970	Daimler Fleetline CRG6LX	Northern Counties H-/-F	Southdown Motor Services	374	RP
TCD 383J	1970	Daimler Fleetline CRG6LX	Northern Counties H-/-F	Southdown Motor Services	383	RP
TCD 481J	1970	Bristol RESL6L	Marshall B45F	Southdown Motor Services	481	R
TCD 490J	1970	Bristol RESL6L	Marshall B45F	Southdown Motor Services	490	RP
BHH 83J	1971	Leyland Leopard PSU3B/4RT	Plaxton C47F	Southdown Motor Services	1835	RP
UUF 116J	1971	Bristol VRTSL6LX	ECW PO-/-F	Southdown Motor Services	516	RP
UUF 328J	1971	Leyland Leopard PSU3B/4RT	Plaxton C53F	Southdown Motor Services	1828	R
SCD 731N	1974	Leyland Atlantean AN68/1R	Park Royal - Roe H43/30F	Southdown Motor Services	731	R
GHV 505N	1975	Bristol LHS6L	ECW B29F	London Transport	BS5	R
RUF 37R	1977	Leyland National 11351A/2R	Leyland National B44D	Southdown Motor Services	37	R
ANJ 306T	1978	Leyland Leopard PSU3E/4RT	Plaxton C53F	Southdown Motor Services	1306	A
HNP 154S	1978	Leyland Atlantean AN68A/1R	East Lancs O43/31F	Brighton Corporation	3	R
TYJ 4S	1978	Leyland Atlantean AN68A/1R	East Lancs H43/31F	Brighton Corporation	4	R
USV 324	1979	Leyland Leopard PSU3E/4RT	Plaxton C48F	Southdown Motor Services	1320	RP
OPV 821	1979	Leyland Leopard PSU3E/4RT	Plaxton C48F	Southdown Motor Services	1321	RP
KAZ 6703	1979	Leyland Leopard PSU5C/4R	Duple C53F	Southdown Motor Services	1339	RP
MAP 340W	1981	Leyland Leopard PSU3F/4R	Plaxton C48F	Southdown Motor Services	1340	R
KOW 274Y	1982	Leyland Atlantean	East Lancs H71F	Southampton Corporation		RP

Notes:

LRV 992	Originally H33/26R
AOR 158B	Originally registered 412 DCD
PRX 187B	Originally registered 415 DCD
PRX 200B	Originally registered 418 DCD
PRX 206B	Originally registered 401 DCD
LFS 296F	Originally H47/32F.
UUF 116J	Originally H39/31F

BHH 83J	Originally registered UUF 335J			OPV 821	Originally registered EAP 921V		
HNP 154S	Originally H43/31F registered TYJ 3S			KAZ 6703	Originally registered EAP 939V		
USV 324	Originally registered BYJ 920T						

St Margaret's Transport Society

Contact Information: St Margaret's High School, Aigburth Road, Liverpool L17 6AB
Telephone: 0151 427 1825
Affiliation: NARTM
Brief Description: Formed in 1979, the Society specialises in single deck half-cabs from the 1940s and 1950s. Meetings are held regularly to carry out restoration of the vehicles. Visitors are welcome but prior appointment is essential. Please contact the address given.

Registration	Date	Chassis	Body	New to	Fleet No	Status
CMS 201	1949	Leyland Tiger PS1	Alexander C35F	Alexander	PA133	R
GWM 816	1951	Crossley SD42/7	Crossley B32F	Southport Corporation	116	RP

Telford Bus Group

Contact address: 65 Sandbach Road, Rode Heath, Cheshire, ST7 3RW
Brief description: The Telford Bus Group has a collection of privately-owned buses and coaches in various parts of England.
The Group has become known for its Bedford VALs of which 12 examples are preserved, with examples of several body types. Other vehicles include Daimler Fleetline 'Mancunian', Seddon Pennine VI, Commer Avenger and Leyland Leopard 'Midland Red S27 type'.
Not all vehicles are restored and some are long term projects.

Registration	Date	Chassis	Body	New to	Fleet No	Status
386 DD	1961	Bedford J2	Plaxton C20F	Talbott of Moreton-in-Marsh		RP
3190 UN	1962	Commer Avenger IV	Plaxton C41F	Wright of Penycae		RP
9797 DP	1964	Bedford VAL14	Duple C52F	Smiths of Reading		RP
EHL 472D	1966	Bedford VAL14	Plaxton C52F	West Riding Automobile Co	3	R
JTH 100F	1968	Bedford VAM14	Duple C45F	Davies of Pencader		RP
UWX 981F	1968	Bedford VAL70	Plaxton C52F	Mosley of Barugh Green		R
RBC 345G	1969	Bedford VAL70	Duple C52F	Cook of Dunstable		RP
WWY 115G	1969	Bedford VAL70	Plaxton C53F	Abbey Coachways of Selby		R
FYG 663J	1970	Bedford VAL70	Willowbrook B56F	Wigmore of Dinnington		RP
VBD 310H	1970	Bedford VAL70	Plaxton C48F	Coales of Woolaston		R
BHO 670J	1971	Bedford VAL70	Duple C53F	Castle Coaches of Waterlooville		R
RNA 236J	1971	Daimler Fleetline CRG6LXB-33	Park Royal H47/29D	SELNEC PTE	2236	A
CDC 166K	1972	Seddon Pennine VI	Plaxton C45F	Bob's of Middlesbrough	26	RP
CDC 168K	1972	Seddon Pennine VI	Plaxton C41F	Bob's of Middlesbrough	28	RP
FAR 724K	1972	Bedford VAL70	Duple C53F	Langley Coaches of Slough		A
JHA 227L	1973	Leyland Leopard PSU3B/2R	Marshall DP49F	Midland Red Omnibus Co	227	RP

Notes:
RNA 236J   Mancunian

TH Collection

Contact Information: Telephone 01263 834829
E-mail: nick@topolino.demon.co.uk
Affiliation: NARTM
Brief Description: A private collection representing coachwork built by Thomas Harrington of Hove. It is believed the vehicles are now all unique examples of the chassis and body combination.
Opening days/times: The collection is not on public view and all vehicles are at varying stages of restoration. Arrangements to visit can be made, strictly by appointment, telephoning first for details.

Registration	Date	Chassis	Body	New to	Fleet No	Status
KD 5296	1928	Leyland Tiger TS2	Harrington C31F	Imperial Motor Services of Liverpool		A
VRF 372	1951	Foden PVRF6	Harrington C41C	Bassett's Coaches of Tittensor		RP
JAP 698	1954	Harrington Contender	Harrington C41C	Audawn Coaches of Corringham		RP
YYB 118	1957	Dennis Lancet UF	Harrington B42F	Hutchings & Cornelius Services of South Petherton		A
PFR 747	1959	Bedford SB3	Harrington C41F	Abbotts of Blackpool		A

Notes:
JAP 698   Former Harrington demonstrator

Three Counties Bus and Commercial Vehicle Museum

Contact address: 83 Millwright Way, Flitwick, Beds MK45 1BQ
Phone: 01525 712091
E-mail: nick.doolan@btopenworld.com
Web site: www.3cbcvm.org.uk
Affiliation: NARTM
Brief description: Established to provide a focus for the preservation, and historical record of buses in Bedfordshire, Buckinghamshire and Hertfordshire. Seeks to ensure a long-term future for the vehicles.
Events planned: Please see enthusiast press for planned Operating Days. Operational vehicles frequently attend local rallies

Registration	Date	Chassis	Body	New to	Fleet No	Status
FXT 122	1939	Leyland Cub REC	LPTB B20F	London Transport	CR 16	RP
DBL 154	1946	Bristol K6A	ECW L27/28R	Thames Valley Traction Co	446	R
CFN 104	1947	Leyland Tiger PS1/1	Park Royal C32R	East Kent Road Car Co		R
JWU 307	1950	Bedford OB	Duple C29F	Lunn of Rothwell		RP
LYR 915	1952	AEC Regent III O961 RT	Weymann H30/26R	London Transport	RT3496	R
MXX 434	1952	AEC Regal IV 9821LT RF	Metro Cammell B39F	London Transport	RF457	R
MXX 332	1953	Guy Special NLLVP	ECW B26F	London Transport	GS32	R
MXX 489	1953	AEC Regal IV 9821LT RF	Metro Cammell B39F	London Transport	RF512	RP
RSJ 747	1956	Albion Victor FT39AN	Heaver C27F	Guernsey Motor Co	69	R
VYO 767	1959	Bristol MW6G	ECW C41F	Tillings Transport		RP
OVL 473	1960	Bristol Lodekka FS5G	ECW H33/27RD	Lincolnshire Road Car Co	2378	R
EFM 631C	1965	Bristol Lodekka FS6G	ECW H33/27RD	Crosville Motor Services	DFG182	R
DEK 3D	1966	Leyland Titan PD2/37	Massey H37/27F	Wigan Corporation	140	R
KBD 712D	1966	Bristol Lodekka FS6G	ECW H33/27RD	United Counties Omnibus Co	712	R
KBD 715D	1966	Bristol Lodekka FS6G	ECW H60RD	United Counties Omnibus Co	715	RP
NBD 311F	1967	Bristol RELL6G	ECW B53F	United Counties Omnibus Co	311	RP
RBD 319G	1968	Bristol RELL6G	ECW B53F	United Counties Omnibus Co	319	RP
UXD 129G	1969	Bristol RELL6L	ECW B48D	Luton Corporation	129	RP
UBD 757H	1969	Bristol VRTSL6LX	ECW H39/31F	United Counties Omnibus Co	757	A

Registration	Date	Chassis	Body	New to	Fleet No	Status
VLW 444G	1969	AEC Merlin 4P2R	MCW B25D	London Transport	MBS444	A
VMO 234H	1969	Bristol LH6L	ECW B41F	Thames Valley Traction Co	214	RP
ANV 775J	1971	Bristol VRTSL/6LX	ECW H39/31F	United Counties Omnibus Co	775	R
WRP 767J	1971	Bristol VRTSL	ECW H39/31F	United Counties Omnibus Co	767	RP
JPL 153K	1972	Leyland Atlantean PDR1A/1	Park Royal H43/29D	London Country Bus Services	AN53	RP
GPD 313N	1974	Bristol LHS6L	ECW B35F	London Country Bus Services	BN45	RP
RBD 111M	1974	Bedford YRT	Willowbrook B53F	United Counties Omnibus Co	111	A
UPE 203M	1974	Leyland National 10351/1R	Leyland National B41F	London Country Bus Services	SNB103	A
HPF 318N	1975	Leyland National 10351/1R/SC	Leyland National DP39F	London Country Bus Services	SNC168	R
SBD 525R	1977	Leyland National 11351A/1R	Leyland National B49F	United Counties Omnibus Co	525	RP
SOA 674S	1977	Leyland Leopard PSU3E/4R	Plaxton C49F	Midland Red Omnibus Co	674	R
UPB 312S	1977	Leyland National 10351A/1R	Leyland National B41F	London Country Bus Services	SNB312	R
GCK 279S	1978	Bedford YLQ	Plaxton C46F	Battersby Silver Grey Coaches		RP
XPK 51T	1978	AEC Reliance 6U2R	Duple C53F	London Country Bus Services	RB51	R
BPL 469T	1979	Leyland National 10351B/1R	Leyland National B41F	London Country Bus Services	SNB469	RP
EPM 134V	1979	AEC Reliance 6U2R	Duple C49F	London Country Bus Services	RB134	A
SVV 587W	1980	Leyland National 2 NL116L11/1R	Leyland National II B49F	United Counties Omnibus Co	587	R
GUW 443W	1981	Leyland National 2 NL106AL11/2R	East Lancs National Greenway B25D	London Transport	GLS443	A
GUW 444W	1981	Leyland National 2 NL106AL11/2R	Leyland National II DP43F	London Transport	LS444	RP
TPD 109X	1982	Leyland Olympian ONTL11/1R	Roe H43/29F	London Country Bus Services	LR9	A
C24 NVV	1985	Ford Transit	Carlyle B16F	United Counties Omnibus Co	24	A

Notes:

RSJ 747   Original Guernsey registration was 1529

Wealdstone & District Vintage Vehicle Collection

Contact address: 91 Graham Road, Wealdstone, Middx HA3 5RE
E-mail: oldbusgarage@sftt.co.uk
Web site: www.sftt.co.uk/busgarage
Affiliation: NARTM
Brief description: A small collection of mainly London buses from the 1950s, examples of which regularly attend rallies. Anyone wishing to visit or assist with the vehicles is welcome. Please write to the address given.

Registration	Date	Chassis	Body	New to	Fleet No	Status
DL 9706	1935	Dennis Lancet	ECW B36R	Southern Vectis Omnibus Co	516	RP
KYY 622	1950	AEC Regent III O961 RT	Park Royal H30/26R	London Transport	RT1784	R
MLL 817	1952	AEC Regal IV 9821LT RF	Metro Cammell B37F	London Transport	RF280	R
MXX 410	1953	AEC Regal IV 9821LT RF	Metro Cammell B41F	London Transport	RF433	R
MXX 430	1953	AEC Regal IV 9821LT RF	Metro Cammell B39F	London Transport	RF453	R
NLE 939	1953	AEC Regent III O961 RT	Park Royal H30/26R	London Transport	RT4275	RP

Notes:

DL 9706   Rebodied 1944

The West Country Historic Omnibus & Transport Trust

Contact address: The Secretary, 33 Broad View, Broadclyst, Exeter EX5 3HA
Web site: www.busmuseum.org.uk
Affiliation: NARTM
Brief description: An Historic Bus, Coach and Lorry Rally is held annually in September at the Westpoint Showground, Clyst St Mary, near Exeter (junction 30, M5). The Trust plans to establish a museum and archive of West Country commercial road transport at this location in the near future.

Registration	Date	Chassis	Body	New to	Fleet No	Status
86 GFJ	1963	Leyland Titan PD2A/30	Massey H31/26R	Exeter City Transport	86	RP
OTA 632G	1969	Bristol RELH6G	ECW C45F	Southern National Omnibus Co (Royal Blue)	1460	R
TDV217J	1970	Leyland Panther PSUR1B/1R	Marshall B—D	Devon General	217	R
VDV 137S	1977	Bristol VRT/SL3/6LXB	ECW CO43/31F	Western National Omnibus Co (Devon General)	937	R
AFJ 726T	1979	Bristol LH6L	Plaxton C41F	Western National Omnibus Co	3306	A
AFJ 727T	1979	Bristol LH6L	Plaxton C41F	Western National Omnibus Co	3307	RP
AFJ 764T	1979	Bristol VRT/SL3/6LXB	ECW H43/31F	Western National Omnibus Co	1157	R
A927 MDV	1983	Ford Transit 160D	Carlyle B16F	Devon General	7	R
C801 FRL	1985	Mercedes L608D	Reeve Burgess B20F	Western National	104	RP
C705 FFJ	1986	Ford Transit	Robin Hood B16F	Devon General	705	RP
C719 FFJ	1986	Ford Transit	Robin Hood B16F	Devon General	719	A
L929 CTT	1994	Iveco 59-12	Mellor B21D	Devon General	1000	R
M627 HDV	1994	Iveco 59-12	Wadham Stringer B21D	Devon General	1029	A

Notes:
TDV217J   Ordered by Exeter Corporation. Previously B47D. Converted to publicity vehicle in 1980
VDV 137S   'Warship' class, named *Victory*

West Midlands Bus Preservation Society

Contact address: Secretary, 22 Beaumont Way, Norton Canes, Cannock WS11 9FQ
Brief description: The main core of the collection is of vehicles from the West Midlands PTE in the period 1969 to 1986. Other artefacts are being collected for inclusion in a planned transport museum.
Opening days/times: Vehicles can be viewed by special arrangement, contact secretary.

Registration	Date	Chassis	Body	New to	Fleet No	Status
DUK 278	1946	Guy Arab II	Roe H31/25R	Wolverhampton Corporation	378	RP
UHY 362	1955	Bristol KSW6B	ECW H32/28R	Bristol Tramways	8322	R
436 KOV	1964	Daimler Fleetline CRG6LX	Park Royal H43/33F	Birmingham City Transport	3436	A
NOV 880G	1969	Daimler Fleetline CRG6LX	Park Royal H43/29D	Birmingham City Transport	3880	RP
TOB 997H	1970	Daimler Fleetline CRG6LX-33	Park Royal H47/33D	West Midlands PTE	3997	A
JOV 738P	1976	Volvo Ailsa B55-10	Alexander H44/35F	West Midlands PTE	4738	R
NOC 600R	1976	Leyland Fleetline FE30AGR	Park Royal H43/33F	West Midlands PTE	6600	RP
WDA 956T	1979	Leyland Fleetline FE30AGR	MCW B37F	West Midlands PTE	1956	A
A103 SUU	1984	Volvo B55-10 Mk III	Alexander H38/30F	London Transport	V3	R

Notes:
DUK 278   Body built 1952
TOB 997H   Gardner 6LXB engine fitted after acquisition by C J Partridge & Son of Hadleigh
WDA 956T   Originally double-deck bus (H43/33F) 6956; rebuilt as single-decker in 1994
A103 SUU   Originally H36/28D

West of England Transport Collection

Contact address: 15 Land Park, Chulmleigh, Devon, EX18 7BH
Affiliation: NARTM
Brief description: A large private collection of vehicles, mainly from West Country major operators. The collection includes buses, coaches and transport memorabilia.
Events planned: 1 October 2006 — Annual WETC Open Day, Winckleigh
Opening days/times: Viewing at other times by prior arrangement with C. T. Shears, tel: 01769 580811.

Registration	Date	Chassis	Body	New to	Fleet No	Status
UO 2331	1927	Austin 20 5PL	Tiverton B13F	Sidmouth Motor Co		RP
JY 124	1932	Tilling Stevens B10A2 Express	Beadle B—R	Western National Omnibus Co	3379	RP W2 to 11
OD 5489	1933	Vauxhall Cadet VY	Mount Pleasant B7	Davis of Rockbeare		R
OD 5868	1933	Leyland Lion LT5	Weymann B31F	Devon General	68	A W 2.10.11
OD 7500	1934	AEC Regent O661	Brush H30/26R	Devon General	DR213	R ''
ADV 128	1935	Bristol JO5G	Beadle B—R	Western National Omnibus Co	222	RP
ATT 922	1935	Bristol JJW6A	Beadle B35R	Western National Omnibus Co	172	RP W2-10-11
AUO 74	1935	Leyland Lion LT5A	(chassis only)	Devon General	SL79	A
FV 5737	1936	Leyland Tiger TS7	Duple C31F	Ribble Motor Services	753	R
ADR 813	1938	Leyland Titan TD5c	Leyland L27/26R	Plymouth Corporation	141	R W 2.10.11
BOW 169	1938	Bristol L5G	-	Hants & Dorset Motor Services	TS676	A
EFJ 241	1938	Leyland Titan TD5	Leyland H30/26R	Exeter Corporation	26	RP
EFJ 666	1938	Leyland Tiger TS8	Cravens B32R	Exeter Corporation	66	R W
ETT 946	1938	Bristol L5G	Beadle B36R	Southern National Omnibus Co	280	A
DOD 474	1940	AEC Regal O662	Weymann B35F	Devon General	SR474	RP W2.10.11
GTA 395	1941	Bristol LL5G	Brislington Body Works B39R	Southern National Omnibus Co	373	RP W2.10.11
DDR 414	1947	Leyland Titan PD1	Weymann L27/26R	Plymouth Corporation	114	R
FFY 401	1947	Leyland Titan PD2/3	Leyland O30/26R	Southport Corporation	84	RP
KHU 624	1947	Bristol K6B	ECW H30/26R	Bristol Omnibus Co	3705	RP
GLJ 957	1948	Leyland Titan PD1A	ECW L27/26R	Hants & Dorset Motor Services	PD959	A W2.10.11
JFJ 606	1949	Daimler CVD6	Brush H30/26R	Exeter Corporation	43	A
LTV 702	1951	AEC Regal III 9621E	East Lancs B35R	Nottingham City Transport	702	A
Q995 CPE	1953	AEC Regent III O961 RT	Park Royal O30/26R	London Transport	RT4588	A
WRL 16	1956	Rowe Hillmaster	Reading B42F	Millbrook Steamboat & Trading Co		A
974 AFJ	1960	Guy Arab IV	Massey H31/26R	Exeter Corporation	74	R W2.10.11
484 EFJ	1962	Leyland Titan PD2D3RA/30	Massey H31/26R	Exeter Corporation	84	A
373 FCR	1963	AEC Regent V	East Lancs H-/-R	Southampton Corporation	353	A
532 DWW	1963	Bedford SB5	Plaxton C41F	Barnsley British Co-op		A
815 KDV	1963	Bristol Lodekka FLF6B	ECW H38/30F	Western National Omnibus Co	2010	A W2.10.11
991 MDV	1963	AEC Reliance 2MU3RV	Marshall B41F	Devon General	991	A W 2-10-11
CTT 513C	1965	AEC Regent V 2D3RA	Park Royal H40/29F	Devon General	513	R W2.10.11
OAE 957M	1973	Bristol RELL6L	ECW B—F	Bristol Omnibus Co	1335	A
GNM 235N	1975	Bristol LHL6L	Plaxton C51F	Caroline Seagull of Great Yarmouth		R
31909	1975	Bristol LH6L	Plaxton C45F	Greenslades Tours	318	A
JFJ 500N	1975	Bristol LH6L	Plaxton C45F	Greenslades Tours	320	A
MPX 945R	1977	Ford Transit	Robin Hood C-F	Angela of Bursledon		A
PTT 106R	1977	Bristol LH6L	Plaxton C37F	Western National Omnibus Co	3406	RP
RUF 40R	1977	Leyland National 11351/2R	Leyland National B23D	Southdown Motor Services	40	R
CRM 927T	1979	Leyland/DAB	Leyland AB64T	South Yorkshire PTE	2006	A
DBV 32W	1980	Bristol VR	ECW	Ribble	2032	R
DBV 43W	1980	Leyland Leopard PSU4E/4R		Burnley & Pendle	43	A W2.10.11
RLN 237W	1981	Leyland-DAB 6-35-690/4	Roe AB—T	British Airways	C310	A
YNW 33X	1982	Leyland Leopard	Plaxton C51F	Shilton of Leeds		R
A749 NTA	1984	Ford Transit	Ford	Devon County Council		A
C748 FFJ	1986	Ford Transit 190D	Carlyle B16F	Devon General	748	A W2.10.11
C671 FFJ	1986	Ford Transit	Carlyle B16F	Devon General	671	RP

Notes:

UO 2331	Body new 1940
JY 124	New body and engine fitted in 1947
OD 5489	Body fitted 1946
OD 7500	Rebodied 1949
ATT 922	Rebodied in the late 1940s
ADV 128	Rebodied 1950
AUO 74	Front end of chassis only
FV 5737	Rebodied 1950
ETT 946	Rebodied 1950
BOW 169	New with Beadle body; acquired by Wilts & Dorset Motor Services (505) in 1952 and converted to breakdown vehicle in 1956
EFJ 666	Used as a snowplough 1952-6
EFJ 241	Converted to tree-cutter in 1958
ADR 813	Rebodied 1953. Originally torque convertor. Now with crash gearbox.
GTA 395	Lengthened and rebodied in 1954
FFY 401	Originally H30/26R
CTT 513C	Restored by the Oxford Bus Museum Trust
31909	Original registration JFJ 498N
RUF 40R	Exhibition vehicle. Originally B44D
Q995 CPE	Original registration NLP581
CRM 927T	Articulated prototype (57ft long)
RLN 237W	Front portion converted to playbus
A749 NTA	Fitted with tail lift for wheelchairs

Westgate Museum

Contact address: Enquiries: Caretaker — Tony Ferris, 107 Westgate Road, Belton DN9 1PY
Brief description: The collection, near Doncaster, is housed in a former Methodist Chapel built in 1865. The site operates under the auspices of the Trolleybus Museum at Sandtoft and the vehicles operate there from time to time.
Opening days/times: Viewing strictly by appointment.

Registration	Date	Chassis	Body	New to	Fleet No	Status
RC 8472+	1944	Sunbeam W	Weymann UH30/26R	Derby Corporation	172	R
RC 8575+	1945	Sunbeam W	Park Royal UH30/26R	Derby Corporation	175	RP
SVS 281	1945	Daimler CWA6	Duple UH30/26R	Douglas Corporation	52	R
DRD 130+	1949	BUT 9611T	Park Royal H33/26RD	Reading Corporation	144	R
LDP 945	1955	AEC Regent III 6812A	Park Royal L31/26RD	Reading Corporation	98	R
WLT 529	1960	AEC Routemaster R2RH	Park Royal H36/28R	London Transport	RM529	R

+ Trolleybus

Notes:

SVS 281	Originally registered FMN 955

Workington Heritage Transport Trust

Contact Information: 22 Calva Road, Seaton, Workington, Cumbria, CA14 1DF
Telephone: 01900 67389
E-mail: wthc@btopenworld.com
Affiliation: NARTM, Transport Trust
Brief Description: A collection based around buses and rail vehicles from the West Cumberland area. It is the aim to open to the public once a suitable building and funding have been arranged.
Events planned: 29 April 2006 — Park & Ride service in connection with Cockermouth Georgian Fair.

Registration	Date	Chassis	Body	New to	Fleet No	Status
109 DRM	1961	Bristol Lodekka FS6G	ECW H33/27RD	Cumberland Motor Services	550	R
AAO 34B	1964	Bristol MW6G	ECW B45F	Cumberland Motor Services	231	R
GRM 353L	1973	Leyland National 1151/1R/0401	Leyland National B52F	Cumberland Motor Services	353	RP
KHH 378W	1980	Leyland National 2 NL116L11/1R	Leyland National B52F	Cumberland Motor Services	378	R

Notes:

KHH 378W	Restored to post-NBC CMS Cumberland Livery

Above: The West of England Transport Collection can boast among its vehicles former Exeter Corporation 66 (EFJ 666), a 1938 Cravens-bodied Leyland Tiger TS8. *Colin T. Shears*

Below: Greater Manchester 1751 (C751 YBA), preserved by the SELNEC Preservation Society, is the sole survivor of 20 Northern Counties-bodied Dennis Domino midibuses new in 1985.

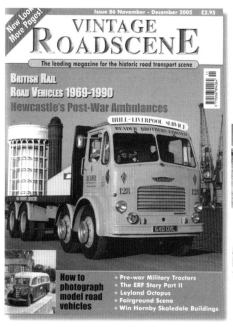

Vintage Roadscene takes readers on a nostalgic trip back to the good c
days of famous fleets, household names and long-past companies fro
the motor manufacturing industry.

Intent on capturing the history of the transport network in detailed article
photography, preservation and even model form, *Vintage Roadscene*
written by a team of transport historians dedicated to taking readers do
memory lane.

Supported by lively, well-informed articles and full colour photographs
covers the restoration of old road vehicles, with life history features, mo
and book reviews, competitions, comprehensive events listings, and ne
of road transport groups.

■ Bi-monthly   ■ ISSN: 0266-8947

The leading magazine for the historic road transport scene

Part 3

Privately Preserved Buses

Devon General Bristol VRTSL3 937
(VDV 137S) is affiliated with the West
Country Historic Omnibus and Transport
Trust. *P. Platt*

PRIVATELY PRESERVED BUSES

This section is included with the help and co-operation of the British Bus Preservation Group (BBPG). There are known to be many excellent privately preserved buses, coaches and some trolleybuses in this country and the list which follows is prepared from data provided by the Group. All the vehicles are owned by BBPG members and every effort has been made to ensure that the information given is correct at the time of going to press.

Condition of the vehicles varies, some having been fully restored (even to public operational standard in some cases); others are undergoing restoration, often a lengthy job with limited resources; some awaiting their turn for the day when the restoration task can be started. Those vehicles which are restored generally make visits to bus rallies up and down the country and details of such events can be found in the bus enthusiast magazines, regularly published.

If you are the owner of a preserved bus, coach or trolleybus which is not listed, you may wish to become a member of the BBPG. Services to their members include a regular Newsletter 'British Bus News', the chance to contact others with similar interests and the ability to share information on vehicle restoration problems, projects and, of course, sources of spare parts. Membership costs is £13 per annum and the BBPG may be contacted at the address below.

British Bus Preservation Group

Contact address: BBPG, 25 Oldfield Road, Bexley Heath, Kent DA7 4DX.
E-mail: info@bbpg.co.uk
Web site: www.bbpg.co.uk
Affiliation: NARTM

Registration	Date	Chassis	Body	New to	Fleet No	Status
PY 6170	1926	Morris Commercial Z 15.9hp	Ch16	Robinsons of Scarborough		R
DB 5221	1929	Tilling Stevens B10A		North Western Road Car Co		A
FM 6397	1931	Leyland Titan TD1	Leyland L51R	Crosville Motor Services	45	RP
FM 6435	1931	Leyland Lion LT2	Leyland B32F	Crosville Motor Services	L7	RP
MV 8996	1931	Bedford WLB	Duple B20F	Howards of West Byfleet		R
BU 7108	1932	Leyland Titan TD2	Massey H-/-R	Oldham Corporation	69	RP
FM 7443	1932	Leyland Cub KP2	Brush B20F	Crosville Motor Services	716	RP
AOG 638	1934	Daimler COG5		Birmingham City Transport	51	RP
AUF 670	1934	Leyland Titan TD3	East Lancs H26/26R	Southdown Motor Services	970	R
DL 9015	1934	Dennis Ace	Harrington B20F	Southern Vectis Omnibus Co	405	RP
JA 5506	1935	Dennis Lancet	Eastern Counties B31R	North Western Road Car Co	706	RP
CCD 940	1936	Leyland Titan TD4	East Lancs H28/26R	Southdown Motor Services	140	A
FM 9984	1936	Leyland Tiger TS7	Harrington C32F	Crosville Motor Services	K101	RP
JA 5528	1936	Bristol JO5G	Brush B31R	North Western Road Car Co	728	RP
BFM 144	1937	Leyland Tiger TS7	ECW B32F	Crosville Motor Services	KA27	R
EUF 181	1938	Leyland Titan TD5		Southdown Motor Services	0181	RP
FHT 112	1938	Bristol K5G	ECW O30/26R	Bristol Tramways	C3209	RP
JA 7770	1938	Bristol L5G	Burlingham B35R	North Western Road Car Co	346	RP
FUF 181	1939	Dennis Falcon	Harrington B30C	Southdown Motor Services	81	A
JK 8418	1939	Leyland Lion LT9	Leyland B32F	Eastbourne Corporation	12	R
EFM 581	1940	Leyland Tiger TS8	ECW B32F	Crosville Motor Services	KA158	RP
EVC 244	1940	Daimler COG5/40	Park Royal B38F	Coventry City Transport	244	R
FNY 933	1944	Bristol K6A	Park Royal H30/26R	Pontypridd UDC	40	RP
HHA 26	1945	Guy Arab II	Weymann UH30/26R	BMMO ('Midland Red')	2574	RP
HKE 867	1945	Bristol K6A	Weymann H30/26R	Maidstone & District Motor Services	DH159	R
HKL 826	1946	AEC Regal I 0662	Beadle OB35F	Maidstone & District Motor Services	OR2	R
ACH 627	1947	Daimler CVD6	Brush H30/26R	Derby Corporation	27	RP
ANH 154	1947	Daimler CVG6	Northern Coachbuilders H30/26R	Northampton Corporation	154	R
CUH 856	1947	Leyland Tiger PS1	ECW B35R	Western Welsh Omnibus Co	856	RP
GOE 486	1947	Daimler CVA6	MCW H30/24R	Birmingham City Transport	1486	R
HLW 214	1947	AEC Regent III 0961 RT	Park Royal H30/26RD	London Transport	RT277	R

Registration	Date	Chassis	Body	New to	Fleet No	Status
HTC 661	1947	Bedford OB	Scottish Motor Traction C29F	Dean & Pounder of Morecombe		R
JDV 754	1947	Bedford OB	Duple C29F	Woolacombe & Mortehoe		R
ENT 778	1948	Leyland Tiger PS1	Burlingham C33F	Gittins of Crickheath		R
JXN 46	1948	AEC Regent III O961 RT	Weymann H30/26R	London Transport	RT1018	R
KHA 311	1948	BMMO C1	Duple C30C	BMMO ('Midland Red')	3311	R
KNN 254	1948	Leyland Titan PD1A	Duple L29/26F	Barton Transport of Chilwell	580	RP
LFM 320	1949	Leyland Tiger PS1/1	Weymann B35F	Crosville Motor Services	KA244	R
LHY 937	1949	Bristol K6B	ECW H31/28R	Bristol Tramways	3774	RP
LUC 250	1949	Leyland Titan 7RT	(chassis only)	London Transport	RTL1073	RP
HWY 36	1950	Leyland Titan PD2/1	Leyland L27/26R	Todmorden Joint Omnibus Committee	18	RP
JOJ 231	1950	Leyland Tiger PS2	Weymann B34F	Birmingham City Transport	2231	R
JOJ 827	1950	Daimler CVG6	Crossley H30/25R	Birmingham City Transport	2827	RP
JXX 487	1950	Bedford OB	Duple B30F	Ministry of Supply		A
KEL 405	1950	Bristol LL6B	ECW FB37F	Hants & Dorset Motor Services	677	R
KNG 711	1950	Bristol L5G	ECW B35R	Eastern Counties Omnibus Co	LL711	RP
KYY 529	1950	AEC Regent III O961 RT	Park Royal H30/26RD	London Transport	RT1702	R
KYY 615	1950	AEC Regent III O961 RT	Park Royal H30/26R	London Transport	RT1777	RP
KYY 647	1950	Leyland Titan 7RT	H30/26R	London Transport	RTL1004	R
DMS 130	1951	AEC Regal III	Alexander C35F	W Alexander & Sons	A104	RP
FFN 446	1951	Beadle-Leyland	Beadle C35F	East Kent Road Car Co		RP
HDL 280	1951	Bristol LL5G	ECW B39R	Southern Vectis Omnibus Co	39	RP
JOJ 207	1951	Daimler CVD6		Birmingham City Transport	2707	RP
LUC 381	1951	AEC Regal IV 9821E	ECW C39F	London Transport	RFW6	RP
LYF 104	1951	Leyland Titan 7RT	Park Royal H30/26R	London Transport	RTL1163	R
LYF 316	1951	AEC Regent III O961 RT	Park Royal H30/26R	London Transport	RT2591	R
MFM 39	1951	Bedford OB	Duple C29F	Crosville Motor Services	SL71	A
RSK 615	1951	Leyland Royal Tiger PSU1/15	Duple DP41F	Jackson of Castle Bromwich		A
URE 281	1951	AEC Regal III	Harrington FC33F	Lymers of Tean		R
LTX 311	1952	Leyland Tiger PS2/5	Massey B35F	Caerphilly Corporation	1	RP
MLL 555	1952	AEC Regal IV 9821LT RF	Metro Cammell B37F	London Transport	RF168	RP
MLL 722	1952	AEC Regal IV 9822E	Park Royal RDP—C	British European Airways	1080	A
NLE 534	1952	AEC Regal IV 9821LT RF	Metro Cammell B39F	London Transport	RF534	R
JDL 40	1953	Bristol KSW5G	ECW L-/-RD	Southern Vectis Omnibus Co	766	A
LWR 424	1953	Bristol KSW6G	ECW -	West Yorkshire Road Car Co	4044	R
MXX 283	1953	AEC Regal IV 9821LT RF	Metro Cammell B41F	London Transport	RF395	RP
MXX 292	1953	AEC Regal IV 9821LT RF	Metro Cammell	London Transport	RF404	RP
MXX 421	1953	AEC Regal IV 9821LT RF	Metro Cammell B39F	London Transport	RF444	R
NLE 673	1953	AEC Regal IV 9821LT RF	Metro Cammell B39F	London Transport	RF673	R
NXL 847	1953	AEC Regal III	Duple C39F	Eastern Belle of Bow		R
NXL 847	1953	AEC Regal III	Duple C39F	Eastern Belle of Bow		R
RAL 795	1954	Daimler CVG6	Massey H33/28RD	Gash of Newark	DD10	RP
UAS 954	1954	GMC PD4501 Scenicruiser	GMC RC43F	Greyhound	T902	RP
395 DEL	1955	Albion Victor	Heaver B35F	Guernsey Motor Co	71	RP
JVH 381	1955	AEC Regent III 9613E	East Lancs H35/28R	Huddersfield Corporation	181	A
MDL 954	1956	Bristol Lodekka LD6G	ECW O33/27R	Southern Vectis Omnibus Co	544	A
WUA 832	1956	AEC Regent V MD2RA	Roe H33/27R	Leeds City Transport	832	A
783 EFM	1957	Bristol SC4LK	ECW B35F	Crosville Motor Services	SC13	R
LSV 748	1957	Albion Victor FT39AN	Heaver B31F	Guernsey Motor Co	73	RP
XCV 326	1957	Bedford SBG	Duple B42F	Harper & Kellow of St Agnes		A
390 DKK	1958	AEC Reliance 2MU3RV	Harrington DP40F	Maidstone & District Motor Services	CO390	RP
TAX 235	1958	Bristol Lodekka LD6G	ECW H33/27RD	Red & White Services	L358	RP
UNB 524	1958	Leyland Titan PD2/40	Metro Cammell H37/28R	Manchester Corporation	3524	R
VFJ 995	1958	Leyland Titan PD2/40	Weymann H31/26R	Exeter Corporation	60	R w/ 2.10.14
120 JRB	1959	Daimler Freeline D650HS	Burlingham C37F	Tailby & George ('Blue Bus Services', Willington)		A
129 DPT	1959	AEC Reliance 2MU3RA	Plaxton C41F	OK Motor Services		RP
3014 AH	1959	Bristol MW5G	ECW B45F	Eastern Counties Omnibus Co	LL452	RP
654 BUP	1959	Leyland Tiger Cub PSUC1/2	Plaxton C37F	Wilkinson Bros of Sedgefield	54	RP
FRE 699A	1959	Bristol SC4LK	ECW B35F	Eastern Counties Omnibus Co	LC556	RP

Registration	Date	Chassis	Body	New to	Fleet No	Status
314 PFM	1960	Bristol Lodekka FS6G	ECW H60R	Crosville Motor Services	DFG33	R
999 PPL	1960	Bedford J4LZ2	Plaxton C29F	Comfy Coaches of Farnham		RP
VLT 196	1960	AEC Routemaster R2RH	Park Royal H36/28R	London Transport	RM196	R
VLT 250	1960	AEC Routemaster R2RH	Park Royal H36/28R	London Transport	RM244	RP
314 DBM	1961	Ford Yeoman	Duple C41F	Travel House of Dunstable		R
8124 WX	1961	Bristol MW6G	ECW C39F	West Yorkshire Road Car Co	CUG27	R
WKG 284	1961	AEC Reliance 2MU3RA	Willowbrook DP41F	Western Welsh Omnibus Co	1284	R
WLT 765	1961	AEC Routemaster R2RH	Park Royal H36/28R	London Transport	RM 765	RP
XKO 72A	1961	Leyland Atlantean PDR1/1 Mk II	Metro Cammell O44/33F	Maidstone & District Motor Services	DH572	RP
811 BWR	1962	Bristol SUL4A	ECW B36F	West Yorkshire Road Car Co	SMA5	R
NAT 766A	1962	Daimler CVG6-30	Roe H39/31F	Grimsby - Cleethorpes Transport	57	R
RCK 920	1962	Leyland Titan PD3/5	Metro Cammell FH41/31F	Ribble Motor Services	1775	RP
3747 RH	1963	AEC Bridgemaster 2B3RA	Park Royal H43/29F	East Yorkshire Motor Services	747	RP
AMX 8A	1963	AEC Reliance 2U3RA	Harrington C51F	Valliant of Ealing		RP
ALM 37B	1964	AEC Routemaster R2RH	Park Royal H36/28R	London Transport	RM2037	RP
BCH 156B	1964	Daimler CVG6	Roe H37/28R	Derby Corporation	156	A
BDL 583B	1964	Bristol Lodekka FLF6G	ECW H38/32F	Southern Vectis Omnibus Co	70	A
BKG 713B	1964	AEC Renown 3B3RA	Northern Counties H38/29F	Western Welsh Omnibus Co	713	RP
TFA 987	1964	Daimler CCG5	Massey H33/28R	Burton upon Trent Corporation	87	R
WOW 993T	1964	Leyland Titan PD3/4	Northern Counties FCO39/30F	Southdown Motor Services	423	RP
BED 732C	1965	Leyland Titan PD2/40	East Lancs H34/30F	Warrington Corporation	51	RP
BOW 503C	1965	AEC Regent V 2D3RA	East Lancs Neepsend H37/29R	Southampton Corporation	366	RP
BUF 272C	1965	Leyland Titan PD3/4	Northern Counties FH39/30F	Southdown Motor Services	272	RP
CTT 774C	1965	Bedford VAS1	Duple C29F	Heard of Bideford		RP
CUV 116C	1965	AEC Routemaster	Park Royal H36/28R	London Transport	RM2116	R
EKP 234C	1965	Leyland Atlantean PDR1/1	Massey H—/—F	Maidstone Borough Council	34	RP
FDB 328C	1965	Leyland Titan PD2/40	East Lancs H36/28R	Stockport Corporation	28	RP
FDB 334C	1965	Leyland Titan PD2/40	East Lancs H36/28R	Stockport Corporation	34	R
FPT 590C	1965	AEC Routemaster 3R2RH	Park Royal H41/31F	Northern General Transport Co	2120	R
CHB 407D	1966	Leyland Titan PD3/4	East Lancs H41/29F	Merthyr Tydfil Transport	142	RP
EDV 505D	1966	Bristol MW6G	ECW C39F	Western National Omnibus Co (Royal Blue)	1423	RP
GEE 418D	1966	Daimler Fleetline SRG6LW	Willowbrook B42D	Grimsby - Cleethorpes Transport	35	R
HAD 915D	1966	Bedford VAM5	Plaxton C45F	Princess Mary Coaches		RP
HHW 452D	1966	Bristol MW5G	ECW B45F	Bristol Omnibus Co	2636	RP
JJD 499D	1966	AEC Routemaster R2RH/1	Park Royal H40/32R	London Transport	RML2499	RP
JJD 539D	1966	AEC Routemaster R2RH/1	Park Royal H40/32R	London Transport	RML2539	RP
HDV 638E	1967	Bristol MW6G	ECW C39F	Western National Omnibus Co (Royal Blue)	1433	RP
LAX 101E	1967	Bristol RESL6L	ECW B46F	Red & White Services	RS167	R
NDM 950E	1967	Bedford VAM14	Duple Midland DP45F	Phillips of Holywell		A
SMK 676F	1967	AEC Routemaster R2RH/1	Park Royal H40/32R	London Transport	RML2676	RP
SMK 716F	1968	AEC Routemaster R2RH/1	Park Royal H40/32R	London Transport	RML2716	RP
SMK 747F	1967	AEC Routemaster R2RH/1	Park Royal H40/32R	London Transport	RML2747	A
JVV 267G	1968	Daimler CVG6	Roe H33/26R	Northampton Corporation	267	RP
PYM 108F	1968	AEC Reliance 6MU3R	Plaxton C30C	Glenton Tours of London		R
STH 100F	1968	Bedford VAM14		Davies of Pencader		RP
YNU 351G	1968	Bristol Lodekka FLF6G	ECW H38/32F	Midland General Omnibus Co	313	R
MJA 895G	1969	Leyland Titan PD3/14	East Lancs H38/32F	Stockport Corporation	95	RP
SVF 896G	1969	Bristol RELH6G	ECW C47F	Eastern Counties Omnibus Co	RE896	RP
UTG 313G	1969	AEC Regent V 2MD3RA	Willowbrook H34/26F	Pontypridd UDC	8	RP
WYP 203G	1969	AEC Reliance 6MU3R	Plaxton C41F	Surrey Motors of Sutton		R
XCH 425G	1969	Daimler Fleetline CRG6LX	Roe H44/34F	Derby Corporation	225	A
PKW 434J	1970	Daimler Fleetline	Alexander H42/28D	Bradford City Transport	434	A
IJI 5367	1971	Bristol RELH6L	Plaxton C49F	Greenslades Tours of Exeter	300	RP
STL 725J	1971	Bedford YRQ	Willowbrook DP43F	Simmonds of Great Gonnerby		RP
TRU 947J	1971	Bristol RELL6G	ECW DP50F	Wilts & Dorset Motor Services	846	R
VOD 123K	1971	Bristol LHS6L	Marshall B33F	Western National Omnibus Co	1253	RP

Registration	Date	Chassis	Body	New to	Fleet No	Status
XRD 23K	1971	Bristol VRTLL6LX	Northern Counties H47/30D	Reading Corporation	23	R
CRU 301L	1972	Bristol VRTLL6LX	ECW H43/31F	Hants & Dorset Motor Services	3301	RP
GBB 516K	1972	Leyland Atlantean PDR2/1	Alexander H48/30F	Tyneside PTE	680	RP
HOR 413L	1972	Leyland National 1151/2R/0403	Leyland National B44D	Gosport & Fareham Omnibus Co	13	RP
JMC 123K	1972	AEC Reliance 6MU4R	Plaxton C34F	Glenton Tours of London	123	RP
NPD 108L	1972	Leyland National 1151/2R/0402	Leyland National B18D	London Country Bus Services	LN8	R
RWC 637K	1972	Bedford		Harris of Grays		RP
TDL 566K	1972	Bristol RELL6G	ECW B53F	Southern Vectis Omnibus Co	866	A
TSP 939K	1972	Leyland Leopard PSU4B/4R	Plaxton C45F	Rennie of Dunfermline		RP
YFM 269L	1972	Bristol RELL6G	ECW DP50F	Crosville Motor Services	ERG269	RP
BPT 672L	1973	Leyland Leopard PSU3B4R	Plaxton C53F	Trimdon Motor Services		RP
HKE 680L	1973	Bristol VRTSL6LX	ECW H43/29F	Maidstone & District Motor Services	680	A
NCD 559M	1973	Bristol VRTSL6LX	ECW PO43/31F	Southdown Motor Services	559	RP
NPD 128L	1973	Leyland National 1151/1R/0402	Leyland National B28F	London Country Bus Services	LNC28	R
OCH 261L	1973	Daimler Fleetline CRG6LX	Roe H44/34F	Derby Corporation	261	RP
OWC 720M	1973	Bristol RELL6L	ECW B53F	Colchester Corporation	20	RP
PKG 587M	1973	Bristol VRTSL6LX	ECW	Cardiff Corporation	587	RP
TGY 102M	1973	Leyland National	Leyland National	London Transport	LS2	A
THM 515M	1973	Daimler Fleetline CRL6	MCW/LT	London Transport	DMS1515	A
THM 712M	1973	Daimler Fleetline CRL6	MCW H44/27D	London Transport	DM1712	RP
GLJ 467N	1974	Bristol VRTSL2/6LXB	ECW H43/31F	Hants & Dorset Motor Services	3315	R
GUG 547N	1974	Leyland Atlantean AN68/1R		West Yorkshire PTE		R
HPK 503N	1974	Leyland National 11351/1R	Leyland National B49F	Alder Valley	201	RP
JUS 774N	1974	Leyland Atlantean PDR1/1	Alexander	Greater Glasgow PTE	LA927	RP
PKH 600M	1974	Bedford VAS	Plaxton C29F	Hull City Football Club		R
RPU 869M	1974	Bristol RELH6G	ECW DP49F	Eastern Counties Omnibus Co	RE849	RP
UMO 180N	1974	Leyland National 11351/1R	Leyland National B49F	Alder Valley	180	R
WPG 217M	1974	Leyland National 10351/1R/SC	Leyland National DP39F	London Country Bus Services	SNC117	A
GPD 318N	1975	Bristol LHS6L	ECW B35F	London Country Bus Services	BN50	RP
JAJ 296N	1975	Bristol RELL6L	ECW B46D	Hartlepool Corporation	96	RP
KDW 347P	1975	Leyland National 11351/1R/SC	Leyland National DP48F	Western Welsh Omnibus Co	ND3975	RP
KDW 362P	1975	Leyland National 11351/1R/SC	Leyland National DP48F	Western Welsh Omnibus Co	ND5475	RP
KPA 369P	1975	Leyland National	Leyland National B49F	Alder Valley	218	RP
KJD 507P	1976	Leyland National 11351A/2R	Leyland National DP36D	London Transport	LS7	A
KOU 795P	1976	Bristol VRTSL3/6LXB	ECW H39/31F	Bristol Omnibus Co	5509	A
LDV 176P	1976	Leyland Leopard PSU3C/4R	Plaxton C47F	Western National Omnibus Co	2436	RP
LWB 377P	1976	Ailsa B55-10	Van Hool McArdle H44/31D	South Yorkshire PTE	377	RP
NDP 31R	1976	Bristol VRTLL3/6LXB	Northern Counties H47/29D	Reading Transport	31	RP
NDP 38R	1976	Bristol VRTLL3/6LXB	Northern Counties H47/29D	Reading Transport	38	RP
NEL 119P	1976	Bristol VRTSL3/501	ECW CH41/29F	Hants & Dorset Motor Services	3345	RP
NOE 576R	1976	Leyland National 11351A/1R	Leyland National	Midland Red Omnibus Co	576	A
NWO 462R	1976	Leyland National 11351A/1R	Leyland National DP48F	Western Welsh Omnibus Co	ND1776	A
UGR 698R	1976	Bristol VRTSL3/6LXB	ECW H43/31F	United Automobile Services	698	RP
OJD 357R	1977	Leyland Fleetline FE30ALR	Park Royal H44/24D	London Transport	DMS2357	RP
RJT 146R	1977	Leyland National 11351A/1R	Leyland National B49F	Hants & Dorset Motor Services	3698	RP
AYJ 100T	1978	Leyland National 11351A/1R	Leyland National B52F	Southdown Motor Services	100	RP
THX 220S	1978	Leyland National 10351A/1R	Leyland National B36D	London Transport	LS220	RP
THX 580S	1978	Leyland Fleetline FE30ALR	MCW H44/27D	London Transport	DM2580	RP
VDV 107S	1978	Bristol LH6L	ECW B43F	Western National (Devon General)	127	RP
WKO 132S	1978	Bristol VRTSL3/6LXB	ECW H43/31F	Maidstone & District Motor Services	5132	RP
WKO 138S	1978	Bristol VRTSL3/6LXB	ECW H43/31F	Maidstone & District Motor Services	5138	RP
WUH 173T	1978	Leyland National 11351A/1R	Leyland National B52F	National Welsh Omnibus Services	N2978	A
YRC 420T	1978	AEC Reliance 6U3ZR	Plaxton C48FL	Silver Line Coaches		
AYR 300T	1979	Leyland National 10351A/2R	Leyland National B36D	London Transport	LS300	RP

Registration	Date	Chassis	Body	New to	Fleet No	Status
BUH 239V	1979	Leyland National 2 NL106L11/1R	Leyland National B44F	National Welsh Omnibus Services	NS8011	A
EPD 511V	1979	Leyland National 10351B/1R	Leyland National B41F	London Country Bus Services	SNB511	A
EPD 543V	1979	Leyland National 10351B/1R	Leyland National B41F	London Country Bus Services	SNB543	A
FDV 827V	1979	Leyland National 2 NL116L11/1R	Leyland National B50F	Devon General		RP
FVM 191V	1979	Bedford CF		Shearings of Altrincham		RP
GSU 866T	1979	Leyland Leopard PSU3C/3R	Alexander (Belfast) B53F	Central SMT Co	T384	RP
HIL 7081	1979	Bedford CFL	Plaxton C17F	Golden Miller of Feltham		R
LSU 381V	1979	Leyland Atlantean AN68A/1R	Alexander H45/33F	Strathclyde PTE	LA1324	RP
WDA 986T	1979	Leyland Fleetline FE30AGR	MCW H43/33F	West Midlands PTE	6986	R
YPL 433T	1979	Leyland National 10351B/1R	Leyland National B41F	London Country Bus Services	SNB433	R
AFB 593V	1980	Bristol LH6L	ECW B43F	Bristol Omnibus Co	462	A
AUP 369W	1980	Leyland Atlantean AN68B/1R	Roe H43/30F	Northern General Transport Co	3469	RP
HFG 923V	1980	Leyland National 2 NL116L11/1R	Leyland National B52F	Southdown Motor Services	123	R
SNS 823W	1980	Leyland National 2 NL116L11/1R	Leyland National B52F	Central SMT Co	N37	A
JCK 852W	1981	Leyland National	Leyland National B41F	Ribble Motor Services	252	RP
PUA 310W	1981	Leyland Atlantean AN68C/1R	Roe H43/32F	West Yorkshire PTE		A
RNE 692W	1981	Bedford CF	Plaxton C17F	Shearings of Altrincham		R
OCW 8X	1981	Leyland Atlantean AN68C/1R	East Lancs H43/31F	Blackburn Borough Transport	8	R
AXI 2534	1982	Bristol RELL6G	Alexander (Belfast) B39F	Citybus	2534	A
UKE 830X	1982	Leyland Leopard PSU3G/4R	ECW C49F	East Kent Road Car Co	8830	A
XFG 25Y	1983	Leyland National 2 NL116HLXB/1R	Leyland National B49F	Brighton Borough Transport	25	RP
A537 TYW	1983	Dodge G08	Wadham Stringer	British Rail		RP
VCO 802	1983	Leyland Tiger TRCTL11/3R	Plaxton C53F	East Kent Road Car Co	8840	R
C41 HDT	1985	Dennis Domino SDA1202	Optare B33F	South Yorkshire PTE	41	RP
C46 HDT	1985	Dennis Domino SDA1202	Optare B33F	South Yorkshire PTE	46	RP
C832 KNK	1986	Bedford CF	Martyn Walker	Regency Cars		RP
D825 PUK	1986	Freight Rover Sherpa	Carlyle B20F	United Transport Buses	032	R
E523 TOV	1999	Iveco 49-10	Carlyle B21F	Carlyle demonstrator		RP

Notes:

AOG 638	Converted to lorry
CCD 940	Originally Beadle L26/26R; rebodied 1950
EUF 181	Coverted to recovery vehicle
HKE 867	Rebodied 1953
LHY 937	Renumbered 1541 in 1964
KYY 615	Previously a training bus
RSK 615	Originally registered LOE 300
FFN 446	Chassis parts from 1938 Leyland TD5
LWR 424	Originally bus 858 (later DGW4); converted to a towing vehicle and renumbered 4044 in 1972
UAS 954	Originally registered in USA
395 DEL	Guernsey registration was 2027
LSV 748	Guernsey registration was 4029
FRE 699A	Originally registered 3003 AH
NAT 766A	Originally registered TJV 100
WOW 993T	Originally registered 423 DCD
WYP 203G	Rebodied 1974
IJI 5367	Originally registered UFJ 229J
THM 515M	Rebuilt as 'Supercar' publicity vehicle
HIL 7081	Originally registered DJF 631T
JCK 852W	Prototype National Greenway conversion
VCO 802	Originally registered FKK 840Y

Right: Originally registered MDL 952, former Southern Vectis Bristol Lodekka 501 (BAS 563) stands outside the depot of the Quantock Heritage collection at Wiveliscombe. *Philip Lamb*

Part 4

Heritage Bus Services

Blue Triangle
Rainham

Contact address: Unit 3C, Denver Industrial Estate, Ferry Lane, Rainham, Essex, RM13 7MD.
Phone: 01708 631001
Operations planned for 2006: Scheduled heritage services not finalised at time of publication, but vehicles frequently appear on rail replacement services.

Registration	Date	Chassis	Body	New to	Fleet No	Status
HLW 178	1947	AEC Regent III O961 RT	Weymann H30/26R	London Transport	RT191	R
KGK 959	1949	AEC Regent III O961 RT	Weymann H30/26R	London Transport	RT2150	
KXW 171	1950	AEC Regent III O961 RT	Saunders Roe H30/26R	London Transport	RT3062	R
LLU 670	1950	AEC Regent III O961 RT	Park Royal H30/26R	London Transport	RT3871	R
LYR 854	1950	AEC Regent III O961 RT	Weymann O30/26R	London Transport	RT3435	R
LYR 969	1952	AEC Regent III O961 RT	Weymann H30/26R	London Transport	RT2799	
MXX 289	1952	AEC Regal IV 9821LT RF	Metro Cammell B39F	London Transport	RF401	
VLT 268	1960	AEC Routemaster R2RH	Park Royal H36/28R	London Transport	RM268	RP
VLT 298	1960	AEC Routemaster R2RH	Park Royal H36/28R	London Transport	RM298	R
WLT 900	1961	AEC Routemaster R2RH/1	Park Royal H36/28R	London Transport	RML900	R
CUV 260C	1965	AEC Routemaster R2RH/1	Park Royal H36/29RD	London Transport	RCL2260	R

Notes:
LYR 854   Converted to open top following de-roofing in 1976

Buckland Omnibus Co
Woodbridge

Contact address: Wayside, The Street, Bredfield, Woodbridge, IP13 6AX.
Phone: 01394 380125
E-mail: ajb@bucklandbuses.co.uk
Web site: www.bucklandbuses.co.uk
Operations planned for 2006: Vehicles available for private hire. Occasional special Felixstowe sea front service — phone for details.

Registration	Date	Chassis	Body	New to	Fleet No	Status
TE 7870	1929	Dennis ES	Brush B29D	Accrington Corporation	57	R
GRP 260D	1966	Bristol MW6G	ECW C39F	United Counties Omnibus Co	260	R
KUL 331D	1966	Bedford VAS2	Willowbrook B29F	Greater London Council	331	A

Notes:
TE 7870   Body rebuilt 1974 by Wyatt

Carmel Coaches
Okehampton

Contact address: Mr A. G. Hazell, Northlew, Okehampton, Devon.
Phone: 01409 221237
Operations planned for 2006: LOD 495 will operate on Dartmoor Rover Network. Please enquire for details.
Sundays and Bank Holidays, May to September.

Registration	Date	Chassis	Body	New to	Fleet No	Status
LOD 495	1950	Albion Victor FT39N	Duple C31F	Way of Crediton		R ✓ 2.9.11
MTT 640	1951	Leyland Titan PD2/1	Leyland L27/26R	Devon General	DL640	R

Cosy Coaches
Killamarsh

Contact address: Cosy Coach Tours, 5 Meynell Way, Killamarsh, Derbyshire, S21 1HG.
Phone: 0114 248 9139
Operations planned for 2006: Please telephone for details.

Registration	Date	Chassis	Body	New to	Fleet No	Status
ATS 408	1948	Bedford OB	Duple C29F	James Mefflan of Kirriemuir		R
MRB 765	1949	Bedford OB	Duple C29F	H D Andrew of Tideswell		RP
CCB 300	1950	Albion Victor FT39N	Duple C31F	Cronshaw of Blackburn		A
ERG 164	1950	Bedford OB	Duple C29F	Paterson of Aberdeen		RP
TDT 344	1955	AEC Regent V MD3RV	Roe H34/28R	Doncaster Corporation	144	RP
YBD 201	1961	Bristol MW6G	ECW C34F	United Counties Omnibus Co	201	A

Cumbria Classic Coaches
Kirkby Stephen

Contact address: Bowber Head, Ravenstonedale, Kirkby Stephen, Cumbria, CA17 4NL.
Phone: 015396 23254
Website: www.cumbriaclassiccoaches.co.uk
E-mail: coaches@cumbriaclassiccoaches.co.uk
Operations planned for 2006: Route 569: Ravenstonedale–Kirkby Stephen–Hawes, Tues (Hawes market day) Easter to October.
Kendal Clipper (circular tour of Kendal), half-hourly, seven days a week during School Summer Holidays. Route 570: Hawes to Ribblehead
viaduct Tuesdays Easter to October

Registration	Date	Chassis	Body	New to	Fleet No	Status
TB 749	1948	AEC Regal III O962	Burlingham C33F	Florence Motors of Morcambe		R
CRN 80	1949	Leyland Tiger PS1	East Lancs B34R	Preston Corporation	75	R
TSK 736	1949	Commer Commando	Scottish Aviation C29F	David Lawson	C8	RP
CWG 286	1950	Leyland Tiger PS1/1	Alexander C35F	W Alexander & Sons (Northern)	PA184	R
MTJ 84	1951	Guy Arab III	Roe C31F	Lancashire United Transport	440	R
JPY 985	1953	Commer Avenger I	Plaxton C29F	Heather Coaches of Robin Hood Bay		R
627 HFM	1959	Bristol Lodekka LD6G	ECW CO33/27RD	Crosville Motor Services	DLB978	R

Notes:

TSK 736	Original registration CMS 9. To be returned to original colours.
JPY 985	Converted to LPG/Petrol

MacTours & Majestic Tour
Edinburgh

Contact address: Edinburgh Vintage Bus Company, 11A James Court, Lawnmarket, Edinburgh EH1 2PB.
Phone: 0131 477 4771
Operations planned for 2006: Hop-on, hop-off open-top tours of Edinburgh operate seven days a week, most of the year.

Registration	Date	Chassis	Body	New to	Fleet No	Status
YSL 334	1951	Leyland Tiger PS1	Guernseybus OB34F	Jersey Motor Transport Co	44	
LST 873	1958	Leyland Titan PD2/40	Park Royal O27/26RO	Barrow in Furness Corporation	165	
JSJ 746	1959	AEC Routemaster R2RH	Park Royal O75R	London Transport	RM90	
JSJ 747	1959	AEC Routemaster R2RH	Park Royal O75R	London Transport	RM84	
JSJ 748	1959	AEC Routemaster R2RH	Park Royal O75R	London Transport	RM80	
JSJ 749	1959	AEC Routemaster R2RH	Park Royal O76R	London Transport	RM94	
WLT 371	1959	AEC Routemaster R2RH	Park Royal O63R	London Transport	RM371	
VLT 143	1960	AEC Routemaster R2RH	Park Royal O75R	London Transport	RM143	
VLT 163	1960	AEC Routemaster R2RH	Park Royal O75R	London Transport	RM163	
VLT 235	1960	AEC Routemaster R2RH	Park Royal O75R	London Transport	RM235	
VLT 237	1960	AEC Routemaster R2RH	Park Royal O75R	London Transport	RM237	
VLT 242	1960	AEC Routemaster R2RH	Park Royal O71R	London Transport	RM242	
VLT 281	1960	AEC Routemaster R2RH	Park Royal O71R	London Transport	RM281	
858 DYE	1961	AEC Routemaster R2RH	Park Royal O63R	London Transport	RM727	
485 CLT	1962	AEC Routemaster R2RH	Park Royal O57R	London Transport	RMC1485	
803 DYE	1962	AEC Routemaster R2RH	Park Royal O63R	London Transport	RM1010	
CUV 203C	1965	AEC Routemaster R2RH	Park Royal H36/28R	London Transport	RM2203	
CUV 210C	1965	AEC Routemaster R2RH	Park Royal O63R	London Transport	RM2210	
CUV 241C	1965	AEC Routemaster R2RH/1	Park Royal H64RD	London Transport	RCL2241	
CUV 248C	1965	AEC Routemaster R2RH/1	Park Royal H64RD	London Transport	RCL2248	
NMY 634E	1967	AEC Routemaster R2RH/2	Park Royal H32/24F	British European Airways	8241	
NMY 646E	1967	AEC Routemaster R2RH/2	Park Royal H56F	British European Airways	8253	
OSJ 636R	1977	Leyland Leopard PSU3C/3R	Alexander OB49F	Western SMT Co	L2636	

Notes:

YSL 334	Originally registered J 5567 and fitted with Reading B34F body
LST 873	Originally registered CEO 952
JSJ 748	Originally registered VLT 80. Extended and converted to open-top
JSJ 746	Originally registered VLT 90. Extended and converted to open-top
JSJ 749	Originally registered VLT 94. Extended and converted to open-top
JSJ 747	Originally registered VLT 84. Extended and converted to open-top
WLT 371	Converted to open-top
VLT 242	Extended and converted to open-top
VLT 237	Extended and converted to open-top
VLT 235	Extended and converted to open-top
VLT 281	Extended and converted to open-top
VLT 163	Extended and converted to open-top
VLT 143	Extended and converted to open-top
858 DYE	Originally registered WLT 727. Converted to open-top
803 DYE	Originally registered 10 CLT. Converted to open-top
CUV 210C	Converted to open-top
NMY 634E	Passed to London Transport (RMA50) in 1979; acquired by Stagecoach at Perth in 1987
NMY 646E	Passed to London Transport (RMA9) in 1979
OSJ 636R	Converted to open-top

Memory Lane Vintage Omnibus Services
Maidenhead

Contact address: 78 Lillibrooke Crescent, Maidenhead, Berkshire, SL6 3XQ.
Phone: 01628 825050
Fax: 01628 825851
E-mail: info@memorylane.co.uk
Web site: www.memorylane.co.uk

Registration	Date	Chassis	Body	New to	Fleet No	Status
KGU 290	1949	AEC Regent III O961 RT	Weymann H30/26R	London Transport	RT1530	RP
KYY 628	1950	AEC Regent III O961 RT	Park Royal H30/26R	London Transport	RT1790	R
LYF 377	1951	AEC Regal IV 9821LT RF	Metro Cammell B37F	London Transport	RF26	R
NLE 643	1953	AEC Regal IV 9821LT RF	Metro Cammell B39F	London Transport	RF643	RP
617 DDV	1960	Bristol MW6G	ECW C39F	Southern National Omnibus Co (Royal Blue)	2250	R
VLT 216	1960	AEC Routemaster R2RH	Park Royal H36/28R	London Transport	RM216	R
253 KTA	1962	Bristol MW6G	ECW C39F	Western National Omnibus Co (Royal Blue)	2270	

Quantock Heritage
Wiveliscombe

Contact address: Bishop's Lydeard, Somerset.
Phone: 01823 251140
Affiliations: NARTM
Operations planned for 2006: Please telephone for details

Registration	Date	Chassis	Body	New to	Fleet No	Status
JG 9938	1937	Leyland Tiger TS8	Park Royal C32R	East Kent Road Car Co		R
AJA 132	1938	Bristol L5G	Burlingham B35R	North Western Road Car Co	372	R
CCX 999	1945	Daimler CWA6	Duple L27/26R	Huddersfield Joint Omnibus Committee		RP
EMW 893	1947	Daimler CVD6	Park Royal B35C	Swindon Corporation	57	A
HUO 510	1947	AEC Regal I O662	Weymann B35F	Devon General	SR510	A
JUO 992	1947	Leyland Titan PD1	ECW L27/26R	Southern National Omnibus Co	2932	A
ACH 441	1948	AEC Regal III	Windover C32F	Trent Motor Traction Co	611	R
JFM 575	1948	AEC Regal III	Strachan B35R	Crosville Motor Services		RP
JNN 384	1948	Leyland Titan PD1	Duple L29/26F	Barton Transport of Chilwell	467	A
JTE 546	1948	AEC Regent III 6811A	Park Royal H33/26R	Morecambe & Heysham Corporation	20	R
JLJ 402	1949	Leyland Tiger PS2/3	Burlingham FDP35F	Bournemouth Corporation	45	R
KTF 594	1949	AEC Regent III 9621E	Park Royal O33/26R	Morecambe & Heysham Corporation	65	R
LJH 665	1949	Dennis Lancet J3	Duple C35F	Lee of Barnet		RP
GWN 432	1950	Dennis Lancet J3	Thurgood FC37F	Super of Tottenham		R
JFJ 875	1950	Daimler CVD6	Weymann B35F	Exeter Corporation	75	R
KEL 131	1950	Leyland Titan PD2/3	Weymann FH33/25D	Bournemouth Corporation	131	RP
KFM 893	1950	Bristol L5G	ECW DP31R	Crosville Motor Services	KG131	R
LFM 302	1950	Leyland Tiger PS1	Weymann B35F	Crosville Motor Services	KA226	R
LFM 717	1950	Bristol L5G	ECW B35R	Crosville Motor Services	KG136	A
LFM 734	1950	Bristol LL5G	ECW B39R	Crosville Motor Services	KG153	A
LUO 692	1950	Leyland Tiger PS2/3	Burlingham C33F	Pridham of Lamerton		A
DCK 219	1951	Leyland Titan PD2/3	East Lancs FCL27/22RD	Ribble Motor Services	1248	R
PHN 699	1952	Guy Arab III	Roe B41C	Darlington Corporation	26	RP
BAS 562	1956	Bristol Lodekka LD6G	ECW O33/27R	Southern Vectis Omnibus Co	507	R
BAS 563	1956	Bristol Lodekka LD6G	ECW O33/27R	Southern Vectis Omnibus Co	501	R
701 AEH	1957	Leyland Titan PD3/4	MCW O36/32F	Potteries Motor Traction Co	H701	RP

W 2.00"

Reg	Year	Model	Body	Operator	Fleet No	R
VDV 752	1957	Bristol Lodekka LDL6G	ECW O37/33RD	Western National Omnibus Co	1935	R
VDV 753	1957	Bristol Lodekka LDL6G	ECW O37/33RD	Western National Omnibus Co	1936	R
GSU 678	1958	Leyland Titan PD2/40	Metro Cammell	Portsmouth Corporation	114	A
NDB 356	1958	Leyland Tiger Cub PSUC1/1	Crossley B44F	Stockport Corporation	403	R
890 ADV	1959	AEC Reliance 2MU3RV	Willowbrook C41F	Devon General (Grey Cars)	TCR890	R
805 EVT	1960	AEC Reliance 2MU3RV	Weymann DP41F	Potteries Motor Traction Co	SL805	RP
LDB 796	1960	Leyland Tiger Cub PSUC1	Willowbrook DP43F	North Western Road Car Co	796	R
3655 NE	1962	Leyland Tiger Cub PSUC1/12	Park Royal DP38D	Manchester City Transport	55	A
572 CNW	1962	Daimler CVG6LX-30	Roe H39/31F	Leeds City Transport	572	RP
DPV 65D	1966	AEC Regent V 2D2RA	Neepsend H37/28R	Ipswich Corporation	65	R
XTF 98D	1966	Leyland Titan PD3/4	East Lancs H41/32F	Haslingden Corporation	45	R
HJA 965E	1967	Leyland Titan PD2/40	East Lancs Neepsend H36/28R	Stockport Corporation	65	R
GNH 258F	1968	Daimler CVG6	Roe H33/26R	Northampton Corporation	258	RP
TDK 686J	1971	AEC Reliance 6U3ZR	Plaxton C53F	Yelloway Motor Services of Rochdale		A
HVU 247N	1975	AEC Reliance 6U3ZR	Plaxton C53F	Yelloway Motor Services of Rochdale		RP
NNC 854P	1976	AEC Reliance 6U3ZR	Plaxton C53F	Yelloway Motor Services of Rochdale		A
WDK 562T	1979	AEC Reliance 6U3ZR	Plaxton C49F	Yelloway Motor Services of Rochdale		R

Notes:

AJA 132	Rebodied 1950
GWN 432	Rebodied 1960
KEL 131	Built with twin staircases and dual doors
DCK 219	White Lady double deck coach
BAS 563	Originally registered MDL 952
BAS 562	Originally registered MDL 953
701 AEH	Converted to open top by Sundekker
GSU 678	Converted to breakdown vehicle. Originally registered ORV991.
572 CNW	Converted to exhibition vehicle

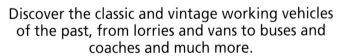

Indices

The Aldershot & District Bus Interest Group numbers among its ranks Alder Valley 127 (KCG 627L), a 1973 Leyland National.

Index of Vehicles by Registration Number

Reg	Page	Reg	Page	Reg	Page	Reg	Page	Reg	Page
101 CLT	61	312 MFC	72	4632 VM	39	654 BUP	109	86 GFJ	102
105 UTU	54	314 DBM	110	47638	82	6545 HA	57	862 RAE	69
109 DRM	104	314 PFM	110	484 EFJ	103	657 BWB	59	866 HAL	45
116 JTD	39	318 AOW	97	485 CLT	116	66	59	869 NHT	68
116 TMD	88	3190 UN	99	488 KOT	64	675 AAM	71	871 KHA	57
120 JRB	109	31909	103	501 KD	88	675 COD	71	872 ATA	74
122 JTD	39	326 CAA	80	503 RUO	75	675 OCV	79	875 VFM	88
129 DPT	109	332 RJO	72	504 EBL	42	6769	81	881 BTF	93
1294 RE	20	333 CRW	26	5056 HA	94	6801 FN	78	8860 VR	39
1322 WA	53	334 CRW	20	507 OHU	68	694 ZO	55	890 ADV	118
138 CLT	23	335 AOW	97	5073 HA	57	70 AUF	98	891 XFM	71
14 LFC	48	348 CLT	80	5212 HA	57	701 AEH	117	9 RDV	75
14 PKR	83	363 CLT	69	528 CTF	93	71 AHI	24	90 HBC	87
1425 P	59	3655 NE	118	532 DWW	103	72 MMJ	86	904 OFM	68
177 IK	24	370 FCR	97	534 RTB	86	7209 PW	54	913 DTT	74
19 XVS	110	371 BKA	88	557 BNG	28	737 DYE	37	918 NRT	23
191 AWL	72	372 BKA	88	56 GUO	94	7424 SP	51	924 AHY	68
1925 WA	83	373 FCR	103	561 TD	86	7514 UA	34	928 GTA	74
198 CUS	81	373 WPU	23	562 RTF	44	756 KFC	48	931 GTA	74
201 YTE	44	3747 RH	110	566 JFM	71	760 CTD	86	932 GTA	74
214 CLT	83	375 GWN	71	569 KKK	27	773 FHA	20	935 GTA	74
217 AJF	87	381 BKM	23	57 GUO	68	78 D140	24	943 KHA	57
217 MHK	23	386 DD	99	572 CNW	118	78 D824	24	952 JUB	35
2206 OI	28	390 DKK	109	574 CNW	75	780 GHA	94	956 AJO	48
221 JVK	74	3916 UB	83	574 TD	44	783 EFM	109	960 HTT	75
236 LNO	23	3945 UE	24	5789 AH	79	7874 WJ	53	9629 WU	59
248 NEA	57	395 DEL	109	583 CLT	86	799 DYE	80	964 H87	59
253 KTA	117	404 RIU	55	595 LCG	80	80 NVO	45	969 EHW	68
256 SFM	88	410 DCD	73	596 LCG	80	802 MHW	57	972 CUF	98
264 ERY	20	414 CLT	39	604 JPU	71	803 DYE	116	972 EHW	68
264 KTA	71	416 DCD	98	6167 RU	67	805 EVT	118	974 AFJ	103
268 KTA	71	419 DCD	98	617 DDV	117	811 BWR	110	975 CWL	72
28 TKR	23	422 CAX	54	6203 KW	34	8124 WX	110	9797 DP	99
297 LJ	67	422 DCD	73	6204 KW	34	815 KDV	103	980 DAE	68
301 LJ	22	4227 FM	44	6220 KW	34	8154 EL	67	991 MDV	103
3014 AH	109	433 MDT	59	6249 UP	92	8156 EL	67	99-64-HB	58
3016 HA	57	434 BTE	44	627 HFM	115	827 BWY	75	999 PPL	110
3035 HA	20	436 KOV	102	6330 WJ	53	828 SHW	81		
304 GHN	65	449 CLT	53	6342 HA	21	85 D2412	24		
304 KFC	48	461 CLT	25	6370 HA	20	850 ABK	48		
305 KFC	48	462 EOT	64	643 MIP	24	858 DYE	116		

Reg	Page	Reg	Page	Reg	Page	Reg	Page	Reg	Page
A103 SUU	102	AAO 771A	86	AEX 85B	28	AHL 694	89	ANB 851	38
A110 WVP	21	ABD 253B	71	AFB 592V	68	AHN 451B	65	ANE 2T	96
A112 HLV	88	ABR 433	92	AFB 593V	112	AHU 803	69	ANH 154	108
A250 SVW	80	ACB 902	43	AFJ 726T	102	AIT 934	55	ANJ 306T	98
A30 ORJ	96	ACB 904	93	AFJ 727T	102	AJA 132	117	ANQ 778	43
A323 GLV	88	ACH 441	117	AFJ 764T	102	AJA 139B	44	ANV 775J	101
A472 HNC	96	ACH 627	108	AFN 488B	78	AJA 152	38	ANW 682	34
A537 TYW	112	ACK 796	93	AFN 780B	78	AJA 408L	96	AOG 638	108
A701 LNC	96	AC-L 379	70	AFS 91B	51	AJX 369	83	AOG 679	20
A706 LNC	39	ACU 304B	92	AFT 930	92	ALJ 340B	67	AOR 158B	98
A749 NTA	103	AD 7156	85	AFY 187X	88	ALJ 973	70	APR 167A	45
A765 NNA	96	ADL 459B	33	AFY 971	43	ALJ 986	28	APW 829B	32
A869 SUL	48	ADR 813	103	AH 79505	28	ALM 37B	110	ARC 515	20
A927 MDV	102	ADV 128	103	AHA 451J	58	ALS 102Y	82	ARC 666T	45
AAA 503C	64	ADX 1	32	AHA 582	56	AML 582H	37	ARD 676	70
AAA 506C	64	ADX 196	32	AHC 442	72	AMX 8A	110	ARG 17B	51
AAA 508C	64	ADX 63B	32	AHE 163	35	ANA 1Y	96	ARN 811C	94
AAA 756	49	AED 31B	66	AHF 850	61	ANA 601Y	96	ARP 601X	71
AAO 34B	104	AEL 170B	67	AHG 334V	86	ANA 645Y	96	ARY 225K	87

ASC 665B	51	BHU 92C	68	C748 FFJ	103	CRU 180C	67	DBN 978	54
ATA 563L	75	BJA 425	38	C751 YBA	96	CRU 184C	80	DBU 246	38
ATD 281J	86	BJK 672D	98	C777 SFS	52	CRU 187C	67	DBV 100W	94
ATD 683	43	BJX 848C	81	C801 FRL	102	CRU 197C	67	DBV 32W	103
ATF 477	49	BKC 236K	88	C823 CBU	96	CRU 301L	111	DBV 43W	103
ATS 408	115	BKC 276K	88	C832 KNK	112	CSG 29C	51	DBV 831W	94
ATT 922	103	BKG 713B	110	CAH 923	32	CSG 43C	51	DBW 613	48
AUD 310J	72	BLH 123B	24	CBC 921	18	CSG 773S	52	DBY 001	81
AUF 670	108	BMS 222	50	CBR 539	92	CSG 792S	52	DCK 219	117
AUO 74	103	BMS 405	50	CC 1087	89	CTF 627B	86	DCN 83	92
AUP 369W	74	BNC 960T	96	CC 7745	56	CTP 200	72	DCS 616	50
AUX 296	49	BND 874C	39	CC 8671	64	CTT 23C	75	DDB 174C	39
AVP 369W	112	BNE 729N	96	CC 9305	27	CTT 513C	103	DDL 50	33
AVX 975G	23	BNE 751N	96	CC 9424	64	CTT 518C	83	DDR 414	103
AWA 124B	51	BNE 764N	96	CCB 300	115	CTT 774C	110	DDW 431V	82
AWG 393	50	BNU 679G	40	CCD 940	108	CU 3593	70	DED 797	43
AWG 623	50	BOK 1V	58	CCG 296K	64	CUH 856	108	DEK 3D	100
AWG 639	50	BON 474C	57	CCG 704C	80	CUH 859	50	DFE 383	35
AXI 2259	84	BOW 162	67	CCK 359	93	CUL 260	28	DFE 963D	69
AXI 2534	112	BOW 169	103	CCK 663	85	CUV 116C	110	DFM 347H	44
AXJ 857	38	BOW 503C	110	CCX 999	117	CUV 121C	81	DFV 146	85
AXM 649	37	BOW 507C	97	CD 4867	19	CUV 203C	116	DGS 536	50
AXM 693	25	BP 9822	19	CD 5125	19	CUV 208C	75	DGS 625	50
AYG 100T	111	BPL 469T	101	CD 7045	49	CUV 210C	116	DHC 784E	98
AYJ 379	50	BPT 672L	111	CDB 224	38	CUV 218C	45	DHN 475	75
AYR 300T	111	BPV 9	32	CDC 166K	99	CUV 219C	57	DHR 192	42
AYV 651	37	BR 7132	19	CDC 168K	99	CUV 220C	80	DHW 293K	70
AZD 203	24	BRS 37	50	CDH 501	20	CUV 229C	37	DIV 83	55
B101 SJA	96	BTF 25	93	CDJ 878	44	CUV 233C	23	DJF 349	45
B106 XJO	48	BTN 113	73	CDK 409C	86	CUV 241C	116	DJG 619C	78
B177 FFS	82	BTR 361B	97	CDL 479C	33	CUV 248C	116	DJP 754	39
B349 LSO	52	BTW 488	23	CDR 679	49	CUV 260C	114	DKY 703	59
B401 NJF	18	BU 7108	108	CDT 636	59	CVF 874	32	DKY 704	70
B65 PJA	39	BUF 122C	98	CDX 516	25	CVH 741	59	DKY 706	59
B901 TVR	96	BUF 260C	98	CEO 720W	65	CVL 850D	35	DKY 712	67
B926 KWM	61	BUF 272C	110	CEO 723W	65	CVP 207	56	DKY 735	21
BAS 562	117	BUF 277C	98	CEO 956	65	CWG 206	38	DL 5084	33
BAS 563	117	BUF 426C	98	CEO 957	65	CWG 283	50	DL 9015	108
BBA 560	38	BUF 427C	98	CET 613	95	CWG 286	115	DL 9706	101
BBK 236B	72	BUH 239V	112	CFK 340	92	CWG 696V	44	DLJ 111L	67
BBW 21V	48	BVP 784V	21	CFN 104	100	CWG 756V	53	DLU 92	25
BCD 820L	42	BWG 39	50	CFV 851	23	CWH 717	38	DM 2583	89
BCH 156B	110	BWG 833L	51	CGJ 188	25	CWN 629C	69	DM 6228	93
BCK 367C	44	BWO 585B	54	CHB 407D	110	CWU 146T	61	DMS 130	109
BCK 939	59	BWS 105L	51	CHF 565	61	CWX 671	34	DMS 325C	51
BCP 671	83	BXA 464B	51	CHG 541	50	CXX 171	25	DMS 348C	81
BCR 379K	97	BXD 576	37	CHL 772	81	CYI 621	55	DMS 359C	51
BD 209	89	BXI 2583	84	CHY 419C	71	CYJ 252	50	DMS 820	50
BDJ 87	59	C 2367	89	CJG 959	78	CZ 7013	60	DMS 823	50
BDL 583B	110	C177 VSF	82	CK 3825	38	D103 DAJ	28	DNF 204	54
BDY 809	28	C201 CBU	96	CK 4474	93	D122 PTT	48	DNF 708C	96
BED 731C	44	C208 FVU	39	CKG 193	70	D176 NON	66	DNW 840T	34
BED 732C	110	C225 CBU	96	CLE 122	37	D275 OOJ	34	DOD 474	103
BEN 177	38	C24 NVV	101	CMS 201	99	D302 JVR	96	DPT 848	89
BFE 419	35	C386 XFD	66	CN 2870	56	D320 LNB	96	DPV 65D	118
BFM 144	108	C41 HDT	112	CN 4740	89	D501 LNA	96	DPV 68D	32
BFS 1L	51	C416 AHT	69	CN 6100	89	D509 MJA	96	DR 4902	42
BFS 463L	51	C45 HDT	59	CNH 699	68	D63 NOF	39	DRC 224	28
BG 8557	61	C46 HDT	112	CNH 860	71	D676 NNE	39	DRD 130	104
BG 9225	61	C526 DYT	37	CNH 862	71	D825 PUK	112	DRN 289	93
BGA 97	73	C526 FFJ	75	CPM 61	42	DAU 370C	45	DSD 936V	52
BHA 399C	57	C53 HDT	53	CPU 979G	23	DB 5070	38	DSG 169	49
BHA 656C	57	C671 FFJ	103	CRC 911	54	DB 5221	108	DTP 823	72
BHH 83J	98	C705 FFJ	102	CRG 811	81	DBA 214C	39	DU 4838	48
BHL 682	75	C719 FFJ	102	CRM 927T	103	DBC 190C	87	DUK 278	102
BHO 543C	80	C724 JJO	48	CRN 80	115	DBE 187	35	DUK 833	21
BHO 670J	99	C729 JJO	72	CRU 103C	67	DBL 154	100	DWB 54H	53

DWG 526	50	ERG 164	115	FFY 401	103	GBU 1V	96	GSI 353	55
DWH 706W	96	ERN 700	93	FFY 402	56	GCD 48	73	GSO 80V	52
DX 3988	32	ERV 252D	67	FFY 404	43	GCK 279S	101	GSR 244	89
DX 5610	32	ERV 938	28	FGS 59D	50	GCM 152E	61	GSU 678	118
DX 5629	32	ESF 647W	52	FHF 451	61	GDJ 435	44	GSU 866T	112
DX 6591	32	ESF 801C	51	FHF 456	44	GDL 764	33	GTA 395	103
DX 7812	32	ESG 652	50	FHN 833	35	GDT 421	59	GTB 903	85
DX 8871	42	ESV 811	40	FHT 112	108	GE 2446	49	GTJ 694	83
DY 5029	83	ETJ 108	49	FJF 40D	87	GEA 174	21	GTP 175F	72
E523 TVO	112	ETS 964	50	FJJ 774	37	GEE 418D	110	GTV 666	59
E570 MAC	65	ETT 946	103	FJW 616	57	GFN 273	78	GUE 247	56
E901 DRG	92	EUD 256K	48	FKF 801D	88	GFU 692	59	GUF 191	98
E903 DRG	92	EUF 181	108	FKF 835E	88	GFY 406	43	GUF 727	35
EA 4181	20	EUF 184	19	FKF 933G	88	GGR 103N	74	GUG 547N	111
EBO 919	70	EUP 405B	74	FKU 758	59	GHA 327D	21	GUJ 608	20
ECD 524	19	EVA 324	50	FLD 447Y	82	GHA 333	56	GUP 907N	92
ECU 201E	92	EVC 244	108	FM 6397	108	GHA 337	56	GUS 926	81
ECX 425	83	EVH 65	72	FM 6435	108	GHA 415D	57	GUW 443W	101
EDB 549	38	EVL 549E	35	FM 7443	108	GHD 215	84	GUW 444W	101
EDB 562	38	EWM 358	43	FM 9984	108	GHD 765	53	GUX 188	55
EDB 575	38	EWS 130D	51	FNY 933	108	GHN 189	65	GVD 47	50
EDS 288A	50	EWS 168D	51	FOI 1629	84	GHN 574	59	GW 713	42
EDS 320A	50	EWS 746W	69	FON 630	20	GHT 127	69	GWJ 724	53
EDT 703	59	EXV 201	28	FOP 429	23	GHT 154	69	GWM 816	99
EDV 505D	110	EXV 253	37	FPT 590C	110	GHV 2N	80	GWN 432	117
EDV 555D	71	EZH 155	24	FPT 6G	94	GHV 505N	98	GWY 690N	34
EF 7380	89	EZH 17	55	FR 1347	42	GJ 2098	25	GYC 160K	69
EFJ 241	103	EZH 170	24	FRB 211H	57	GJB 254	48	GYS 896D	81
EFJ 666	103	EZH 231	55	FRC 956	57	GJF 301N	87	GZ 7638	55
EFJ 92	38	EZH 64	55	FRE 699A	109	GJG 739D	78	H74 ANG	79
EFM 581	108	EZL 1	55	FRJ 254D	39	GJG 751D	27	HA 3501	56
EFM 631C	100	F115 PHM	37	FRJ 511	54	GJX 331	34	HA 4963	20
EFN 178L	78	F300 SSX	82	FRP 692	71	GK 3192	36	HA 8047	21
EFN 592	78	F305 DRJ	96	FRP 828	71	GK 5323	36	HAD 915D	110
EGA 79	41	F575 RCW	86	FRU 224	67	GK 5486	36	HAH 537L	71
EGN 369J	25	F685 YOG	21	FRU 305	55	GKA 74N	88	HAX 399N	69
EGO 426	25	FAE 60	68	FSC 182	50	GKD 434	88	HBD 919T	71
EGP 1J	37	FAM 2	68	FSL 615W	82	GKP 511	59	HBF 679D	57
EHA 424D	94	FAR 724K	99	FTB 11	38	GKV 94	94	HCD 347E	73
EHA 767D	57	FAS 982	50	FTO 614	59	GLJ 467N	111	HD 7905	53
EHA 775	20	FBG 910	61	FTR 511	97	GLJ 957	103	HDG 448	57
EHL 344	75	FBN 232C	66	FTT 704	69	GM 6384	50	HDL 280	109
EHL 472D	99	FBR 53D	92	FUF 181	108	GN 8242	25	HDV 638E	110
EHT 108C	75	FBU 827	38	FV 5737	103	GNB 518D	96	HDV 639E	51
EKA 220Y	88	FCD 294D	98	FVA 854	81	GNC 276N	39	HE 12	89
EKP 234C	110	FCI 323	24	FVM 191V	112	GNF 15V	96	HEK 705	39
EKU 743	59	FCK 884	93	FW 5698	35	GNF 16V	96	HET 513	42
EKU 746	59	FDB 328C	110	FW 8990	59	GNG 125C	32	HF 9126	49
EKV 966	26	FDB 334C	110	FWG 846	50	GNH 258F	118	HFG 923V	112
EKY 558	59	FDL 676	33	FWH 461Y	96	GNJ 583N	78	HFM 561D	71
ELP 223	79	FDL 927D	33	FWL 371E	48	GNM 232N	23	HFO659	50
ELP 228	25	FDM 724	57	FWX 914	34	GNM 235N	103	HFR 501E	81
EMS 362V	82	FDO 573	35	FXH 521	28	GO 5170	25	HFR 512E	86
EMW 893	117	FDV 827V	112	FXT 122	100	GO 5198	37	HFR 516E	86
EN 9965	96	FDV 829V	75	FYG 663J	99	GOE 486	108	HGA 983D	81
END 832D	96	FEA156	21	FYS 839	70	GOH 357N	21	HGC 130	25
ENT 778	109	FEL 105L	67	FYS 988	41	GOU 732	94	HGG 359	81
ENW 980D	34	FEL 209V	67	FYS 998	41	GOU 845	64	HGM 335E	51
EO 9051	65	FEL 751D	45	FZ 7897	60	GPD 313N	101	HGM 346E	51
EO 9177	65	FES 831W	52	GAA 580	64	GPD 318N	111	HHA 26	108
EOD 524D	45	FET 617	95	GAA 616	64	GRM 353L	104	HHA 637	56
EOI 4857	60	FET 618	59	GAJ 12	59	GRP 260D	114	HHF 15	88
EPD 511V	112	FFM 135C	44	GAN 744J	92	GRS 334E	81	HHN 202	73
EPD 543V	112	FFN 399	78	GAX 2C	71	GRS 343E	51	HHP 755	83
EPM 134V	101	FFN 446	109	GBB 516K	111	GRY 48D	87	HHW 452D	110
EPW 516K	79	FFU 860	35	GBB 524K	92	GRY 60D	57	HIL 7081	112
ERD 152	59	FFV 447D	51	GBJ 192	28	GSC 667X	52	HJA 121N	96

HJA 965E	118	JAP 698	100	JOW 928	97	KBD 712D	100	KOW 910F	97
HKE 680L	111	JBD 975	71	JP 4712	38	KBD 715D	100	KOX 663F	20
HKE 867	108	JBN 153	39	JPA 190K	25	KBO 961	70	KOX 780F	57
HKL 826	108	JC 5313	83	JPL 153K	101	KCG 627L	64	KPA 369P	111
HKR 11	59	JCK 530	86	JPT 901T	92	KCK 869	93	KPT 909	42
HLF 820	61	JCK 542	93	JPT 906T	74	KCK 914	93	KRN 422	44
HLJ 44	79	JCK 852W	112	JPY 985	115	KD 3185	83	KRR 255	40
HLW 159	43	JCP 60F	42	JRA 635	89	KD 5296	100	KRU 55F	67
HLW 178	114	JDJ 260K	44	JRJ 281E	39	KDB 408F	39	KSV 102	85
HLW 214	108	JDL 40	109	JRN 29	22	KDB 696	79	KSX 102X	52
HLX 410	25	JDN 668	59	JRN 41	93	KDJ 999	44	KTC 615	43
HMA 99W	44	JDV 754	109	JRR 404	56	KDL 885F	33	KTD 768	43
HNB 24N	96	JEL 257	68	JRT 82K	32	KDT 206D	59	KTF 594	117
HNP 154S	98	JF 2378	20	JRX 823	87	KDT 393	59	KTJ 502	89
HNP 989J	97	JFJ 500N	103	JSC 900E	51	KDW 347P	111	KTT 42P	75
HNW 131D	34	JFJ 506N	71	JSF 928T	52	KDW 362P	111	KTT 689	20
HOR 413L	111	JFJ 606	103	JSJ 746	116	KED 546F	85	KTV 493	59
HOR 590E	80	JFJ 875	117	JSJ 747	116	KEL 110	67	KTV 506	59
HOR 592E	80	JFM 238D	29	JSJ 748	116	KEL 131	117	KUF 199F	98
HOU 904	64	JFM 575	117	JSJ 749	116	KEL 133	67	KUL 331D	114
HOV 685	56	JFM 650J	44	JSX 595T	52	KEL 405	109	KUO 795P	111
HPF 318N	101	JFT 413X	92	JT 8077	33	KET 220	53	KUS 607E	66
HPK 503N	111	JFV 527	93	JTD 300B	44	KFM 775	57	KVF 658E	79
HPW 108	68	JG 8720	64	JTE 546	117	KFM 893	117	KVH 219	59
HPW 133	35	JG 9938	117	JTF 920B	59	KFN 239	78	KVH 473E	34
HRG 209	50	JHA 227L	99	JTH 100F	99	KGK 529	95	KVO 429P	45
HRN 249G	94	JHA 868E	57	JTU 588T	52	KGK 575	95	KW 1961	28
HRN 31	93	JHL 701	92	JUB 29	83	KGK 758	79	KW 2260	34
HRN 39	93	JHL 708	75	JUD 597W	48	KGK 803	25	KW 474	35
HRN 99N	86	JHT 802	50	JUE 349	57	KGK 959	114	KW 6052	58
HSC 173X	52	JJD 405D	80	JUM 505V	34	KGM 664F	51	KW 7604	35
HSD 86V	82	JJD 499D	110	JUO 992	117	KGU 142	25	KWE 255	53
HTB 656	38	JJD 524D	75	JUS 774N	111	KGU 284	22	KWT 642D	34
HTC 661	109	JJD 539D	110	JV 9901	59	KGU 290	117	KXW 171	114
HTF 586	38	JJG 1P	78	JVF 528	48	KGY 4D	37	KXW 435	95
HTF 644B	44	JK 8418	108	JVH 373	84	KHA 301	20	KY 9106	34
HTT 487	74	JKC 178	88	JVH 378	84	KHA 311	109	KYY 529	109
HUD 476S	48	JLJ 402	117	JVH 381	109	KHA 352	20	KYY 615	109
HUO 510	117	JLJ 403	67	JVO 230	45	KHC 367	87	KYY 622	101
HUP 236	73	JMC 121K	18	JVS 541	50	KHH 378W	104	KYY 628	117
HVM 901F	39	JMC 123K	111	JVU 755	38	KHL 855	75	KYY 647	109
HVO 937	40	JMN 727	59	JVV 267G	110	KHU 28	68	KYY 961	79
HVU 244N	39	JMS 452E	81	JVW 430	23	KHU 326P	69	L247 FDV	48
HVU 247N	118	JN 5783	42	JVW 976W	73	KHU 624	103	L674 UKF	66
HWO 334	57	JNA 467	38	JWB 416	53	KHW 306E	57	L929 CTT	102
HWV 294	71	JNB 416	26	JWS 594	49	KHW 630	68	LA 9928	36
HWY 36	109	JND 646	38	JWU 307	100	KID 154	24	LAA 231	64
HX 2756	37	JND 728	54	JWU 886	34	KJA 299G	44	LAE 13	69
HYM 768	37	JND 791	38	JWW 227N	78	KJA 871F	39	LAK 309G	34
HYM 812	70	JNK 681C	86	JWW 375	59	KJD 401P	37	LAK 313G	34
HZA 230	55	JNN 384	117	JWW 376	59	KJD 507P	111	LAX 101E	110
HZA 279	55	JO 5032	48	JWW 397	59	KLB 721	69	LC 3701	36
HZD 593	55	JO 5403	48	JX 7046	83	KLB 908	95	LCD 52	28
IB 552	19	JOJ 207	109	JX 9106	83	KLB 915	95	LDB 796	118
IJI 5367	110	JOJ 222	20	JXC 194	79	KLJ 346	67	LDJ 985	44
ILI 98	24	JOJ 231	109	JXC 288	25	KMN 519	88	LDP 945	104
IY 1940	55	JOJ 245	57	JXC 323	69	KNG 374	32	LDS 201A	51
IY 7383	24	JOJ 526	20	JXN 46	109	KNG 711	109	LDV 176P	111
IY 7384	55	JOJ 533	57	JXX 487	109	KNG 718	79	LED 17P	44
IY 8044	24	JOJ 548	20	JY 124	103	KNN 254	109	LEN 101	75
J 2503	43	JOJ 827	109	JYC 855	94	KNV 337	71	LEO 734Y	65
JA 5506	108	JOJ 847	20	K232 DAC	26	KOD 585	74	LEO 735Y	65
JA 5528	108	JOJ 976	57	KAG 856	81	KOM 150	26	LEV 917	85
JA 7585	38	JOV 613P	58	KAH 407	32	KON 311P	58	LF 9967	89
JA 7770	108	JOV 714P	21	KAH 408	28	KOU 791P	69	LFJ 862W	75
JAA 708	80	JOV 738P	102	KAL 579	56	KOW 274Y	98	LFM 302	117
JAJ 296N	111	JOW 499E	97	KAZ 6703	98	KOW 909F	97	LFM 320	109

Reg	No.	Reg	No.	Reg	No.	Reg	No.	Reg	No.
LFM 717	117	LUC 381	109	MTB 848	38	NKJ 849P	80	OBN 502R	96
LFM 734	117	LUO 692	117	MTC 540	93	NKU 245X	34	OC 527	56
LFM 753	68	LUS 524E	51	MTE 639	50	NLE 534	109	OCH 261L	111
LFM 756	88	LVK 123	73	MTJ 771S	88	NLE 537	37	OCK 985K	28
LFM 767	34	LWB 377P	111	MTJ 84	115	NLE 603	80	OCK 988K	79
LFR 529F	86	LWB 388P	53	MTL 750	18	NLE 643	117	OCK 997K	86
LFR 540G	86	LWR 424	109	MTT 640	115	NLE 672	25	OCU 769R	92
LFS 288F	51	LYF 104	109	MUA 865P	78	NLE 673	109	OCU 807R	92
LFS 294F	51	LYF 316	109	MUT 253W	87	NLE 882	80	OCW 8X	112
LFS 296F	98	LYF 377	117	MV 8996	108	NLE 939	101	OD 5489	103
LFS 303F	51	LYM 729	92	MWW 114D	75	NLJ 268	67	OD 5868	103
LFS 480	50	LYR 533	34	MXX 23	57	NLJ 272	67	OD 7500	103
LFW 326	35	LYR 542	59	MXX 261	80	NLP 645	42	ODK 705	83
LG 2637	54	LYR 826	25	MXX 283	109	NMA 328D	54	ODL 400	33
LHA 870F	20	LYR 854	114	MXX 289	114	NMS 358	81	OED 217	22
LHC 919P	66	LYR 910	25	MXX 292	109	NMS 366	50	OEM 788S	88
LHL 164F	75	LYR 915	100	MXX 332	100	NMY 634E	116	OFC 205	48
LHN 784	59	LYR 969	114	MXX 334	25	NMY 636E	51	OFC 393	48
LHN 785	84	LYR 997	23	MXX 364	37	NMY 646E	116	OFC 902H	72
LHN 860	65	M627 HDV	102	MXX 410	101	NMY 658E	80	OFM 957K	61
LHT 911	85	M939 XKA	39	MXX 421	109	NNB 125	38	OFN 721F	78
LHW 918	68	MAH 744	32	MXX 430	101	NNB 547H	96	OFR 970M	86
LHY 937	109	MAL 310	45	MXX 434	100	NNB 589H	96	OFR 989M	21
LHY 976	68	MAP 340W	98	MXX 481	79	NNC 854P	118	OFS 777	50
LIL 9929	52	MBN 177	93	MXX 489	100	NNU 123M	40	OFS 798	50
LJ 500	67	MCK 229J	78	MYA 590	25	NNU 124M	40	OHK 432	35
LJF 31F	66	MCN 30K	92	MZ 7396	55	NNU 234	67	OHU 770F	69
LJH 665	117	MDJ 555E	44	NAC 416F	48	NOB 413M	58	OHY 938	68
LJW 336	20	MDL 880R	33	NAE 3	71	NOC 600R	102	OJ 9347	20
LJX 198	83	MDL 954	109	NAG 120G	51	NOE 544R	58	OJD 172R	25
LJX 215	83	MDT 222	59	NAH 135P	79	NOE 576R	111	OJD 357R	111
LLU 670	114	MFM 39	109	NAH 941	79	NOV 796G	57	OJD 903R	81
LLU 829	28	MFN 898	78	NAT 766A	110	NOV 880G	102	OJF 191	87
LLU 957	95	MFR 306P	94	NBB 628	28	NPD 108L	111	OJI 4371	86
LLU 987	95	MHU 49	68	NBD 311F	100	NPD 128L	111	OJO 727	72
LMA 284	38	MHY 765	53	NBN 436	66	NPD 145L	27	OLD 589	37
LMJ 653G	42	MIL 8338	96	NBU 494	39	NRA 78F	40	OLD 714	35
LMS 168W	82	MJ 4549	64	NCD 559M	111	NRG 154M	29	OLJ 291	42
LMS 374W	52	MJA 891G	39	NCK 106J	94	NRG 26H	81	ONF 865H	96
LN 4743	29	MJA 895G	110	NCK 338J	94	NRH 802A	66	ONO 49	23
LN 7270	89	MJA 897G	39	NCS 16P	51	NRN 586	93	ONO 59	35
LNA 166G	96	MKB 994	88	NDB 356	118	NSF 757	81	ONU 425	71
LNN 89E	45	MLL 555	109	NDH 959	70	NSJ 502	51	OOX 825R	21
LOD 495	115	MLL 722	109	NDK 980	39	NTF 466	44	OP 237	20
LOG 301	20	MLL 740	25	NDL 656R	51	NTT 661	74	OPV 821	98
LOG 302	20	MLL 817	101	NDL 769G	65	NTT 679	74	ORB 277	57
LOU 48	64	MLL 952	79	NDM 950E	110	NTU 125	94	ORC 545P	45
LOW 217	97	MMW 354G	71	NDP 31R	111	NTW 942C	23	ORJ 83W	39
LRA 801P	40	MN 2615	36	NDP 38R	111	NTY 416F	51	ORS 60R	51
LRN 321J	94	MNC 525W	96	NDV 537G	75	NUD 105L	72	ORU 230G	67
LRN 60J	69	MNS 10Y	82	NEA 101F	57	NUW 567Y	37	ORV 989	72
LRV 992	98	MNW 86	34	NEH 453	23	NVK 341	73	OSJ 620R	84
LRV 996	72	MO 9324	19	NEL 119P	111	NWO 462R	111	OSJ 629R	52
LST 873	116	MOD 978	67	NFN 84R	78	NWU 265D	34	OSJ 636R	116
LSU 381V	112	MOF 90	20	NFS 176Y	52	NWW 89E	75	OSK 831	92
LSV 748	109	MOO 177	79	NFW 36V	36	NXL 847	109	OST 502	24
LSX 16P	51	MOR 581	64	NG 1109	33	NXL 847	109	OT 8283	64
LTA 772	42	MPU 21	71	NGE 172P	81	NXL 874	94	OT 8592	64
LTA 813	94	MPU 52	23	NHA 744	57	NXP 506	50	OT 8898	64
LTC 774	38	MPX 945R	103	NHA 795	57	NXP 775	80	OT 8902	64
LTF 254	83	MRB 765	115	NHN 250K	92	NXP 997	37	OTA 632G	102
LTN 501	43	MRT 6P	32	NHU 2	68	NZE 598	55	OTA 640G	94
LTU 869	55	MSD 407	81	NJA 568W	96	NZE 620	55	OTB 26W	66
LTV 702	103	MSD 408	81	NJO 703	48	NZE 629	55	OTT 43	94
LTX 311	109	MSF 122P	81	NJW 719E	57	O 9926	56	OTT 55	42
LUC 210	25	MSF 465P	81	NKD 536	88	OAE 954M	68	OTV 137	59
LUC 250	109	MSF 750P	51	NKD 540	88	OAE 957M	103	OTV 161	45

OU 9286	80	PTF 727L	94	RRS 46R	52	SOU 456	64	THM 712M	111
OUM 727P	18	PTT 106R	103	RRU 901	67	SOU 465	64	THX 220S	111
OV 4090	56	PTW 110	23	RRU 903	20	SP 5139	29	THX 580S	111
OV 4486	56	PUA 310W	112	RRU 904	67	SPT 65	92	THX 646S	80
OVF 229	79	PUF 165H	98	RSC 194Y	82	SPT 963V	74	TJ 6760	93
OVL 465	35	PUM 149W	78	RSD 973R	82	SPU 985	86	TJO 56K	72
OVL 473	100	PV 817	32	RSG 825V	82	SR 1266	26	TKU 467K	34
OWC 182D	71	PV 8270	32	RSJ 747	100	SRB 424	26	TMS 403X	82
OWC 720M	111	PV 9371	32	RSK 615	109	SRJ 328H	39	TMS 585H	51
OWE 116	53	PVH 931	70	RSL 905	92	SS 7486	50	TNA 496	39
OWE 271K	58	PW 8605	89	RT 4539	64	SS 7501	50	TNA 520	39
OWS 620	50	PWL 413	48	RTC 645L	44	SSA 5X	82	TNB 759K	96
OWW 905P	78	PWL 999W	72	RTJ 422L	86	SSF 237H	51	TOB 997H	102
OWX 167	75	PWS 492S	85	RU 2266	67	SSN 248S	82	TPD 109X	101
OWY 750K	78	PY 6170	108	RU 8678	49	SSX 602V	52	TPJ 61S	37
OZ 6686	55	PYM 108F	110	RUF 186	73	STH 100F	110	TRJ 109	44
PAJ 829X	92	Q124 VOE	57	RUF 37R	98	STJ 847L	86	TRJ 112	39
PAU 204R	81	Q507 OHR	68	RUF 40R	103	STL 725J	110	TRN 481V	94
PBC 113G	87	Q995 CPE	103	RV 6360	43	STO 523H	45	TRN 731	94
PBC 734	26	RAG 400	81	RV 6367	72	SUK 3	57	TRU 947J	110
PBC 98G	87	RAG 411	50	RWB 87	53	SV 6107	93	TRY 122H	87
PBJ 2F	79	RAG 578	50	RWC 637K	111	SVF 896G	110	TSJ 272	83
PCG 888G	97	RAL 795	109	RWU 534R	84	SVS 281	104	TSJ 47S	82
PCG 889G	97	RB 4757	83	SB 8155	20	SVV 587W	101	TSK 736	115
PCK 618	93	RBC 345G	99	SBD 525R	101	SWS 671	50	TSO 16X	82
PCN 762	92	RBD 111M	101	SBF 233	57	SWS 715	50	TSP 939K	111
PCW 203J	92	RBD 319G	100	SCD 731N	98	SWV 155J	92	TTD 386H	39
PDH 808	57	RBW 87M	72	SCH 117X	45	SYK 569F	98	TTR 167H	97
PDJ 269L	44	RC 2721	35	SCH 237	21	TAX 235	109	TTT 781	83
PDL 519	33	RC 4615	56	SCN 268S	92	TB 749	115	TUG 20	73
PDU 125M	26	RC 7927	20	SCS 333M	51	TBC 164	18	TUJ 261	53
PDU 135M	58	RC 8472	104	SCS 366M	51	TBC 50X	87	TUO 497	71
PFE 542V	36	RC 8575	104	SDK 442	39	TBD 279G	71	TUO 74J	75
PFN 788M	78	RCH 629L	40	SDL 268	33	TBK 190K	73	TUP 859	74
PFN 865	45	RCK 920	110	SDL 638J	33	TCD 374J	98	TV 4484	58
PFN 867	78	RCM 493	61	SDX 33R	66	TCD 383J	98	TV 9333	59
PFR 346	86	RCP 237	87	SDX 57	23	TCD 481J	98	TVS 367	81
PFR 554H	86	RCS 382	50	SEO 209M	65	TCD 490J	98	TWH 807K	66
PFR 747	100	RCU 588S	92	SFC 610	48	TCK 465	93	TWH 809K	66
PHA 319M	21	RCU 838S	92	SFV 421	93	TCK 726	94	TWL 928	48
PHA 370M	58	RD 7127	70	SG 2030	28	TCK 821	81	TWM 220V	88
PHJ 954	23	RDB 872	69	SGD 407	23	TCO 537	92	TWT 123	75
PHN 699	117	RDH 505	57	SGD 500	81	TDH 912	21	TWW 766F	34
PHN 831	92	REN 116	39	SGR 935V	74	TDJ 612	44	TWY 8	75
PJX 232	34	RFE 416	35	SHA 431	57	TDK 322	53	TXJ 507K	39
PJX 35	75	RFM 408	71	SHA 645G	57	TDK 686J	118	TYD 888	50
PKG 587M	111	RFM 641	44	SHN 301	92	TDL 564K	33	TYJ 4S	98
PKH 600M	111	RFM 644	44	SHN 80L	40	TDL 566K	111	UAS 954	109
PKW 434J	110	RFU 689	71	SJ 1340	50	TDL 998	87	UBD 757H	100
PND 460	39	RGS 598R	79	SKB 168	88	TDT 344	115	UBN 902	66
PNF 941J	96	RHS 400W	52	SKB 224	88	TDV217J	102	UCS 659	51
PNU 114K	40	RJT 146R	111	SKB 695G	88	TE 5110	55	UCX 275	21
POR 428	64	RKC 262	88	SLT 56	37	TE 5780	83	UDT 455F	59
POU 494	80	RLN 237W	103	SLT 57	37	TE 7870	114	UEO 478T	65
PRA 109R	81	RMS 400W	82	SLT 58	25	TE 8318	35	UF 1517	19
PRN 145	93	RN 7588	93	SMK 676F	110	TET 135	53	UF 4813	19
PRN 79K	94	RN 7824	38	SMK 716F	110	TF 6860	34	UF 6473	19
PRN 906	93	RN 8622	93	SMK 747F	110	TF 818	35	UF 6805	19
PRX 187B	98	RNA 220J	96	SMM 90F	80	TFA 987	110	UF 7428	19
PRX 200B	98	RNA 236J	99	SMS 120P	51	TFF 251	71	UFC 430K	48
PRX 206B	98	RNE 692W	112	SND 455X	96	TFN 980T	78	UFF 178	50
PSJ 480	44	ROD 765	83	SND 460X	96	TFU 90	50	UFJ 292	92
PSJ 825R	53	RPU 869M	111	SNS 823W	112	TGM 214J	51	UFJ 296	74
PTC 114C	39	RRM 148M	79	SO 3740	49	TGY 102M	111	UFM 52F	61
PTD 640S	96	RRM 386X	82	SOA 674S	101	THL 261H	78	UFM 53F	71
PTE 944C	39	RRN 405	86	SOE 913H	57	THM 515M	111	UFP 233S	87
PTF 718L	94	RRN 428	93	SOI 3591	84	THM 692M	61	UGB 196W	82

UGR 698R	111	VF 8157	32	VYO 767	100	WW 4688	70	XX 9591	25
UHA 255	57	VFJ 995	109	VZI 44	55	WWH 43L	96	Y 9608	75
UHA 941H	57	VG 5541	94	VZL 179	55	WWJ 754M	59	YBD 201	115
UHA 956H	57	VH 2088	83	WAD 640S	79	WWM 904W	88	YD 9533	64
UHA 969H	20	VH 6188	67	WAJ 112	50	WWY 115G	99	YDB 453L	96
UHA 981H	58	VH 6217	67	WBN 955L	96	WYP 203G	110	YDK 590	39
UHG 141V	82	VHB 678S	82	WBR 246	34	WYW 6T	25	YDL 135T	33
UHY 359	68	VJG 187J	78	WBR 248	92	WYW 82T	66	YDL 315	87
UHY 360	68	VJO 201X	72	WCG 104	80	WZJ 724	55	YFM 269L	111
UHY 362	102	VK 5401	43	WDA 700T	21	XAK 355L	34	YFM 283L	71
UHY 384	68	VKB 711	88	WDA 835T	58	XBO 121T	52	YFR 351	86
UK 9978	21	VKB 841	88	WDA 956T	102	XBU 17S	39	YFS 310W	52
UKA 23V	88	VKB 900	88	WDA 986T	112	XBU 1S	96	YG 7831	89
UKA 562H	88	VL 1263	35	WDF 569	57	XC 8059	36	YHT 958	68
UKE 830X	112	VLT 140	42	WDK 562T	118	XCH 425G	110	YHY 80	69
ULS 716X	52	VLT 143	116	WDS 112V	82	XCV 326	109	YJG 807	78
ULS 717X	52	VLT 163	116	WEX 685M	78	XCW 955R	94	YL 740	48
UMA 370	39	VLT 188	75	WFM 801K	34	XDH 516G	57	YLG 717F	34
UMO 180N	111	VLT 196	110	WFN 912	27	XDH 519G	21	YLJ 147	67
UNB 524	109	VLT 216	117	WG 1620	49	XDH 56G	57	YLJ 286	28
UNB 629	39	VLT 235	116	WG 2373	81	XDH 72	70	YNA 321M	96
UO 2331	103	VLT 237	116	WG 3260	49	XFG 25Y	112	YNU 351G	110
UOA 322L	40	VLT 242	116	WG 4445	81	XFM 42G	51	YNW 33X	103
UOU 417H	80	VLT 250	110	WG 8107	49	XG 9304	50	YNX 478	48
UOU 419H	80	VLT 268	114	WG 8790	49	XGM 450L	81	YPL 433T	112
UP 551	43	VLT 281	116	WG 9180	49	XHA 482	57	YPT 796	74
UPB 312S	101	VLT 298	114	WH 1553	35	XHA 496	57	YR 3844	36
UPE 203M	101	VLT 44	23	WHA 237H	92	XHO 370	64	YRC 194	45
URE 281	109	VLW 444G	101	WHL 970	75	XJA 534L	96	YRC 420	111
USV 324	98	VM 4439	38	WHN 411G	92	XKC 789J	88	YRT 898H	28
UTC 672	38	VMO 234H	101	WJY 758	34	XKO 72A	110	YSD 350L	51
UTF 732M	94	VMP 10G	81	WKG 284	110	XLG 477	34	YSG 101	51
UTG 313G	110	VMP 8G	51	WKJ 787	94	XLV 140W	44	YSL 334	116
UTN 501Y	74	VNB 101L	39	WKO 132S	111	XM 7399	36	YT 3738	22
UTU 596J	57	VNB 132L	96	WKO 138S	111	XMS 252R	52	YTE 826	28
UTV 229	83	VNB 173L	96	WLT 371	116	XMS 422Y	82	YWB 494M	48
UU 6646	25	VNB 177L	96	WLT 506	20	XNG 770S	32	YWL 134K	72
UUA 212	92	VNB 203L	96	WLT 529	104	XNX 136H	20	YYB 118	100
UUA 214	34	VO 6806	42	WLT 736	34	XO 1038	25	YYJ 914	51
UUF 110J	73	VO 8846	45	WLT 765	110	XON 41J	21	YYS 174	81
UUF 116J	98	VOD 123K	110	WLT 900	114	XPK 51T	101	ZC 714	55
UUF 328J	98	VOD 550K	75	WNG 864H	58	XRD 23K	111	ZD 7163	55
UVL 873M	36	VOD 88K	75	WNL 259A	74	XRU 277K	67	ZH 3926	55
UWH 185	66	VOI 8415	84	WNO 478	23	XSL 945A	50	ZH 3937	55
UWX 981F	99	VPT 598R	74	WNO 556L	79	XSN 25A	50	ZH 4538	55
UXD 129G	100	VR 5742	38	WOW 993T	110	XTA 839	74	ZI 9708	55
UZG 100	55	VRD 186	21	WPG 217M	111	XTC 530H	81	ZJ 5904	24
UZH 258	24	VRD 193	59	WRA 12	53	XTP 287L	73	ZJ 5933	55
VBD 310H	99	VRF 372	100	WRL 16	103	XTF 98D	118	ZL 2718	55
VCO 802	112	VRU 124J	67	WRP 767J	101	XU 7498	89	ZL 6816	55
VCW 597Y	92	VSC 86	50	WS 4522	49	XUA 73X	78	ZO 6819	55
VD 3433	49	VSS 158M	81	WSD 756K	81	XUF 141	98	ZO 6857	55
VDL 264K	33	VTU 76	34	WT 7101	34	XUO 721	74	ZO 6881	55
VDV 107S	111	VTY 543J	92	WT 7108	43	XUS 575S	82	ZO 6949	55
VDV 137S	102	VUD 30X	72	WT 9156	83	XVU 341M	96	ZO 6960	24
VDV 752	118	VUP 328	74	WTE 155D	51	XVU 352M	39	ZS 8621	24
VDV 753	118	VV 5696	71	WTS 266T	52	XVU 363M	96	ZU 5000	24
VDV 760	53	VV 8934	35	WTS 270T	82	XVX 19	23	ZU 9241	55
VDV 798	74	VVK 149G	92	WTS 708A	92	XW 9892	22	ZY 1715	24
VDV 817	74	VVP 911	57	WUA 832	109	XWS 165K	51	ZY 79	55
VER 262L	48	VWM 83L	88	WUH 173T	111	XWW 474G	78		
VF 2788	32	VY 957	38	WV 1209	32	XWX 795	59		

Index of Museums, Collections and Heritage Bus Services